DAVISON OF DUKE
His Reminiscences

Wilburt Cornell Davison

DAVISON OF DUKE

His Reminiscences

Edited by
JAY M. ARENA, M.D.
and
JOHN P. McGOVERN, M.D.

DUKE UNIVERSITY MEDICAL CENTER
Durham, North Carolina

Printed in the United States of America by
The Ovid Bell Press, Inc., Fulton, Missouri

DAVISON OF DUKE – HIS REMINISCENCES is dedicated to all of Duke University Medical Center's graduates and trainees, past, present, and those yet to come, with the hope that Dave's humanistic approach to medicine will continue to touch their lives and endure.

PREFACE

IN HIS WILL, Wilburt C. Davison left explicit directions that Jay M. Arena and John P. McGovern were "to edit and publish any and all of the reminiscences, diary, etc. . . . ," if they wished. Needless to say, we were delighted to undertake this editorial endeavor because of our enduring esteem and affection for "the Dean." We have selected the fiftieth anniversary celebration of the Duke Medical Center as a most appropriate time to share this valuable, historic, and fascinating document with all Duke alumni and friends.

Because of the vast amount of material that was available, we faced a number of difficult editorial decisions regarding the content, organization, size and style of this volume. One decision, however, was easy: to leave the "reminiscences" intact, except for minor editing, so as not to lose the flavor and style of the individual who founded Duke Medical School and whose more than thirty years' leadership guided the Medical Center toward its present eminence. We dampened our initial desire to use the "reminiscences" and other papers as the core around which to build our own, more fully documented and comprehensive biography of the Dean, and contented ourselves instead with choosing selective supporting material to enhance his personal account.

This book could not have been published without the encouragement and generous aid of many individuals. It would be impossible to list all of Dr. Davison's friends and colleagues who cherished and loved him, and who, either directly or indirectly, had a role in *Davison of Duke – His Reminiscences*. A partial list would include: Elon H. Clark; G. S. T. Cavanagh; William G. Anlyan; Mary D. B. T. Semans; Helen M. Thomas; H. Grant Taylor; Eugene A. Stead, Jr.; Martin M. Cummings; Talmage L. Peele; and three remaining members of the original Duke faculty, J. Deryl Hart; David T. Smith; and Edwin P. Alyea. We also would especially like to thank Michael A. McCormick for his support and editorial assistance as well as Ovid H. Bell, Leslie L. Wildrick, and Julia Q. Mitchell for their varied and valued contributions to this project. Finally, we greatly appreciate the generous contributions of the Duke Foundation, the Davison Club, the John P. McGovern Foundation and the Texas Allergy Research Foundation. Their support means that the entire proceeds of this book can go directly to the Scholarship Endowment of Duke University Medical Center.

JMA
JPM

INTRODUCTION

FOR THOSE WHO KNEW Wilburt Cornell Davison this volume will bring to life a rich, warm, and valued relationship, and for those less fortunate students and alumni hopefully it will enlighten them as to the unique qualities of this giant of a man who laid the foundation and built upon it a great medical center — Duke.

Many tributes have been written about "The Dean" by his students, colleagues, associates, and admirers; some of these will be found in another section of this book. The authors of these tributes have, in turn, extolled his commanding presence, his warm and friendly personality, his contagious enthusiasm and humor, his medical prescience and astuteness, his numerous contributions to pediatrics and medical education, his idolatry of Sir William Osler, and, above all, his dedication and single-mindedness in successfully building, staffing, and operating Duke University School of Medicine for 35 years. They have described his combination of physical and mental bigness, his quick mind and tongue, his invariable good manners and his unostentatiousness, his simple dress, his Spartan manner, his enjoyment in driving a Renault, his fondness for foods (all kinds — especially Josh Turnage's barbecue and Berghoff's German sandwiches and beer), and his lifetime of successful accomplishments that resulted in a personality that consistently made little of his own role. Although he was among the first to air-condition his pediatric ward, he resisted the mounting pressure to air-condition his offices. Meetings between those who knew him always give rise to shared fond recollections, remembrances and experiences; they invariably reflect a tone of great personal loss. As one said, "I was a bigger person in his presence." Although "The Dean," if he were alive, would loudly decry the flattering statements and sentimentality expressed above, it was he who not only enumerated and published the 261 adulatory phrases taken from the writings about Sir William Osler but forcibly reiterated, in the same article, how much Osler disliked adulation.

Dr. Wilburt Cornell Davison, the man who more than any other charted the course for the Duke University Medical Center to become the institution of excellence it is today, died June 26, 1972, at the age of 80, in the hospital he helped build.

Though he is no longer with us physically, he has left his indelible imprint and style — youthful faculty leadership, flexibility, informality, involvement in innovation and change, and, above all, the desire to meet the needs of people with love and compassion.

It was 1926 when the 34-year-old pediatrician and assistant dean of the Johns Hopkins Medical School attracted the eye of Duke President William Preston Few, who was searching for a man to develop the Duke School of Medicine. The eminent Dr. William H. Welch recommended that "Davison would be the best man for Dr. Few to secure to develop the school."

In the years that followed, no detail was too small for Dr. Davison's concern, and he sometimes joined the labor crew in overalls to help build stone on stone. But he built in something else at Duke equally as strong — flexibility.

It was this demand for flexibility that pressed him, as a Rhodes Scholar at Oxford, to request of Sir William Osler permission to complete the first two years of medical training in one year. Years later at Duke he built into the medical curriculum flexibility for successive generations of medical students.

From 1927 to 1960, while he was dean of the School of Medicine, Duke was Davison and Davison was Duke. "On all of the walls, under the paint, one finds inscribed, 'Davison was here.'"

A native of Grand Rapids, Michigan, and the son of a Methodist minister, he earned his AB degree at Princeton in 1913 and then went to Oxford where he earned BA and BSc degrees. He returned to Hopkins for his MD.

World traveler, tradition wrecker, consultant to governments, detester of idleness, personification of informality, recipient of honors, author, molder of men — Davison was all of these. But above all else he was a teacher and compassionate physician.

During a newspaper interview in the later years of his life, Dr. Davison lamented what he felt was a de-emphasis on humanism in medicine as he reflected on his own philosophy:

> Medical Schools across the nation are filled with all kinds of scientific types who don't have a lot of personal interest in students or patients as individuals.
>
> That's wrong. You ought to know both your students and your patients by their first names.

All fields need more humanistic people, but it is particularly so in medicine. It just doesn't take that much more time to be nice to people, to treat patients or students with compassion and dignity.

CONTENTS

ILLUSTRATIONS

DAVISON OF DUKE
His Reminiscences

CHAPTER I

GROWING-UP (1892-1909)

M Y URGE to become a physician started at the age of three when my legs were scalded from a boiling food pot which I had investigated either through greed or scientific curiosity. Indeed, the physician who treated me also gave me my first pediatric and psychologic instruction by providing me with candy so that I yearned to return to his office for the daily painful treatments, rather than dreading the visits like so many children. The old Michigan doctor in 1895 used the now forgotten sugar "buttons" on a strip of paper as his bait, but only recently have pediatricians gone back to the practice of "winning over" children with sweets. Now even tongue depressors are made like lollipops. These burns produced a lasting impression on my mind as well as permanent scars on my legs which, later to my delight, were accepted as smallpox vaccination so that I was excused from many school revaccinations.

Fourth of July fireworks clinched my determination to study medicine. While firing a toy cannon which I had been forbidden to use, I looked closely at it to see why it had not gone off when I ignited it, and just then it did. Fortunately, I had a quick blink reflex and only my eyelids and face were peppered with powder. Even though the family physician spent two hours in painfully extracting powder grains, I still have blue stains around my eyes. While on the operating table, I knew definitely that I wanted to be a doctor.

Our family had a second near tragedy with fireworks when a lighted firecracker fell into the basket which contained our Fourth of July supply. The effects of the *Blitzkrieg* which followed were avoided only by "hitting the dirt" until the last rocket and Roman candle had whizzed by. After these two accidents with fireworks, I have been rabid for their prohibition. The Fourth of July tetanus deaths of those days were appalling. Most recently, states have now made fireworks illegal but they still are too easy to obtain, especially in the South at Christmas time.

A high school football injury which required two operations was the next milestone in my medical education. Being kept out of school for a year permitted the consolidation of my rapid growth into

3

The Davison family (circa 1894)

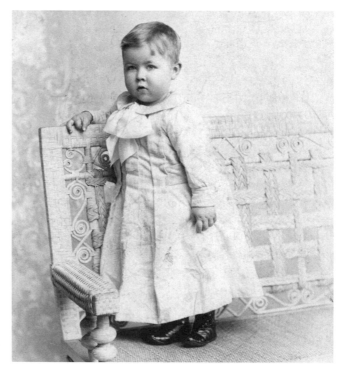

Davison as a toddler

a sturdy though unfortunately massive physique. My parents' fear about my loss of education led to their providing a tutor, Dr. Towles, a retired Harvard clergyman, whose daily assignment was six hours of Greek with two hours of quizzes. As a result I learned to work and concentrate.

MICHIGAN

Instead of arriving in Long Island like my forebears, I was born 28 April 1892 at 54 Hovey Street, corner of Deloney Street, in Grand Rapids, Michigan, in the parsonage of the Joy Memorial Methodist Episcopal Church which was the first appointment or "charge" given to my father who had been graduated from Princeton and married the preceding year. However, I was brought back to Long Island at the age of six weeks by my Aunt Nellie. Aunt Nellie, who was a maiden lady at the time, went to my Grandmother Cornell and asked if I were a "spastic" because I held out my arms so stiffly all day. Grandmother Cornell, having raised innumerable children and grandchildren, undressed me and found that the shirt which I was wearing had shrunk so much in the washing and had become so tight that I couldn't put my arms down. My mother brought me back to Grand Rapids later in that year. In 1895, my father was given a new church at Greenville, Michigan. My earliest memories are the river there, my goat and wagon, going to kindergarten, and my mother's attempts to learn to ride a "safety" bicycle behind the woodpile.

LONG ISLAND

In 1897, when I was five years old, my father "exchanged" his Michigan church for one in Brooklyn. However, this new church, in spite of previous promises to the contrary, turned out to be an assistantship which my father refused to accept, thereby establishing a reputation for independence at the sacrifice of a year's salary and giving me a lifelong distrust of the promises of politicians, church, medical, and otherwise. I did not visit Michigan again for forty years and then the cold and rain made me regret the trip, especially after twenty years in the sunny South.

From 1897 to 1898 we lived with my Davison grandparents at 577 Putnam Avenue, Brooklyn. Although below the legal age, I was admitted to Public School No. 44 because my mother had taught there before her marriage. My only recollection of that period is using a school slate, seeing one of my cousins who attended the same

5

school, and being paid a penny a day to learn to write with my right hand instead of my left. Fortunately for my finances, psychologists had not then discovered that teaching left-handers to write right-handed might be deleterious to future health and happiness. As a matter of fact, the only harm done was that I never learned to write legibly either way, which has bothered examination readers and secretaries ever since. Some, if not all of my good marks in quizzes, undoubtedly were due to the instructor's inability to read my answers. Psychologists now have revised their condemnation of this teaching and cannot find much difference in left-handers who write right or left-handed. The latter, though, certainly are handicapped by school and college lecture chairs which always are built for right-handers.

In April, 1898, my father was appointed to Grace Church, Bay Ridge, at that time a delightfully sleepy suburb of New York City and an ideal spot for young children. New York harbor had not yet been contaminated, and truck farms were ripe for melon thefts. I learned to swim by being thrown off a breakwater in New York harbor by a kindly but misguided friend of my father. I would have been rescued if I had sunk, but I didn't know it, so I managed to paddle ashore without help and have been able to swim ever since. It was a good pediatric lesson, for I realized, as everyone else now does, that children should be allowed to learn to swim gradually without being forced. Swimming also gave me a lasting lesson which helped my medical career. When my father asked me if I had been swimming and smoking one afternoon, like any small boy, I denied the charge, as going to the bay had been forbidden that day. However, one of the good church members had reported me. The subsequent spanking was thorough and ended with my father's statement that he did not mind the disobedience in swimming and smoking but lying was not to be tolerated. The lesson was indelible. I have been honest ever since.

The Spanish-American War was the great excitement of that period. Every boy had a picture of the *Maine*, which had been sunk in Havana harbor in February, 1898. Learning to read was greatly accelerated by the desire to follow the newspapers. I vividly remember taking a twenty-mile bicycle trip with my father to Camp Black at Mineola, coming back by train exhausted, and going with my father who preached to the troops at Fort Hamilton. On another occasion I watched the celebration for Admiral Dewey on his return to New York from Manila, and, best of all, I was one of the school children who helped raise the flag at Owl's Head on the Shore Road when Dewey's flagship, the *Olympia*, passed up the bay. I also had my first lesson in physics at this time for, when I was puzzled by seeing the smoke of the saluting guns of the battleship across the harbor before I could hear them, my teacher explained the difference in the rates of travel of light and sound waves. A little later I saw my first motion picture, a staccato reel of Troop C on its return from the war, which Mr. Anthony Fiala, the explorer, showed in the church. I have been a movie addict ever since.

The advent of the automobile in 1899 was thrilling. One of my father's friends kept his machine in the parsonage barn and it was a source of interest to all of the youngsters.

Attending Public School No. 102 for six years (1898-1904) made very little impression on me. My only recollection was the choice once offered me by the principal of being caned or taking a note home to my father for some now forgotten misdemeanor. Naturally, I chose the note and though my father whipped me anyway, the gamble seemed worth taking.

Most of the memories of this period were of extracurricular activities. Winters in Bay Ridge were great fun, for ponds and hills were numerous. Skating and playing hockey were the best, although I was once knocked unconscious while skating. Tobogganing and bob-sledding filled many afternoons.

The farms of Bay Ridge were a delight. Uncle Ad, Mr. Adrian de Nyse, had one of the larger ones and kept baskets of peaches, apricots, apples, and melons ready for small boys. His only anger was in catching us destroying food, as when we staged a target match with a loft full of onions. These wide-open spaces are now covered with apartments and tenements.

A pony was a long awaited and, at first, a delightful addition to the family, but as he was stubborn and delighted in throwing riders and attempting to roll on them, I developed a fear rather than a love of horses. The animal was tractable when harnessed to a dog-cart or sled, and I made my spending money by taking other boys for rides.

Dogs were a great source of joy as well as sorrow. Every child should have one. The joy came from the sense of possession and the affection which only a dog can show. The sorrow was seeing "Spot"

7

Davison, age 5

killed by a trolley and having an unlicensed dog captured by the dog-catcher. Fortunately, the family relented and the animal was redeemed from the pound.

Many Michigan friends visited us, and father and I always took them to Ellis Island to see the daily arrival of the hordes of immigrants.

Father also enjoyed going to see fires and, as he always wore a clerical vest like a priest's, the Irish firemen would let him through the lines. He took me to one of these and when the fireman stopped me, father told him that I was his son. The fireman said, "Father, you wouldn't be fooling me?"

One of the most dangerous weapons a small boy can have is an air rifle, particularly if he is feuding with two brothers who live next door. My parents finally confiscated mine after I had won a battle by planting a BB shot in the forehead of one of my opponents where it remained for several weeks.

I remember being given chloroform so that the doctor could remove my tonsils while I was lying on the flat-top desk in my father's study. It probably was a "snip" operation because the tonsillectomy had to be repeated when I had diphtheria in 1921 and became a carrier.

The only other illness I had in Bay Ridge was an erroneous diagnosis of trachoma at the age of ten. I had follicular conjunctivitis, and still have it for that matter, but trachoma was so prevalent at that time because of the influx of immigrants that any granulations of the lids were called trachoma. The therapy was terrible — going to an ophthalmologist in Brooklyn every Saturday to have him roll my lids up and down and rub the conjunctiva with a copper sulfate crystal. I have been wearing glasses ever since. I learned in Formosa in 1954 that trachoma quickly responds to the new wonder drugs.

The summer when I was ten stands out in my memory. The family stayed at Belle Island on the Connecticut shore of Long Island Sound. A sudden, violent squall capsized and sank the twenty-foot sloop which I was sailing with my father. Fortunately, a hand hold of the boat remained above water, but the hour of clinging with waves breaking over me until rescued made a lasting impression. Several other boats and seven lives were lost during the storm. I always attributed the catastrophe to having a black cat aboard the sloop. The cat was drowned. That summer, I probably had poliomyelitis because I limped for a month following what I thought was a stone

9

bruise. Twenty years later some atrophy of my right calf and short-ening of my right leg were noted.

An influence, which probably increased my determination to study medicine, was the digging up of an ancient graveyard belonging to my father's church. The city had bought the cemetery for a new road, and hundreds of skeletons were disinterred and packed into a huge vault in front of the church. I shall always remember a large worm crawling out of one of the skulls and the grave-digger picking it up and, while looking at the skull and knocking out the worm, said, "and that was Uncle Henry."

Like most small boys, I became enthusiastic over stamp collecting but became bored with it although I had accumulated a valuable assortment, the best of which I obtained dishonestly. The *Youth's Companion* had an advertisement that for one dollar, one hundred different, valuable stamps could be bought. I saved a long time for the dollar, and I was permanently embittered when I received one hundred common American stamps. They were all different, but they certainly were not valuable. However, the company sent several sheets of good stamps on approval. I kept them, partly through greed, and partly in revenge, for being cheated out of my dollar. I quaked whenever the company sent threatening letters about the return of their approval stamps, because I knew my father would chastise me severely if he learned of my guilt. I still have the stamps. Though I have lost all interest in them, I hope that the company does not still delude small boys.

Comments made to children sometimes have a lasting effect. While visiting my Cousin Bertha, I held up a walking party to cut a cane from some bushes. My knife was dull, and the branch tough, but finally, after a long struggle, the cane was obtained. My elder cousin, either in annoyance at the delay, or in admiration, commented on my determination. At any rate, I took it as a compliment and made determination, "stick-to-itiveness," as one of my grammar school teachers described it, a fetish for the rest of my life. It turned out to be a mixed virtue, for I wasted many hours finishing useless things which I had started, such as movies and books, which bored me from the beginning.

Another childhood memory which had a lasting beneficial effect was the story about my great grandfather, who died in 1889 at the usual Davison age of sixty-nine. During his last illness, one of his neighbors thoughtfully called on him to console him. However,

10

Davison on his favorite pony

instead of thanking his friend for the visit, Old Bill, as he was called on Long Island, demanded repayment of some money owed to him. This would-be mourner came out of the farm house muttering "that so-and-so, like all the Davisons, never forgets." I have always tried to improve my memory for faces and facts. Remembering faces was a necessity because, as a Methodist preacher's son, I had to be able to recognize each member of a new church every few years. In regard to facts, one of my instructors at Princeton told me that I had such a good memory for useless details that he never knew whether I understood the subject itself. But, he was kind and gave me the benefit of his doubt with a "First Group."

In 1904, the six-year limit at the Bay Ridge church was reached, and my father was transferred to the Williams Avenue Church in the slums of East New York. Except for a brief automobile trip with my mother in 1917, I did not visit Bay Ridge again until some thirty years later. I had gone to New York on the 12th of October, 1947, and found that I could not make the appointments which I had hoped because of the Columbus Day holiday, which New York and Massachusetts apparently celebrate though no one else does. So I went to Bay Ridge by myself on "a sentimental journey" and spent one of the most delightful afternoons of my life in going over the old church, parsonage, and the new parish building. It brought back many happy memories. The church looked a wee bit smaller than while we were there, but the parsonage was just the same. The living room, which I used to think was so large, seemed quite modest in proportion. Mrs. Bergen, who wanted to adopt me forty years before, had died the preceding year. The preacher, Dr. Frederick W. Poton, who had been there sixteen years and who was a friend of my Father, drove me past her house and then drove me to Fort Hamilton, Coney Island, and Rockaway Beach. All of the once open fields are completely filled with apartment houses.

The year that we lived in East New York, 1904-5, I attended Public School No. 76. My clearest memory of that school was the principal's discussion of the origin of family names. He mentioned Bakers, Smiths, etc., but was much annoyed when one bright student, fortunately not me, asked if the principal's name, A. A. Ashmun, had any significance. The crowded city streets and the absence of playgrounds as well as scarlet fever and diphtheria in the family made my father ask for a transfer to a less congested and more

The Reverend William L. Davison, the Dean's father

healthy charge. Fortunately he was assigned to Jamaica in April, 1905.

The summer, when I was twelve, my father and I camped at Hemlock Beach near Fire Island on the south side of Long Island and were so enamored with the surf and sand that a bungalow was purchased. Hemlock Beach is now part of the Long Island Estate Park called Jones Beach. Summers there gave me plenty of swimming practice, a rugged constitution, and big feet from going barefoot. The first gained me my college letter at Princeton and my half-blue at Oxford, the second provided good health, and the third made shoes a torture, even the huge wide ones built especially for me. My only exploits, aside from learning to sail and repair contentious motor boats, were winning a swimming race at the Unqua Yacht Club, Amityville, and rescuing Margie Miller from drowning. The latter episode was all a mistake. She was screaming for help because she had lost her water wings while in deep water. I plunged in at the first scream and had commenced to tow Margie ashore, but she lost her head and clutched both of my arms. As I knew the approved Red Cross life-saving remedy for this dilemma, namely a sharp slap to the face, I applied it. I broke her hold and rescued her but she never spoke to me again. And she was a nice girl, too.

The sanitary facilities at Hemlock Beach were very primitive and consisted of a "Chick Sales two-holer." For light reading there, we kept a copy of *Wit and Wisdom* by the Reverend Sidney Smith, or it may have been by another author. The book was lost when a storm swept the house out to sea. After a few summers we knew the stories by heart but they were new to weekend guests who could not refrain from retelling them, usually at lunch. One of my sister's and my greatest delights was embarrassing the guests, as well as our parents, by rudely reminding everyone that we knew the source of their jokes and funny stories. No amount of punishment by my mother would stop us.

The U.S. Coast Guard, in 1904, when I first encountered it, consisted of a series of Coast Guard Stations, housing a captain and a crew of eight, every five miles along the coast. In addition, it had a few cutters for rescue at sea. In 1904, the captain at Hemlock Beach was Bill Davis, who had been one of the gunners on the *Monitor,* which defeated the *Merrimac* off Hampton Roads on the 9th of March, 1862. At sixty-seven, four years younger than I am now, he seemed very old and austere and had little contact with his Coast

Guard crew or with us children. His successor was Israel Von Nostrand, one of the most lovable characters I have ever known. His relations with the crew were very amiable, and all of them, Captain Israel and the crew, could not have been kinder to us as small children.

Some of us walked with the Coast Guard crewman on his sunset patrol. At the "halfway hut," two and a half miles up the beach, he waited until the Coast Guardsman from the next station met him, and then each of them walked back to their respective stations. This patrol was going on all along the coast every four hours on the lookout for ships. There were only two wrecks during the ten years we had a cottage at Hemlock Beach. One was a ship carrying cylinder oil which ran aground with no casualties, but it was exciting to watch. Everyone on the beach as well as on the mainland had at least one barrel of cylinder oil as a prize. The other ship was a fruit liner carrying bananas and, except for the United Fruit Company's gift of bananas to cure celiac disease at the Johns Hopkins Hospital twenty years later, I have never seen so many bananas at one time. Everyone had several stalks of green bananas and in spite of being soaked with salt water, many of them ripened.

My greatest adventure with the Coast Guard was being allowed to participate in the capsize drill which they were required to do each year. We launched a life boat which was built for a captain and a crew of eight. I took the place of one man who was ill. The boat was a "self-bailer" with the floor of the boat a few inches higher than the surrounding water so that any wave which came aboard drained off through small portholes. After we rowed out about a mile, the captain ordered all of us to get on one side with bridle ropes, as they were called, to pull the boat over. We did and when we counted heads there was one missing. As I was the best swimmer I was asked to swim under the boat to find the missing member of the crew. I brought him out. His neck had been caught in one of the bridle ropes, and he was half drowned but still chewing tobacco when I rescued him.

Occasionally, we would spend a weekend during the winter at Hemlock Beach. On one of these visits we were marooned by a storm and had to eat seagulls and clams, known to transmit infectious hepatitis.

The family spent ten summers at Hemlock Beach, and probably would still go there if a winter storm had not washed the cottage out

15

to sea. My father wrote me in 1915 while I was in Serbia that the Coast Guard had notified him that when it was last seen a mile from the shore the refrigerator was still on the back porch.

JAMAICA

Jamaica, in 1905, was a typical Long Island village with growing pains. Though streetcars rattled through from the city, most people went to Brooklyn and New York by steam trains. The tunnels and electric expresses were still in the future. Father's wooden Methodist Church and parsonage, like most of the better houses of the town, were on the main street. The schools were splendid. Jamaica had just been incorporated into New York City so the standards were excellent and as the immigrant invasion had not reached the town, the classes were small and the students not only native-born but mostly the descendants of the early settlers. My best teachers in the Jamaica High School were Miss Wilkins in mathematics and Miss Lydia F. Root and Dr. Edward C. Chickering in Latin. My later luck with these subjects in college emphasizes the fact that good teachers are an essential part of education. The results may not be due to their actual didactic instruction but to their ability to arouse the student's interest and enthusiasm in the subject so that he learns unconsciously. Educational experts should devise means or tests for the identification of these good teachers and for the elimination of the duds. Promotion by seniority and the retention of unstimulating instructors may produce academic security and freedom for the educators, but these safeguards have reduced most of the so-called educated to standardized mediocrity. Perhaps it can't be helped in universal democratic education. Fortunately, Jamaica High School had not quite reached the mass production stage, and I obtained a fair secondary education.

Classes were small, informal, and amusing. One day, Cecil Kenyon, one of my classmates, translated Livy's account of Scipio's defeat of Hannibal by "the Roman soldiers goosed the elephants with spears so that they were disconcerted and fled." Another time he translated Caesar's report of the effort to rid the woods of bears by placing sharp stakes under the trees into which the bears had climbed and then shaking the trees as "the bears fell out of the trees and were impaled on the stakes and were expectorated to death." When he was reprimanded for his queer translation, he blandly

16

replied that he knew the word meant "spit" but thought it was too vulgar a word for a lady teacher.

High school students took social fraternities even more seriously than do collegians. I was delighted to be elected to one and attended chapter and even national meetings. Now I cannot even remember its name. Honor societies had not yet percolated into the high schools, but several of us who were ardent Greek students formed one in that field.

I had grown too rapidly to be a good athlete but football in 1907 with its five yards in three downs required only weight, and I had plenty of that. On a hard tackle, the left side of my neck was badly bruised but it didn't make me play any worse than usual. However, two months later the swollen neck nodes had to be removed. I enjoyed this experience at the Long Island College Hospital. Apparently, some of the damaged tissue remained, for the wound did not heal and a second operation was necessary a few months later. I also enjoyed that week in the hospital. The pathology report was "non-tuberculous," an obvious error. As a matter of fact, except for the disfiguring scar on my neck which is now hidden by fat, the injury, operations, being kept out of school for a year, and the previously mentioned tutoring were among the best things that ever happened to me.

Northern Methodist preachers must sign a pledge not to smoke before they can be ordained, but when my father, an extraordinarily healthy-looking man, came before the bishop, the latter said, "It is so obvious from your appearance that you don't smoke — the pledge is unnecessary." My father lost faith in bishops for he had been smoking since the age of sixteen, but, at any rate, he could smoke legally, though he was discreet about it. I shall always remember how embarrassed he became when I offered one of his church members a box of his cigars.

Grandfather Davison was one of the old school who believed that pleasure and sin were synonymous. His efforts to persuade my father to stop smoking having proved unavailing, he bribed him with a car. Nowadays that may seem a low reward for giving up one of the all too few pleasures of life, but in 1908 an automobile, a two-cylinder Autocar with a coffee-crank steering lever, was something else. Mechanically, it was a terrible car, and a trip, or rather an expedition, of thirty miles without a catastrophe or a puncture was a triumph. But the joy of riding forty miles an hour when the car did go and the fun and mechanical education of fixing it when it didn't were almost too much happiness for a youth of fifteen out of school because of a football injury. However, I did sprain my back permanently by trying to crank the engine after I had forgotten to put oil in it. As I hadn't commenced to smoke at that age, I didn't realize the price my father was paying for the car. The following year when I went off to college and couldn't help fix the car, it fell to pieces like the one-horse open shay. To prevent my father's returning to smoking, my grandfather gave us a second-hand Pope-Toledo which was more powerful than perfect, but it too fell apart so my father resumed smoking and everybody except my grandfather was happy.

My grandfather was one of the violently religious men of the nineteenth century. He had family prayers, attended church regularly and even built a small mission church so that additional services could be held, but he was quite unscrupulous during the rest of the week. His zeal was responsible for my father's being a preacher instead of an engineer. Grandfather also was an ardent prohibitionist, and I did not understand, until I studied medicine, why his attic was filled with hundreds of empty patent medicine bottles, including Lydia E. Pinkham's Vegetable Compound, a Female Remedy! The fifteen to thirty per cent alcohol which most of these remedies contain is responsible for the sense of well-being which they produce as well as for their huge sales during prohibition. However, I do not believe that grandfather was a hypocrite. He did not realize that he was drinking liquor though he certainly enjoyed his "medicine." No one spoiled his pleasure by telling him that he was a self-deluded toper.

My great-grandfather was fairly wealthy, having a large farm and a lumber and ship yard at Oceanside and schooners which carried timber from North Carolina to Long Island. When he died in 1889, he gave his three sons most of his money and left small endowments for his daughters because he didn't trust his sons-in-law. My grandfather, with his brother George, became commission merchants and wholesale dealers in butter and cheese at 182 South Street, New York. Later he ran a general store at Oceanside, Long Island, which he received in payment of a debt, and a restaurant in Brooklyn. Finally, in the nineties he realized the possibilities of Long Island real estate because New York was becoming crowded, and the surburban migration had started. Grandfather would buy farms,

18

divide them into lots, build houses on them and sell them at an auction at a good profit. I remember one of his sales — at low tide the place was a mud-flat and at high tide some of it was under water. Sales were held at half-tide. At another one of his developments, a householder told me that the reason that he bought his home from grandfather was because grandfather had pointed to a large oak tree and said "that tree alone was worth fifty dollars." The householder said that the statement was true but that when the deed was signed he found that the tree was not even on grandfather's land.

One of the great benefits of living in Jamaica was that I saw my grandmother Davison frequently. She and grandfather had a home at Oceanside, as it was called, though it was ten miles from the ocean. I spent most of my weekends and vacations there. I also spent a month there during my second year of high school when I had what was diagnosed as chorea but was much more likely a tic, with my head frequently jerking to the right. I again enjoyed a fortnight at Oceanside during my freshman year at Princeton when I was temporarily suspended because I had not realized that members of the crew were required to go to morning chapel like ordinary students. My grandmother Davison and I were great friends, and she was always helping me financially and otherwise. She died in 1915 while I was in Serbia.

Christmas dinners at 92 Hart Street, Brooklyn, my grandmother Cornell's house, were tremendous, with twenty or more aunts and cousins. Her attic was a delight as it was filled with all of the toys, Horatio Alger and Henty books of my uncles and aunts. Uncle Jim, my mother's younger brother, took my sisters and me every year to the circus and Buffalo Bill Wild West shows at the old Madison Square Garden. His older brother, Minne, always gave us money. Grandmother Cornell lived to be over ninety, dying in the early nineteen twenties. I am said to resemble her but do not know whether I shall inherit her longevity as my mother did. My grandfather Cornell died at sixty before I was born. I am the first male Davison to reach seventy-one.

One of my most vivid memories of Jamaica is seeing the almost immediate effect of a hypodermic in relieving my father's suffering during a ptomaine attack. Within seconds he was asleep.

One of the most exciting events of my youth was seeing the battleship *Connecticut* launched. Through a member of the church my father and I received invitations to the christening ceremony at the Brooklyn Navy Yard. Some regal-looking woman, probably the wife of the Governor of Connecticut, hurled the tethered bottle of champagne at the ship as she slid down the ways. The bottle did not burst but a quick-witted Irish sailor retrieved it and smashed it against the bow with the words, "You're the *Connecticut* by God."

When I returned to high school after my hospital experience, I had no difficulty, thanks to Dr. Towles' tutoring, in making up the studies I had missed the previous year, and I was graduated on the 30th of June, 1909. The only outside activities during this last year in high school were dramatics and public speaking. Both, by giving me confidence before an audience, helped me in my medical career. Though Miss A. W. Ward was an excellent teacher, I never learned to be a good public speaker, or good actor for that matter, but I could speak on my feet without palsy of the knees even though I was conscious of making a poor talk. I even sang in a town performance of "The Mikado" that year, my last musical effort.

In 1909, I took the Princeton entrance examinations. Either they were easy or my tutoring had been good, because I passed. I also learned a very good lesson in psychology. At Adelphi Academy in Brooklyn where I took the June exams, proctors constantly watched the students for cheating. As a result, it was rampant; notes on cuffs and bits of paper were frequently and surreptitiously consulted by everyone except me as far as I could see. I was honest, possibly by nature but more likely because I had been well tutored and it had not occurred to me to prepare any "cribs" in advance. In September, the same group of students took the balance of the college entrance examinations at Princeton. An instructor distributed the papers, briefly described the honor system, requested that the examinations be left on the desk before noon, and departed. The group was stunned from the shock of being without proctors, and possibly from the sense of wasted efforts on the crib notes. At any rate no one used them and during the following four years at Princeton I never saw a student cheat.

When I was notified that I was admitted to Princeton I felt that at last I had reached the height of my ambition. The only flaw was that I realized I was leaving home for good. I hated especially to part from my mother who had unostentatiously loved and helped me in thousands of ways. I ardently loved both my father and mother, but I was closer to her. I always felt that she alone understood me, probably better than I did myself, and for that matter, sometimes too well for my own desires though not for my own good. I could tell her my hopes and she would plan with me and not laugh at me no matter how foolish my ideas seemed. I always disliked being laughed at and being thought ridiculous, even though I realized how much I deserved it. As I grew older, I learned to hide my discomfort and to bear it with a grin, though I rarely enjoyed a laugh at my own expense.

In all my life I had never seen my mother angry or other than sympathetic. If anyone was rude to her, as children and parishioners sometimes unintentionally were, she would rarely show how much she was hurt and would cover her feelings with a smile. She was always cheerful under the hardships of being a minister's wife living in ugly parsonages with even more hideous furniture, making ends meet on an inadequate salary, being polite to boring callers and attending endless meetings, to mention just a few of her trials. The book and the movie, *One Foot in Heaven* is an all-too-true portrayal of the vicissitudes of a preacher's home. I had never known anyone to be more unselfish and solicitious than my mother; she always thought first of the comfort, well-being, and happiness of others. In addition to my deep love for her, I had unbounded admiration for her limitless ability to meet all situations.

CHAPTER II

PRINCETON (1909-1913)

A FTER three years of high school and one year of being tutored, I entered Princeton at the age of seventeen. As my father had gone to Princeton, no other university was even considered. In reality, my mother was responsible for both of our going to Princeton. In 1887, when my father wavered between Harvard and Princeton, the fact that he was engaged to Mattie Cornell in Brooklyn, made Princeton, just fifty miles away, much more desirable than Harvard. I had not heard the rumor that Princeton would admit any son of an alumnus provided he could at least read and write, or else I would not have taken the entrance examination so seriously and worked so hard to pass them.

Finances were a problem, as my father had only his preacher's salary. To lighten the load during my freshman year, I was given a reduced board rate in the university dining halls in return for watching the cigar stand one evening a week. Princeton also allowed me to sign a note for my first year's tuition which carried a proviso that I would be given scholarships for the next three years if I obtained a "second group" average. As my preparation had been sound, and as I was reasonably diligent, I maintained a "first group" average and so paid no tuition during my four years.

Although I was grateful for this assistance, I have felt ever since that loans and not scholarships should have been used for those last three years. I repaid the loan as soon as I was able, but when I tried to repay the scholarships and also have my 1913 class fund credited with the amount, the Princeton treasurer informed me that the check could be credited to the scholarship fund or to the class fund but not to both. Not knowing anything of accounting, I thought that Princeton must not need the money or my suggestion would have been accepted. I, therefore, included the amount of my Princeton scholarships in a gift to Duke, an illustration of the lack of sense of obligation produced by scholarships. Student loan funds accomplish the same purpose as scholarships, and as they must be repaid, they are not used by students who do not need them. As a matter of fact, I should not have taken the scholarships because my grandfather died during my freshman year and left the family reasonably well-to-do.

When my grandfather Davison died, my father was made administrator of the estate, a colossal job, as the assets were all in real estate scattered over Long Island without any written lists of their location. My grandfather carried all of the information in his head and superstitiously believed that if he made a will or even if he carried life insurance he might die suddenly. He died suddenly anyway, woke up on the morning of the 20th of November, 1909, gasped and dropped back dead. My father rose to the occasion although he had never had any financial training except trying to live on his salary and battling with church mortgages. He had the title records in Long Island counties traced and located most of my grandfather's property. He also was assigned to the Fleet Street Church, an ancient organization with very few members which had been endowed by the Brooklyn Rapid Transit Company because half of the building had been torn down for the extension of the subway. As a result, my father's church duties were light and he was able to devote most of his time to settling the estate. The only property which gave him any difficulty was a small store and apartment building in Lynbrook. The rents were paid promptly and everything seemed serene until my father learned that the apartments upstairs were being used as a brothel. I don't think he was as much worried from the moral point of view as from the fear that the newspapers would learn that a Brooklyn preacher was collecting rent from a bawdy house. At any rate, he promptly sold the building to its occupants for whatever they offered and then spent the next twenty years bemoaning the fact that the value of the property had increased tenfold after he sold it.

I went to Princeton with four chief aims: to prepare for the study of medicine, to obtain my college letter in athletics, to try for a Rhodes Scholarship, and to gain a Phi Beta Kappa key. This fourth ambition grew from the lasting impression made on me as a small boy by hearing my father describe the finding at a quarry at the Brandywine battle-field in Pennsylvania, of one of the original Phi Beta Kappa keys issued in 1776 at the College of William and Mary and belonging to one of Washington's young officers who had fallen in the battle. The story made me decide to try for one of these historic keys, but when I went to college, I found that to have a record entitling me to it, I had to change my habit of working at night because, in those days at any rate, obvious studying at Princeton was

23

looked down upon as "greasy poling." Those who wanted the good opinion of their fellow students and who hoped to be elected to an upper class club did as little work as was necessary to stay in college. My only solution to this dilemma was to get up at 6 a.m. and to study before breakfast, so that no one, except my room-mate, would detect my guilt. The plan was a success. I found I could do more and better work in two hours early in the morning than at night. It also helped establish an early rising habit which has been useful throughout my life, and it gave me an undeserved reputation for being able to get good marks without studying. I also learned that the only requisites for a Phi Beta Kappa key were hard work, a good memory, and a proper selection of courses that were easy or interesting. Any student can shine by hard work if the task is easy or interesting. One of my instructors demonstrated this axiom by substituting pornographic Latin for the required reading. I never saw students work so hard. As Val Havens said to me later at Oxford, a Phi Beta Kappa key is of little use: if it is worn in the United States, the wearer is accused of false pride and if worn in England, no one recognizes it.

During my freshman year, choice of courses was forbidden, but as mathematics, Latin and Greek were required, subjects in which I had been tutored, I received marks of first and second "groups." As fifth group is passing, I was rated as a good student, to my father's dismay. He feared for my future and reminded me that the man who had led his Princeton class of 1891 was teaching county school while the student who had stood at the foot of his class was editor of a New York newspaper. However, I did want that Phi Beta Kappa key and counted on my interest in medicine to avoid the fate of the county school teacher. During the next three years, I took all of the biology courses possible, as they were easy and interesting. This choice of easy courses hurt my conscience a little so I indulged in a few other courses because I thought I needed them. I also found that by getting permission to count the best five of these courses, a practice no longer allowed, I made a fair record and received my Phi Beta Kappa key on the 13th of March, 1913.

For anyone six feet tall and weighing 170 pounds, athletics was a necessity to maintain campus respectability. Besides, I wanted a college letter, as athletic prowess was at that time one of the requirements for a Rhodes Scholarship. Because of my size, *rowing* seemed to be the easiest means toward this end but how I hated it.

To sit on a sliding seat in a shell, gradually wearing away the skin of my backside, watching the head of the man in front, pulling with back and arms, pushing with legs, getting the oar quickly away from my body at the end of the stroke to avoid catching a "crab," and blistering my hands and fingers — if that was fun or sport, I couldn't see it. At any rate, I "made" the freshman and junior varsity crews.

I enjoyed rowing only on three occasions. During the interclass race, the junior boat was leading the freshman crew in which I was rowing by three lengths. Suddenly, just before the finish, the junior boat stopped and sank, and the freshman crew won, giving us our class numerals, a very proud moment. After the race it was learned that one of the juniors had allowed his foot to come out of the foot supports and in trying to replace it, had pushed it through the paper-thin hull of the boat. The cold swim didn't harm the juniors, and most of them had their class numerals anyway. Again, during practice, I had a lighter moment when Ben Howell, rowing in front of me, was slow in "feathering" his oar and the resulting "crab" deposited the unfortunate victim in the weeds and mud at the bottom of Lake Carnegie. The third episode seemed funny enough at the time. Our crew had just lost a race, and, as was customary, they threw Ben Michael, the coxswain, overboard as soon as the shell reached the boat-house. Innumerable of Ben's female relatives had collected at the boat-house to greet him. They shrieked in unison when he was pitched into the lake and several swooned when he came up to the surface with every hair on his body, and he was hairy as an ape, startlingly revealed through his dripping white shirt and shorts. That was in 1909 before hairy chests and other things were as daringly exposed as they are now.

During my sophomore year my father would not permit me to row, as one of his friends, a former Cornell oarsman, had dropped dead from a heart attack. A year later I had dug up enough records of crew men dying of old age to convince my father that rowing did not damage the heart. I have since learned that I was wrong, but, at any rate, I made the junior varsity that year. As my chance of making the varsity during my senior year seemed slim, and as chemistry, physics, and biology laboratory periods occupied most of my afternoons, I did not row regularly during my last year in college.

Swimming was as bad as rowing, if not worse. I found that my speed was inadequate for racing, so I played water polo. If any game should be abolished, water polo, as played in this country, leads the list. English water polo is fun, but in the American game, drowning, strangling, gouging, biting, and kicking were encouraged by the coaches and practiced and endured by the players. I loathed it, but I still wanted a college letter and finally won it though I never was a good water polo player; my size and buoyancy made up for my lack of aggressiveness and my dislike of punishment. Most of the team developed chronic sinus infections. I have spent the rest of my life treating mine and trying to persuade college authorities to substitute English water polo for the American variety. The English game has not been popular in this country because it seems too "sissy" in contrast to the more manly, native sport, but, at any rate, American water polo has been dropped by many universities, including Duke.

Track and tennis were more fun. I learned to "put the shot" and "throw the hammer" and obtained an occasional fourth place medal. The training I received from Keene Kitzpatrick was invaluable later at Oxford where the competition was easier. The tennis was for pleasure only and though of a very low degree of proficiency, I could win a friendly game once in a while.

At the end of my sophomore year in 1911, I decided to enter medical school without completing the Princeton course and discussed the question with Carter Wood, who at that time was Dean of the College of Physicians and Surgeons of Columbia University. He said that two more years of college, though pleasant, were unnecessary and, in fact, the two years thus saved could be more profitably used in additional hospital work after medical school. I therefore applied for admission to "P and S" and was admitted. However, my father would not give me permission and said even though the junior and senior years at Princeton might be a waste of time, the course should be completed. As I was a minor, I had no alternative but to obey but I am still convinced that Carter Wood was right and that two years of college preparation are preferable to four.

My first experience with surgery, except for having my tonsils removed and my neck nodes drained after a football injury, was watching J. M. T. Finney operate at the Johns Hopkins Hospital. I was spending the Easter vacation of 1911 in Baltimore with a classmate, Bing Bagby, with whom I had intended to study medicine. It was natural that we should wish to watch an operation, a mistake too many premedical students make. Finney gave us permission so we arrayed ourselves in gowns and entered the operating room. Finney, a former Princeton and Harvard football player, as

26

well as a Princeton Trustee, chuckled and assured us that we would enjoy the sight as the victim that morning was a Harvard student. All went well until the blood started and then my friend paled and fled. He decided then and there that a medical career was not for him, and he became a professor of psychology at Chapel Hill. I had a similar experience the following year which would have ended medicine for me were it not for Dr. John B. Deaver. Deaver had lectured to the Premedical Club at Princeton in the spring of 1912 and had invited the students to watch him operate at the German (now the Lankenau) Hospital the following Saturday morning before the Penn-Princeton baseball game. Tom Mabon, a classmate, and I went. As we entered the room, Deaver was removing a breast tumor, one of the most extensive and bloody operations. I stood it for ten minutes and then bolted for the garden in the rear of the hospital. The smell of the ether and the sight of the blood made me decide then and there to study law. Having replanned my life, I still wanted to see the baseball game so returned to the operating room door to summon Tom Mabon who was enjoying the carnage within. His father was a physician, and he was accustomed to it. I could not attract Tom's attention through the glass door but Deaver saw my pale green face, surmised my predicament, and beckoned me to enter. I shook my head so Deaver, in his rubber gloves and sterile gown, strode toward me to fetch me. I was ashamed to show the white feather and too, I was afraid Deaver would think me ungrateful, so I swallowed hard, entered, and to my surprise enjoyed the operation and forgot the ball game and my decision to study law. I have sympathized with entering medical students ever since.

The summer of 1911 at Montauk Point was the most important of my life because I met Atala Scudder and fell in love with her at first sight. I am still in love with her, and we have been married nearly fifty years.

RHODES SCHOLARSHIP

My studying, my selection of courses in which good grades were obtainable, and my athletics were planned solely to help my application for a Rhodes Scholarship which I had wanted ever since I had read of their creation in 1903. The qualifying examinations in Latin, Greek, and mathematics were held in Trenton on the 15th and 16th of October, 1912, and were not difficult. When I learned that my classmate, Wilder Penfield, also had passed the qualifying exam-

27

inations in New Jersey, it was obvious to me that Wilder could easily beat me. The four criteria for appointment at that time were scholarship, leadership, athletics, and letters of recommendation. Wilder's and my scholastic records were similar, but he was class president and All-America football tackle. Happily for me, I remembered that a candidate could apply from his home state as well as that in which he had attended college so I asked the Oxford authorities to transfer my application to New York.

No limit was placed on the number of the letters of recommendation so I obtained fifty or more from everyone whom I thought would be laudatory, including Woodrow Wilson and Henry Van Dyke. My father also collected a number of enthusiastic letters about me, even one from our Congressman who did not even know me. In general, the approbation of these was in inverse proportion to my acquaintance with the writers. When all of these letters had been assembled, Walter Boone, a classmate, and I read them and selected the ten most mendacious. They were successful.

After receiving the Rhodes Scholarship, my next six months at Princeton were very pleasant, culminating in a B.A. degree *cum laude* on the 10th of June, 1913.

My only two experiences in politics were amazingly effective. Earle McClintock (Princeton, 1911), Dan Lawrence (1910), who later founded *U.S. News*, and my classmate, Bob Ober, who later was killed in World War I, collected a group of brass-lunged 1913ers, including me, to sit in the gallery of the 1912 Democratic Convention in the Baltimore Armory and help nominate Woodrow Wilson who had been our President at Princeton. In relays we kept up a continuous bellow of "We want Wilson." Whenever one squad became exhausted, they would rest while the others continued during the voting. Champ Clark led during the ballots for the first two days but could not secure the necessary two-thirds vote. Because of the noisy gallery, or in spite of it, Wilson's vote kept increasing until finally William Jennings Bryan and Boss Murphy of New York capitulated and threw their weight to Wilson, who finally was nominated. The only reward for the "We Want Wilson" shouters was an invitation to march in Wilson's inaugural parade in Washington on the 4th of March, 1913. After a few miles of walking on the pavements of Pennsylvania and other avenues, the group decided they were being punished rather than rewarded.

My other political activity also ended in a parade. Atala's mother was very active in the women's suffrage campaign and asked me to collect some classmates to march in the New York Suffrage Parade. As our railroad fares were being paid, we accepted gladly. A day in New York would compensate for the amusement our friends would have at seeing us marching down Fifth Avenue. Either as a result of our parade or of natural evolution, the women received the vote.

Both of these incidents may explain the ease with which a handful of communists can arouse students into mob action in Latin America and Japan. Every student loves a parade as a lark and during the excitement they become just as vicious as their leaders. One Latin American student said that the communists not only pay you a dollar per day to riot but also supply you with a bag of stones.

CHAPTER III

OXFORD (1913-1916)

I SOON learned that whoever organized the "sailing party" for the forty-three Rhodes Scholars elected that year would receive free transportation. As the Rhodes Scholarship income of £300 ($1,500) would not start until arrival at Oxford, I arranged with the Cunard Company for accommodations on the S.S. *Franconia* sailing from Boston on the 30th of September, 1913, and wrote to my future Oxford classmates. Thirty-one of them joined the sailing party and several of them visited me in Brooklyn en route to Boston. The voyage was delightful — good weather, pleasant companions and the usual deck and indoor games. The program of the ship's concert for the benefit of the Seamen's Charities was largely composed of Rhodes Scholars, some of whom could sing, recite, and act. We reached Liverpool on the 8th of October, 1913, and went directly to Oxford.

Arriving in Oxford is an experience for the unsophisticated. The ancient buildings, the antique or absent plumbing, the left-hand traffic, the personal servant or "scout" and other strange customs left my companions and me starry-eyed. Scouts as a matter of fact are the real masters of the Oxford Colleges. Mine terrified me from the start. We had been told that we had to bring our own table silver, and when my scout unpacked my "luggage" and saw my butter spreaders which my mother had given me at a great sacrifice, he did not recognize them and said scornfully, that they could be used as fish knives until I could find something better.

All Rhodes Scholars are at once bewildered, amazed, and delighted by the difference in the Oxford educational system, the beauty of their surroundings, and by the greatness of the opportunity before them. Oxford itself is wonderful. The old buildings with their venerable associations and memories arouse an enthusiasm in Americans as well as in the English that cannot be equalled. An American feels that he is a part of an educational institution that was established centuries before the western hemisphere was dreamed of. Every college is complete in itself, with its own chapel, dining hall, and junior and senior "common" rooms. Some are more famous than others, but each is magnificent. One cannot help being interested in architecture when he is constantly confronted with masterpieces. The historic Thomas (called the Isis at Oxford) and the bit of England surrounding Oxford are delightful.

Being a member of a minority group is good experience in realizing that one must have a sense of responsibility toward the group. Anything any of us Americans did which "wasn't done" hurt the rest of us. The members of a majority group are interested in a small minority as a curiosity. They tolerate but don't like a larger minority unless it conforms to local customs, and they hate and fear a large minority. We fell in the second category and tried to remain inconspicuous by more or less successfully following the majority. American tourists in Europe usually are examples of minorities without a sense of responsibility to their country. Much of the ill-will we have caused in Europe is due to our utter disregard of local customs.

John D. Hayes, a senior Rhodes Scholar at Merton, whom I had known at Princeton, took us in hand and indoctrinated us into Oxford customs, manners, habits, and clothes. "Never speak to anyone unless you know him and preferably let him speak first" was the first rule, and "cautious inquiries in advance about whether a thing is done" was the second. Due to the natural shyness of the average English undergraduate, they seemed unfriendly, but one soon realized that the English really liked the Americans. We soon learned to like them, and these friendships have lasted fifty years. However, for the first three days at Oxford, no one seemed in the least concerned with me and my academic relations to the university. The captains of the athletic teams were the only Englishmen I met in that period, and they were only interested in inviting me to engage in different sports.

Language differences presented a problem at first. Not only are many words accented differently at Oxford, but the words themselves may have a different meaning. As I had grown up around New York where polyglot accents are the rule rather than the exception, I did not have much difficulty; in fact, I frequently was called in to translate for some of the Rhodes Scholars from the deep South. Sooner or later, most of us acquired some Oxford expressions and were accused of trying to imitate a British accent, but it usually was unconscious. I was very much chagrined a few years ago after

31

speaking at a medical meeting to be told by Stanhope Bayne-Jones that my accent was a terrible mixture of Long Island, Oxford, and North Carolina.

The rule that anyone who was not in his college by midnight led to many accidents. At Merton, a student could get over the garden wall by having a hansom cab back up to it and bribing the cabby to place his horse blanket over the broken glass set in concrete which topped the wall. However, unless the youth was particularly sober, and many were not, he might forget to jump clear of the glass greenhouse which the college dons had built on the inside of the wall to trap the unwary returning undergraduate. Unfortunately, my room was next to the college garden, and at least one night every week I, as a medical student, had to dress cuts and bruises and pick glass from wounds. I suppose it was good training in medicine because I had to keep first-aid emergency equipment constantly on hand. There also was a reverse rule that all non-members of the college had to be out before midnight. Later, when I was an intern at the Radcliffe Infirmary, I had to treat one of my friends who stayed too long in a college to which he did not belong. He climbed out of a window and jumped down on what he thought was a lawn. Unfortunately, the college authorities had erected an iron spiked fence under the window. My friend survived my treatment, though the spikes penetrated six inches into his thigh. To add insult to injury, he was fined twenty pounds when he was caught.

After I had registered with the Merton porter, a college servant who was more potent than the warden or head don, I tried to discover how to study medicine. My first contacts with the Oxford educational system were catastrophic. Every Oxford undergraduate has a tutor who directs his program. I was assigned to Dr. Marsh, an ancient chemistry don. Our first and last meeting was unpleasant. Marsh informed me that no Americans knew any chemistry but that he would give me an examination to see how elementary the tutoring should be. I didn't know much chemistry but as I had completed all of the usual courses required in this field, I saw no reason for repeating them. It would have been better for me to have continued to know Marsh as a tutor, but I was going to study medicine and, at that stage, I felt that chemistry was something which one studied and discarded like short trousers. After a stormy discussion, March and I decided that future sessions would be mutually unprofitable so I was given permission to study medicine untutored.

The next step was to be admitted to the university as a "foreign senior student" and then to visit the medical laboratories which consisted of the anatomy, physiology and pathology buildings, a museum and library. All of the courses given were posted on a large sheet on the physiology door. I arranged a schedule, pronounced "schedule" at Oxford, to cover the usual first two years of medicine in one year. I saw no good reason why I couldn't do it. I had become accustomed to hard work at Princeton, carrying enough extra courses and even graduate studies so that I could have been graduated in three years if the regulations had not prevented it. I asked one of the instructors if this plan were permissible and was firmly told, "It isn't done." In answer to my inquiry of "why," the same reply was received. I later found that the statement "it isn't done" was supposed to and usually did end all Oxford arguments. However, I was inexperienced and pressed the case. Finally, I was told to select my own courses under the supervision of Sir William Osler, the Regius Professor of Medicine and Dean of the Medical School, who had lived in the States and would know how to handle an argumentative American student who did not understand Oxford traditions.

An appointment was made, and I rang the bell at 13 Norham Gardens, Sir William's house, with fear and trembling because to me and most Americans the name Osler was the pinnacle of medicine. By that time, I profoundly regretted even considering my proposed crowded schedule, but as the appointment had been made, I had to make the call. When the door opened, I had decided to withdraw my request, to apologize for my temerity, and to retreat in haste. I was delightfully surprised when a small man came to the door and said cheerily before I could open my mouth, "I am Sir William and have heard of your request which I think is very foolish, but, of course, you can do anything you please, and now let's have tea." I was amazed as he took me by the arm and propelled me into the drawing room, introducing me to Lady Osler with, "Grace, here is a new American colt who is wrecking a medical school tradition. Give him some tea." Both of them were so charming and friendly that I soon felt that I had two friends at Oxford. My awe immediately turned to adoration and devotion. This extremely pleasant and informal reception was the first of many delightful memories I shall always cherish of the Oslers. Sir William never mentioned the two-year-in-one medical school schedule again, but I soon found

33

**13, NORHAM GARDENS,
OXFORD.**

1915

I shall not make a visit on Sunday. I have a cold. Cannot go to Clevedon Monday or Tuesday as I have to join Dr. Collier in the medical examination.

Wm Osler

**13, NORHAM GARDENS,
OXFORD.**

1916

Mr. Penfield writes that he will arrive at 3.30 tomorrow — I have told Mr. Lyttes — Telephone please if it is not convenient for you to meet him — Sincerely

Monday.   G. R. Osler

Typical cards to Davison from the Oslers

that though I could and did attend all of the courses, my knowledge of their content remained very meager. I had exceeded the limit beyond which medical education could be accelerated. At any rate, from 1913 to 1914, I studied anatomy, bacteriology, biochemistry, histology, pathology, pharmacology, physiology, physical diagnosis, attended Osler's ward rounds at the Radcliffe Infirmary, played water polo and ice hockey, threw the hammer and put the shot for the Oxford varsity, and rowed in fours, torpid* and the eight for my College. I also put in a summer term in anatomy at Edinburgh. It was a busy year.

At the end of each year, the dons of the college summon each undergraduate to appear before them to be complimented, or more often reprimanded, for their work, depending on the report of their tutors. When I attended this "don rag," as it was called, the dons were nonplussed, as I apparently was the only student they had ever had who escaped having a tutor. Finally, they asked me for a report on myself. Naturally, I gave a good one. The warden, a gloomy old man, ordered the Dean to enter on the college books, "Mr. Davison says he has done very well." I never had to attend another don rag.

Merton had the oldest library in England. It was built in 1377 by Bishop Rede. It consisted of a beautiful, panelled room with ancient books and manuscripts chained to the desks to prevent the medieval scholars from borrowing them. No modern books disgraced the shelves. I needed a Howell's *Physiology* for reference and had the temerity to suggest that the librarian purchase one. He was quite indignant because some of William Harvey's manuscripts were there and as Harvey had been warden of Merton in the 1640's, why should anyone want anything better. I tried to explain that considerable additions to physiology had accumulated during the three centuries since Harvey. He finally agreed to present the matter to the dons of the college. They were so amused at my American brashness that they authorized the purchase.

None of us, while in residence at Oxford before World War I, took our studies very seriously. We were supposed to do our hard work during the winter, spring, and summer vacations. The first two were of six weeks each and the last was of three months. In other words, Oxford has three terms of two months each and vacations of six months. During "term" we spent most of our time in "sports," as

---

* A torpid is a College's second boat, the eight being the first.

athletics were called in England. I was too tired after rowing, water polo, hammer throwing and shot putting to study at night; in fact, I had a hard time keeping up with my laboratory work, for the British take their sports very seriously, especially rowing. However, I did try to obtain permission to dissect at night. Arthur Thomson, the Scottish professor of anatomy, was horrified (the Scotch take education very dourly) and said that never would he allow his laboratory to be prostituted to athletics. Thomson required us to carry all of the tarsal bones in one pocket and the carpal bones in another so that he could call on us to produce any particular one. At that time in 1913, fifty years ago, I could spot each one of them by the feel of it. Now, I cannot even remember their names. At any rate, Thomson said that I had to work at regular laboratory hours or not at all. I chose the latter, and I can now readily see that if World War I had not intervened, I should have learned very little medicine during the balance of my Rhodes Scholarship.

ROWING

To carry a combined medical and athletic schedule had its difficulties. Training at Oxford proceeded on the theory that if one survived he could row. We had to consume a heavy breakfast of porridge, fish, eggs, toast, marmalade, an orange, and a pint of beer. Rowing practice from two to four was followed by tea and biscuits, a practice which I avoided until forced into it. Tea drinking at Oxford is automatic. Life just doesn't go on without it. My initiation into the habit came very quickly. Pathology lectures were from five to seven after rowing practice. After the third class, Alexander G. Gibson, the lecturer, warned me that I had to drink tea or fail the course because I had slept through the preceding lecture. I have been drinking tea ever since.

The crew dined in "hall" at seven-thirty. The evening menu had only two variations, fruit and meat. The first was either prunes or figs, respectively known as black and brown "starters" because of their laxative effect. The meat was beef and mutton for three days each, with chicken on Sunday. The fixed ingredients of the evening meal were soup, fish, sweetbreads, spinach, cabbage, Brussel sprouts, pudding, port, and beer. Food in England, and particularly at Oxford, was wholesome rather than delicious, but the excellent beef, mutton, cheese and hot mustard more than made up for the greens, sprouts, puddings and amateur cooking. I had to run two

Rowing for his College at Oxford

miles daily around Christ Church meadow in order to keep my weight under 196 pounds (14 stone).

To overcome staleness, each member of the crew was ordered to get tight at dinner four days before the races. In spite of quantities of champagne, beer and port, I put the other members of the crew to bed and was nearly dropped from the crew for my "lack of cooperation."

The Merton boat did so well in Eights Week that the college decided to enter the Henley races in July. We practiced and sweated and really developed a good crew with a fair chance of winning. Then, without warning, Court von Wurmb or "von Grub" as we called him, a German Rhodes Scholar, who rowed number six, said he had been ordered home. He was irreplaceable so the race was "scratched." I was disappointed as one of my ambitions had been to row at Henley. However, I thought I would have another chance next year. Little did I realize that von Wurmb's order to return to Germany at the end of June foreshadowed the First World War. In spite of him being German, I liked him.

My only claim to fame in Oxford rowing was that I had the widest oar on the river. Because of my weight and previous rowing training the usual Oxford six-inch bladed oar was too small for me and one with a seven-inch blade had to be built. It now hangs on the wall of my study together with my golf club and swimming cap as a trophy of discarded and unlamented physical activity.

WATER POLO

The Oxford tradition decreed that members of a college crew or boat could not engage in any other sport. However, as I wanted a "blue" and doubted whether I should win one in rowing, I practiced water polo in the late afternoon after rowing. I was varsity goalkeeper but as I was not supposed to play, I was registered as "A. Keep" in the program of the matches. We won all of our games except that against Cambridge, and I made my "half blue."

Water polo gave me one of the best lessons in the difference between American and British athletics. At Princeton and other American universities, the object is to win by every means allowable under the rules, but at Oxford, the game was more important than the score. In one London match, my opponent could outplay me so I allowed him to swim over me and then blasted him out of the water with a powerful, underwater kick. He kept away from me in the future, but Mellows, the Oxford captain, had seen the performance and promptly put me out of the game with "it isn't done." As J. Frank Dobie commented, "An English university consists of 3,000 men, every one of whom would rather lose a game than play it unfairly."

TRACK

I surreptitiously practiced hammer-throwing and shot-putting in the morning before breakfast. At Princeton, I was one of the worst hammer-throwers and shot-putters, or weight-putter as it is called in England, but I found at Oxford that only four others knew anything about these events and they were senior Rhodes Scholars who would leave at the end of the year. Instead of awarding useless medals for winning track and crew races, Oxford gave the successful competitors credit at the local jewelers. In that way, I acquired a wrist watch, tobacco case and a beer tankard which are still useful. Medals, on the other hand, are cherished for a day and then placed in a trunk to be forgotten. The only amusement I ever had with medals was one day when Sandy, my younger son, then a small boy, and I were hunting for something else in the attic and found my old medals. Sandy politely inquired about each of them and I probably boasted of my prowess. He then found the Victory Medal which everyone received in the First War. When Sandy learned what it was, he gazed at me with admiration and exclaimed, "Daddy, I didn't know that you had won the war too."

Oxford does not do prep school recruiting or give athletic scholarships, but few undergraduates escape being a member of one or more teams. Even the Prince of Wales, later King Edward the VIII and still later the Duke of Windsor, who was a fellow student at Oxford, entered into all of the usual activities and played soccer for his college, Magdalen. He was treated and wanted to be treated like the rest of us. One day in going to my dressing room, at the Merton Baths, at which the water polo team practiced, I found that someone had left his clothes there. As the varsity had prior rights, I promptly heaved out the intruder's garments just as the owner, the Prince of "Pragger Wagger" as he was called in Oxford slang, appeared. I was much embarrassed, but he quickly collected his scattered belongings, apologized for "barging in" on the varsity and disappeared into the realms set aside for the undergraduates, followed by a water-polo ball powerfully thrown by Loudoun-Shand, a Scotch varsity player.

ICE-HOCKEY

Just before the winter vacation, Tom Means, a Yale Rhodes Scholar at Merton, asked me if I could play ice hockey. Naturally, anyone who had been brought up on Long Island could play hockey, but I, truthfully, told him that I was no good at the game. He said that it would make little difference as the other members of the Oxford hockey team were equally poor and invited me to go to Murren, Switzerland, to play against Cambridge, our expenses being paid by Sir Henry Lunn's Alpine Club which owned the hotels there and wanted the match played to attract guests. I, of course, accepted.

As I had never been on the continent the trip was memorable. The altitude of Murren, 5,000 feet, bothered us for the first few days. We had to rest after fifteen minutes of skating. I found that the Oxford team, as Tom Means had told me, was very weak. Our goal-keeper, Tatton, couldn't skate and defended the net with one hand, holding onto the frame with the other. One of the forwards, Lord something, I have forgotten, played with a monocle which would tinkle on the ice every few minutes and force him to stop playing until he could replace it. I played cover point, or guard, but as the Cambridge players, who practiced with us, were much faster I decided that "body-checking" was the only possible defense, especially when I learned that the referee did not know the rules. It was of no use. On the 23rd of December, 1913, Cambridge defeated us 10 to 0. Tom Means and I were covered with bruises, but the game was fun and the post-match banquet was sumptuous.

Murren has one of the longest and fastest tobaggan or "luge" runs in the world. It was cut in the deep snow and then "iced" by flooding the track with water. Tom Means and I tried it once. A cable car took us and our "luges," which are like our old-fashioned "belly-whopper" sleds, to the top of the mountain where the run started. Tom insisted on going down first as I was inexperienced. He told me to follow after an interval of one minute so that we would not collide. I had the fright of my life for the speed soon reached sixty miles an hour. The little sled would careen around the turns and give me a ghastly view of the Jungfrau valley thousands of feet below. Half way down the mountain, I heard loud shrieks and cursing. Obviously, someone was in trouble so I managed to stop my sled by gradually sliding off backwards, much to the damage of my clothes and abdomen. I found Tom Means bleeding like a stuck pig and swearing like a marine. I finally learned that he had sighted a St. Bernard dog standing on the edge of the run ahead of him with a gleam in his eye. Tom shouted to the animal to leave him alone and that if he wanted something to eat, a much better nourished man was following him. The dog had been trained to rescue and didn't understand Tom anyway. As Tom shot past him, the St. Bernard reached down and caught him by the seat of his trousers and held on. When I arrived, Tom had lost a fistful of buttocks, and the dog had disappeared.

In spite of my ignorance, Tom insisted that I treat him so I tied a large handkerchief around his bleeding leg and carried him down to the hotel on my sled. I had a vague recollection that an antiseptic was needed so asked the hotel porter if he had any. He produced an ancient bottle of something with a carbolic odor and an unreadable German label. I carefully applied the molasses-like stuff on the wound and bandaged it. Three hours later, Tom was still in pain, so I removed the dressing and found that the whole area had been burned down to a depth of a quarter of an inch. Tom was wild but I assured him that this "cauterization" was necessary to prevent hydrophobia and tetanus. The wound finally healed but Tom had a six inch square brand as a permanent memento of his encounter. The experience was a lasting lesson to me to avoid using any drugs whose labels I could not read. I apparently had applied pure Lysol which should have been diluted with 500 parts of water. Duke Hospital later had signs on all wards "Do not give medicine without reading the label three times." As soon as Tom could walk, we went to Grundelwald, Switzerland, for another week of winter sports. I even tried skiing which, at that time, was almost unknown at home. I never learned to ski with confidence, but a jump of a couple of feet gave me as much thrill as 100 feet produced in a professional.

We returned from Switzerland via Paris and that winter of 1913-1914 was the busiest "holiday" I ever had. My most interesting medical experience was seeing two lepers at the St. Louis Hospital. Like all first-year medical students, I was afraid of catching every disease I saw, and leprosy was popularly thought to be very infectious. As a matter of fact, I have since seen many lepers in the "Far East" without a qualm, but those first two worried me for months.

At this time I made an effort to understand and enjoy music. Both my parents played and sang. I was rocked to sleep throughout infancy with the songs of *Carmina Princetonia* by my father who had been on the Princeton glee club for four years. I sang in a boy's choir,

Davison in Switzerland

The Oxford ice hockey team in Switzerland.
Davison, first from right on second row.

struggled with piano and violin lessons, played second violin in the Jamaica High School orchestra, attended concerts, symphonies and operas in this country and abroad but finally learned to my great regret that I did not appreciate music. Except for Gilbert and Sullivan, music actually bored me. Probably, many others are like me though they won't admit it. The only tunes I can readily recognize are the *Volga Boat Song* and the *Star Spangled Banner*, and I sometimes cannot even differentiate between them.

I never learned to like opera, but I did enjoy one performance of *Samson and Delilah* in Paris. Tom Means and I had two-franc seats which we found were in the top-most heaven, from which the stage was completely invisible. We decided that we had been cheated so, between the first and second acts, while everyone was promenading in the foyer, we slipped into two good seats in the first balcony. When their owners returned, they furiously argued with us but we merely shrugged our shoulders, insisted that we could not understand French and seemed so innocent that the ushers removed the irate Frenchmen and locked the doors of the entrance to the balcony. Tom and I greatly enjoyed the second act, but we were too slow in disappearing at the end of it. Two huge gendarmes were waiting for us and despite our struggles, they heaved us down the marble steps of the main entrance. We did not see the third act but the fun was worth the discomfiture. Several years later at the Quadrangle Club in Chicago, I was introduced to H. G. Hudson, president of Illinois College, who told me that he had been a Rhodes Scholar from 1911 to 1914. I replied that I had been one from 1913 to 1916 and that we should have known each other. He rather rudely assured me that he didn't remember me. Finally, he exclaimed "Of course I remember you, you were the Rhodes Scholar who started a riot by being thrown out of the Paris Opera House." Such is fame!

SPRING VACATION

Early in 1914, William H. Cornell, who had employed me to spy on his bookkeeper at Montauk Point in 1911, wrote that this ex-employee had sued him for being dismissed and that he needed my testimony at the trial. Needless to say, I arranged to return to the States during the Easter vacation as I was much in love. The trial was a joke. As soon as I entered the courtroom, the ex-bookkeeper recognized me and realized that I knew that he had been engaging in a rival fish business which invalidated his contract. He promptly withdrew his suit, and I had a very happy vacation with Atala at Bryn Mawr and Atlantic City. I returned on a cruise ship, the *Cretic*, from Boston on the 2nd of April, 1914, to Gibraltar via the Azores and Madeira. I made a fascinating detour to Tangiers in North Africa and then returned to Oxford through Spain and France. While in Madrid, I had the pleasure of meeting Professor Ramon y Cajal and Dr. Rio-Hortega, the famous neurohistologists who were friends of Sherrington, the professor of physiology at Oxford. I also visited their laboratory at the medical school.

The summer vacation of 1914 was delightful. Atala and her family spent June at Oxford and July in London and Paris, and I was their guest. The only cloud, to which I paid no attention at the time, was meeting Sherley Morgan, a Princeton classmate, in front of the Opera one afternoon, at the end of July. He told me that he had just lunched with some French officers who had told him that all Europe would be at war within a week. I was incredulous, but Sherley said that his friends had told him that Austria had made impossible demands on Serbia because of the assassination of their Archduke and that Germany would declare war in support of Austria. In the bright sunshine of a peaceful Paris afternoon, this rumor sounded like a pipe dream.

After Paris, Atala went with her mother and sister to Donaueschingen in the German Black Forest for a few days with the intention of later attending the Wagner festival at Bayreuth. Judge Scudder and I travelled to Vevey in Switzerland to await their return. Two days later, Hell broke loose. Sherley Morgan's friends were right — Germany, Austria, Serbia, France, Belgium, and Russia were at war. As telegraph wires had been cut, I started for Donaueschingen on Swiss trains crowded with troops. Switzerland had mobilized to preserve her neutrality.

The story is told that one of the German generals asked the Swiss commander what he would do if the Germans decided to invade with an army of a million. The Swiss replied that he had a million sharpshooters, and they would kill the million Germans. "What if I send two million Germans?" asked the German general. "Each of our men would fire twice," replied the Swiss.

I had no difficulty in entering Germany and rode the even more crowded German troop trains. The German soldiers were happily excited about fighting Russia and did not realize that England would declare war. When I reached Donaueschingen, I found that Atala and her mother and sister had left for Vevey where I joined them the next day.

We spent the balance of August in Switzerland, Judge and Mrs. Scudder staying in Vevey and Atala and her sister at St. Lagier at the school they had attended as children. I had a room in a nearby pension, studied medical books all morning and walked and climbed mountains all afternoon. No one had any money; the banks were still closed. One of the most delightful experiences was walking with Atala to Montreux, ten miles along the Lake of Geneva, with twenty cents we had been hoarding for the return trip on the train. We were so hot and tired that we decided to splurge our twenty cents on raspberry ice and walk home. It was worth it. Food seemed to be plentiful. We had the most delicious rabbit stews almost daily for lunch. However, we noticed just before we left St. Legier that all of the village cats had disappeared. We haven't eaten rabbit since.

Our return to Paris in September was comfortable because our State Department had arranged for a special train for Americans. The situation in Paris was hectic. The Germans had penetrated to Senlis, almost at the gates of Paris and were close to Rouen. The French government had departed for Bordeaux. That afternoon, Atala and I saw the first air-raid in history. The only damage was to a Frenchwoman who picked up one of the hot fragments of a bomb as a souvenir. That evening, Marshal Joffre requisitioned all of the taxicabs to transfer his troops from the trains coming from the south to those leaving for the north so that he could make a stand on the Marne. As Paris was having its first black-out, and the taxi lights were dimmed, the traffic was chaotic and dangerous.

As all of the channel boats were being used to bring the British Army to France, our government sent the U.S. battleship, *Tennessee*, to Le Havre to pick up any stranded Americans. Atala and I finally obtained seats on the train to Le Havre, spent the night in a warehouse, and embarked on the *Tennessee* the next day. The crossing from Le Havre to Weymouth was delightful, and we reached London five days after leaving Switzerland, a journey usually made in twenty-four hours.

Atala had to return to Bryn Mawr, and after she sailed, I went to Edinburgh to study anatomy at Surgeon's Hall under Professor J. Ryland Whitaker until the autumn term started at Oxford. Whitaker was the most famous anatomy teacher in Great Britain, and his lectures were delightful. He would explain intricate structures like the internal ear in such simple terms that even I could understand them, and then make the whole class recite his description in unison until it was memorized. I understand that the Turks teach the Koran that way. It may not be modern pedagogy but I can still remember the anatomy I learned from Whitaker.

Professor Whitaker gave me a baby to dissect. I was unable to finish it before leaving for the autumn term at Oxford so I wrapped the infant in several newspapers to retain the embalming fluid and carried the bundle with me. Naturally, I was worried because transporting a body without a permit made me liable to a fine of fifty pounds. I placed the parcel in the luggage rack in the far corner of the railway compartment and hoped that no one knew that I was the owner. Unfortunately, the weather was hot and the embalming fluid dripped on the passenger sitting underneath. She was indignant that anyone would leave wet, smelly packages in luggage racks but, as I heartily agreed with her, my ownership was not detected.

Oxford, in October, 1914, had changed from the previous spring term. Most of my English friends had joined up and we Americans wanted to help. The first opportunity came in November. Herbert Hoover had been placed in charge of the Belgian Relief Commission and needed some youngsters to administer the food distribution in Belgium. He sent Perrin C. Galpin to Oxford for recruits. I had been elected president of the American Club before the war; in fact, I made so many bad decisions that I held the title of hereditary monarch, so I asked for volunteers at the next meeting. The whole club offered to go but Galpin could only use twenty. They did yeoman service. Most of the others engaged in other war activities in England, France, and even Egypt and India.

Osler gave me a letter to Dr. Richard Derby, who, with Dr. Joseph A. Blake, was chief of the hospital of the American Ambulance Service which the American colony in Paris had organized in the Lycee Pasteur, a new school building at Neuilly. Dr. Derby was bewildered about my status so I was assigned first as an orderly which is good training in gaining sympathy for the patients, next as a catheter specialist on the paraplegic wards, and, finally, as an anesthetist.

Most of the non-medical aides were New York and Paris society people. One of the former, Miss Frances Howland, was later responsible for my interest in pediatrics. One of the most amusing incidents was the puritanical row which one of the Rhodes Scholars

46

had with a Franco-American medical student who had lived all his life in Paris. They had been discussing one of the very attractive *infirmieres* and the Franco-American casually mentioned that she was the mistress of a well-known Frenchman. "What do you mean?" said the outraged American. The reply was "She sleeps with him." The pure American promptly knocked out the Franco-American. When the latter was revived, the American told him that he must never say anything like that again. "But everyone knows about it" was the naive reply, and he was knocked out again.

Benjamin Jablons, the pathologist, let me work in the autopsy room. He was a good teacher and had a fine sense of humor. His reply to George W. Crile of Cleveland who was to come to the American Hospital in December was a classic. Crile was very much interested in shock and wrote Jablons to save sections of the liver, spleen, suprarenal, testes and ovaries of everyone who died in shock. In regard to the last organ Jablons remarked, "I believe that Crile does not know the meaning of hors de combat."

Everyone worked like horses, possibly because we all ate horse meat from the cavalry animals killed at the battle of the Marne. Most of the wounds at that time were from shrapnel. High explosive shells were not used until 1915. One of the most pathetic patients was a young Frenchman who had been lying in a trench when a shrapnel bullet struck the handle of his bayonet which was in his belt scabbard and drove one of the rivets through his spine completely paralyzing his legs. Some of the men would have as many as twenty pieces of shrapnel in their bodies, and they were hard to locate. Finally, Joseph A. Blake, the chief surgeon, and Arthur U. Desjardins, who later was roentgenologist at the Mayo Clinic, decided to operate on the X-ray table. Everything went well until the anesthetist struck his head against the high tension wires and was nearly electrocuted.

Most of the patients appreciated the attention which they received, but an occasional one made our lives miserable by frequent unnecessary calls. One of them especially irritated his orderly, who was a Paris society swell. Finally, in revenge, this orderly placed a urinal in the refrigerator and a bedpan on the stove. The next call was the last unnecessary one. After this hot and cold treatment, the patient was very cooperative.

Unfortunately, I have seen many people die and shall always be deeply affected but never so much as when I lost my first patient. I was giving an anesthetic to a young French soldier whose hip and

47

pelvis had been badly smashed by a shell. After the wound had been debrided of clothing and bone and shell fragments, and Carrel-Dakin tubes and solution inserted, the surgeon wrapped the whole area with plaster of Paris bandages, including the abdomen and thorax, causing respiration to become so feeble that the patient died.

In the winter of 1914-1915, the Serbs, or Yugoslavs, as they are now called, asked the French for medical and surgical teams, so I obtained permission from Lord Milner and Mr., later Sir, Francis Wylie of the Rhodes Trust, H. M. Vernon, my new Oxford tutor, and W. H. Fyfe, the Dean of Merton and the Oxford Vice-Chancellor and joined one of the units as an anesthetist. I left the American Ambulance Hospital at Neuilly on the 25th of January, 1915, and sailed from Marseilles on the 27th of January, 1915, on the Messageries Maritime Steamer, *Caledonian*, for Salonika. F. F. Gardner, the chief surgeon of the outfit, Elsie Jessup, the chief nurse, and I were the advance party. The others members were to come later. Gardner had acquired a cold in Malta and had an idea that eating raw onions would cure it. They didn't but they certainly made life miserable in the cabin, and we could not go on deck because of the storm. Going by train up the Vardar Valley from Salonika to Nis was hazardous for the comitadji bands of Bulgars and Macedonian Serbs. The Bulgarian Revolutionary Committee in Macedonia had blown up the bridge over the Vardar River and we had to ride on the train platforms, ready to jump if the temporary trestle gave way.

The original Serb plan had been for us to operate a surgical base hospital at Nis, but the fighting was over when we arrived on the 4th of January, 1915. However, due to crowding from the Austrian invasion, one of the worst epidemics of typhus broke out among the Serb Army, the civilian population, Austrian prisoners, and especially among doctors and nurses. Instead of being an anesthetist in a surgical team at Nis, I became a typhus specialist at Krusevac on the 11th of February, 1915, and looked at rashes, took temperatures, and administered aspirin for the terrific headaches of typhus. The only Serbian I learned was "Where is the pain?" and "Are you feeling better?" The only thing we knew about typhus was that it was louse-borne. The patients died like flies (20 per cent mortality). Fourteen of the Americans in Serbia contracted typhus and three died.

The only way to keep free of lice was eternal vigilance and cleanliness. Picking the cooties whenever they were felt, and frequent "seam inspection" of underwear and clothes also were necessary because one never knew whether the lice which were removed had been on some patient and had become infected. One night, Gardner felt a louse crawling around on him but couldn't locate it. I tried unsuccessfully to help him by candle light and finally we concluded that the cootie was hiding in Gardner's umbilicus. At any rate I sealed him off with hot candle grease which may have smothered him though it was painful for Gardner. Bathing was a necessity, but bath-tubs were scarce. We succeeded in buying in the market large pig-troughs hollowed out of single logs and with a little practice we were able to take fairly thorough baths without tipping over at every move.

I had a very healthy respect for typhus because every day it killed someone I knew. Finally, our Austrian cook came down with it. I was so sure that I would get it and was so afraid that I wouldn't make the diagnosis that I took my temperature frequently. Fortunately, it remained normal. If it had reached 99 degrees, I probably should have died of fright.

Our only recreations in Krusevac were walking, horse-back riding, and drinking Turkish coffee. The first was almost impossible because of the mud, and my only experience with the second cured me of ever wanting to ride again. I had borrowed a horse from a Serb cavalry officer who neglected to teach me the necessary words to control the animal. The horse started off at a gallop, heading for the Morava river. As soon as he was half-way across, he stopped and refused to go any further. I exhausted my Serbian, English and American vocabulary but was marooned there with my legs at right angles to keep them out of the water until a Serb peasant waded out and rescued me. However, I still like Turkish coffee.

In addition to typhus, the Serbian population suffered from a food shortage. They shared their food with the Austrian prisoners but neither group had enough to eat. Scurvy finally broke out among the Austrians, and it was not controlled until one of them suggested that onions might cure it. Onions were plentiful and soon cured the scurvy, but the odor from the prison camp could be detected for miles. The reason the Serbs themselves did not get scurvy was because their national dish is paprikas, a mixture of meat and red peppers. After a Serbian meal, I always had to keep my mouth open to cool off. It is now known that the red peppers in paprikas contain large amounts of ascorbic acid which prevents scurvy.

The Serb diet was almost as bad as their typhus epidemic. Lambs were the main dish, and everything was utilized including the eyeballs, lungs and intestines (chitlings). Swallowing an eyeball is an experience to be avoided.

Finally, as in all epidemics, the number of cases waned and as the weather became warmer, typhus gradually disappeared. The medical profession, usually, gets and sometimes takes credit for stopping epidemics, but this typhus outbreak in Serbia ceased because most of the population caught the disease and either died or recovered. On the 25th of February, 1915, we received word from Paris that the remainder of our unit could not come but that a Harvard unit with Richard Strong, Hans Zinsser, and Joe Hopkins would handle the typhus epidemic, so I decided to return to Oxford for the examinations of the "Honour School of Physiology" for which I had originally registered along with the other subjects of the first two years of medical school. F. F. Gardner, the surgeon of our unit, also planned to return. The other members were absorbed into the Serbian Medical Corps. On our way south we spent the first night in Nis, the temporary capital, where we were joined by a Cambridge medical student, named Squires, from a neighboring unit who also was returning to England for his examinations.

While Gardner, Squires, and I were dining in a Nis coffee shop, we saw a tall, thin, white-mustachioed man enter. I recognized him as Sir Thomas Lipton, for I had seen his pictures many times in the New York papers during the yacht races for America's Cup when I was a boy. Besides, one of my Serb friends had told me that Lipton had brought out a medical unit to Serbia from England on his yacht, the *Erin,* a few days before. He looked at everyone in the room and finally came to our table and said "You are not Serbians, are you?" We thanked him for the implied compliment and told him our nationalities. He asked if we could speak Serbian, and we told him our knowledge was sufficient only for medical questions and for ordering meals. He said he was primarily interested in the latter as he was hungry and that if we would order the best meal the place afforded, he would like to join us and pay the bill. Needless to say we obliged. Sir Thomas told us that he had been born in Ireland and had been in business in Aberdeen, Scotland, New Orleans, and London

50

so he could speak four languages, Irish, Scotch, American, and English, but that the Serbian language and especially their cyrillic alphabet were beyond him. It was a jolly meal, for Lipton was a famous raconteur and through his international tea business and his yacht racing, he apparently knew everyone worth knowing. When he learned that we were returning to England, he invited us to go on his yacht which would leave Salonika three days hence. We were delighted and left for Salonika that night. When we arrived, we took turns sitting on the dock for fear that the *Erin* might sail without us.

On the 27th of Feburary, 1915, during one of the intervals of waiting, I wandered through a Salonika fort but was soon stopped by a guard who prodded me with a bayonet. I protested in perfect grammatical ancient Greek but could not make myself understood. After a very uncomfortable and vain attempt at an explanation of my reason for being out of bounds, the Greek soldier laughed and said in New Yorkese, "Youse is an American, ain't you?" I admitted the fact, not knowing whether it would get me into even more trouble since the United States had not then joined the Allies. However, the Greek dropped his rifle, embraced me and would have kissed me except for my rapid footwork, and insisted on my spending the evening with him. He had immigrated to America as a boy and had been in the fur business on 42nd Street, New York. Just before the war he returned to Greece to visit his old parents and had been drafted into the army at the outbreak of hostilities. To see a fellow American was like manna from heaven to him, and he was hospitality personified.

Sir Thomas finally arrived with five more guests whom he had invited to sail with him, Dr. Hodge from the American Red Cross Hospital at Gevgelija, a British admiral who had been in charge of the Serb artillery, the Serb ex-ambassador to Turkey, the editor of the *Daily Mail*, and Prince Paul, the nephew of King Peter of Serbia who was returning to Oxford for his examinations. It was a joyous party for the luxury of the yacht was a delightful contrast to the squalor of the crowded Serb villages. Unfortunately, just before we sailed, Dr. Hodge said he had a headache. We immediately looked for a typhus rash and to our dismay found it. We had to carry him ashore to a Greek hospital. All of us volunteered to remain with him but as Gardner was the only medical graduate he decided to stay and join in at Naples.

The Dardanelles campaign started the day we arrived in Greece.

Athens was in a turmoil. Apparently, the strategy consisted in having the British fleet and the Anzac troops storm the Dardanelles while the Greek Army marched around the Aegean Sea and attacked Turkey from the north. The plan was sound but the Greeks were not. As far as I could learn, Venizelos, the Greek premier, had made the agreement, but the Queen, who was the Kaiser's sister, prevented its consummation. Constantine, the King, didn't count in the battle between the Queen and the prime minister. The people were all for fighting the Turks, and the street riots were violent. Finally, Venizelos resigned and returned to his home in Crete in order to restore peace in Athens. But the British were left holding the bag in the Dardanelles, and a disastrous show it turned out to be. Winston Churchill, the advocate of the campaign, was blamed, but the fault lay with the Greek queen. We spent several days in the midst of this exciting international intrigue. Prince Paul would lunch with the King who was a distant relative of his; Sir Thomas would lunch with the British Minister; the Serb ambassador would visit his diplomatic friends, and because I was on Lipton's yacht, the American minister thought that I was a VIP and often invited me to lunch. In the evening at dinner on the *Erin*, we would trade the gossip we had gleaned during the day. During the furor, Lipton learned that the British needed a hospital ship so he named me, a second-year medical student, the chief surgeon on the *Erin* with Squires, a Cambridge first-year medical student, as assistant surgeon and cabled Lord Fisher of the British Navy that the *Erin* was ready to be the hospital ship for the Dardanelles expedition. The offer was nearly accepted, and we made elaborate plans but finally word came that a British hospital ship had arrived at Mudros and our chance to become famous vanished. All of us were disappointed so we continued the return voyage to England.

Our next stop was at Naples on the 7th of March, 1915. The editor of the *Daily Mail* was very keen on obtaining more news of the situation in Italy, which had not yet declared war against Austria and Germany, and dared me to cross these countries on an over-land trip to England, promising me fifteen pounds for a newspaper story, a tempting sum for any Rhodes Scholar. Gardner arrived from Salonika as Hodge had recovered from typhus so we decided to make the trip together.

Except for Prince Paul, who later returned to Oxford and gave me a royal lunch in his rooms at Christ Church, and the editor of the

Daily Mail, who paid me fifteen pounds the following month in London, I never saw Sir Thomas and his other guests again. The *Erin* continued safely on her way to England, but on her next voyage to Serbia she was sunk by a submarine off Sicily and the survivors were brought to Taranto.

Gardner and I obtained new passports from the American consul as our previous ones were covered with allied visas indicating that we had served in France and Serbia. The only other papers of identification I had were letters from Bishop John L. Nuelsen, the Methodist Resident Bishop in Europe and a friend of my father, and from Bishop William Burt for whom I was named and who had lived in Rome for many years.

Although the Italians were still allies of Austria and Germany, their hatred of them was so great that they declared war on the side of England and France a month after our visit. Except for often being mistaken for German spies, our trip north through Italy via Rome, Florence, Bologna, Venice and Verona was very pleasant. In Florence, I called on Dr. Maria Montessori, but she was too busy to see me. Visiting Vittorio Putti's clinic at Bologna temporarily increased my ambition to become an orthopaedist.

Our entry into Austria on the 19th of March, 1915, was without mishap though the Austrian guards in Innsbruck seemed suspicious of two traveling American citizens. Our first trouble came when we crossed the Austrian-German frontier at Rosenheim. We were arrested and quizzed for hours at the guard house. We maintained that we could not speak German which was more or less true, and the German officers refused to speak English though most of them could. They finally allowed us to proceed to Munich but placed two guards in the compartment with us. As we thought these guards probably could understand English we kept silent during the three hour journey, which was hard for me. When the train pulled into Munich we dawdled in getting off so that our guards became bored. Finally they happened to look the other way, and we ran down the station stairs like rabbits and haven't seen the guards since. We went to a pension frequented by Rhodes Scholars in peacetime and registered without difficulty. We took most of our meals in an automat to avoid speaking our American-German. As a matter of fact, no one paid any attention to us, which hurt our egos, but we enjoyed sight-seeing and even visited the military hospitals.

A convalescent wounded major who was staying at our pension

became very friendly. He was a Bavarian and not very keen for this Prussian War and would discuss it as disinterestedly as any American. I asked him one day what they would do when Kitchener's new army entered the field. He said Germany was not worried as they planned to use gas. In my innocence, I thought the gas would be used in artillery to conserve gunpowder.

Gardner and I continued our trip north visiting Heidelberg, Wiesbaden, Frankfurt, and Cologne. We anticipated trouble at the Dutch border so as an alibi we engaged passage on the Holland-American Line steamer sailing from Rotterdam to New York the following week. We told the agent we would pay for the tickets in Holland and that if anything prevented our going, we would cancel the tickets. It was a fortunate precaution for we were arrested by the German guards at the Dutch border, searched from head to foot; our scanty baggage was pawed over and even my umbrella was broken into small pieces to see if anything was concealed in the frame. The steamship tickets were the deciding factor in our favor, and we were released.

As soon as we reached Holland we cancelled our Holland-American passage to New York and sailed from Rotterdam to London on the *Zeeland* on the 11th of April, 1915. At noon a periscope broke the surface a few hundred yards away. There was no panic on the unarmed Dutch channel boat, but everyone removed coats and shoes expecting to have to swim. A few minutes later the conning tower became visible, and we really were worried as we thought we should be shelled. Finally, the conning tower opened and a sailor appeared. Instead of going forward to man the deck gun, he went aft and unfurled a Union Jack. The sigh of relief among the passengers nearly lifted the channel boat out of the water.

As soon as I reached London, I called on the editor of the *Daily Mail*. After the interview at a sumptuous lunch, he gave me the fifteen pounds. His newspaper, the next day, carried a more-or-less accurate account of our trip. The editor was not as naive as I was about the gas story. Apparently, the Germans had been experimenting with poison gas for some time and though the British secret service undoubtedly knew about it, our story was the first public news. Perhaps the editor thought his fifteen pounds was well spent. The gas story had an interesting sequel. The Germans started to use poison gas at Ypres a few weeks after my return to Oxford. Professor Haldane who had studied mine gases was sent out from Oxford and brought back several rubber balloons filled with it. He asked all of the medical students to collect their urine in large bottles. Haldane then bubbled the gas through the urine and delightedly found that it was neutralized. He told us that when the first wave of gas came over at Ypres, one of the French officers who was a chemist, recognized it as chlorine and ordered his men to urinate on their spare socks and to tie them around their mouths and noses as he knew that urine would neutralize chlorine. These improvised gas masks were successful, but Haldane said the British Tommies refused to use them and said they would rather die like gentlemen, and many of them did. As a result of his experiments, Haldane and others soon devised less objectionable gas masks for the British Army. However, our American masks in 1917 contained urates.

OXFORD EXAMINATIONS

I reached Oxford in May, 1915, to prepare for the physiology examinations or "Schools." Oxford was deserted; only thirty-seven students were left in Merton College. Athletics and social activities were gone. All of the British undergraduates who could pass the physical requirements were in the Armed Services, and I drilled with the Oxfordshire Volunteer Corps. Only a few women, Americans and other foreign students remained although the government was searching out the medical students and ordering them back to complete their courses because of the shortage of medical officers and civilian physicians. During World War II, all the countries involved required their medical students to stay in school and become doctors as quickly as possible. Studying for examinations was hard work after roaming around the war-torn Continent and also after the delightful non-scholastic previous year at Oxford. My only benefit from the war, and it was an important one, was the cessation of athletic and social activities and the realization that learning medicine was a serious job. Another year like my first one at Oxford would have made me a chronic loafer and ruined me. But I had certainly enjoyed that end of the Edwardian era.

H. M. Vernon, who was assigned to me as tutor on my arrival from Serbia, soon made me return to the daybreak study schedule I had followed at Princeton. His method of tutoring was to require the reading of a series of articles on some subject in physiology and the presentation of a long paper on it each week. His caustic criticisms of the content of my compositions as well as of their lack of literary merit stung me into studious activity. I learned to write easily and voluminously on dull subjects and may even have learned some physiology. After two months of this slavery, Ken Waters (Kenneth F. Darrell Waters), an English medical student, invited me to spend the week before the examinations at his home in London. According to Oxford tradition, a week's holiday was needed to prevent staleness during the "schools," as the final examinations are called. It was a delightful interlude with tennis as a substitute for books and papers on physiology.

Apparently this plan has merit, for Ken Waters and I received "firsts" in the examinations. Ken earned his "first" but Sir Gowland F. Hopkins, the chief examiner, tempered my grade with mercy. During the oral examinations, or "viva," he gave me only two questions, neither of which I could answer. He first asked me what I thought of Ehrlich's side-chain theory. Never having heard of it, I answered, "I don't think much of it." "That is exactly my view," said Sir Gowland. The next question was "How many calories does a working man need every day?" Not having the vaguest idea, I hazarded "300." "Don't you mean 3,000?," said Hopkins. I agreed at once. We then chatted about Serbian food habits, on which I was eloquent, and I was the first American to obtain a "first" in physiology. The next day I was notified that Merton College had awarded me twenty pounds worth of books for getting a first. I appreciated the gift but as I had all of the medical books I needed I asked the Warden of the College whether I could use the prize for a microscope. I was sharply told that "it isn't done." I persisted, but it took a meeting of the college dons before they allowed this breach of tradition.

As soon as my examinations were over I returned to the States for a fortnight's holiday with Atala. It was all too short, but I had promised to return to Oxford in August for research work on paratyphoid vaccine with George Dreyer, the Professor of Pathology, so I returned on the *Philadelphia* on the 31st of July, 1915.

RESEARCH

Research in Great Britain is more hampered than in the United States because the Anti-Vivisection Society and a Royal Commission persuaded Parliament to pass a very strict law about the use of animals. As a result, it is necessary to obtain a license before any animal experiments are permitted, a procedure usually requiring many weeks or months. An example of the harm produced by this British law of 1876 was the delay in producing a triple, typhoid-paratyphoid A and B vaccine. In 1915, cases of paratyphoid fever were becoming very numerous, especially among the forces on the Dardanelles and in Mesopotamia. The sanitary conditions on the Gallipoli peninsula were bad because of the heat, flies, and lack of sanitation among the Anzacs as well as among the Turks. According to a story, current at the time, there was considerable argument among the troops as to whether a captured Turk smelled worse than their goat mascot. Bets were laid and the colonel was asked to settle the controversy. He fainted at the first sniff of the goat, but the Turk's backers finally won because the goat swooned with the prisoner was led in. Typhoid, paratyphoid, and dysentery, both amebic and bacillary, were worse problems than wounds.

The shortage of nurses and orderlies on the hospital ships from these areas sometimes made it necessary for bedpans to be passed from one patient to the other until they were filled. As a result, some of the patients caught each others' infections, especially paratyphoid, and the cases were difficult to diagnose when they arrived in England. Osler was very anxious to study these mixed infections with Dreyer's agglutination technique, and I applied, with his help, for assignment to the *Aquitania*. However, the Admiralty did not want any Americans in the Dardanelles campaign.

A paratyphoid vaccine was needed, and Dreyer, Professor of Pathology at Oxford, knew from his previous work on mixed vaccines that adequate protection could be provided by adding paratyphoid bacilli to the typhoid vaccine. However, Sir William Leishman, the British Army pathologist, feared this mixture might interfere with the efficacy of the typhoid vaccine. The only way Dreyer could convince Leishman was by experiments, and he told me that if I would inoculate some human volunteers and rabbits with mixed triple typhoid-paratyphoid A and B vaccine, and some others with straight typhoid or paratyphoid A or B vaccines (as controls), and then test their immunity by agglutination tests, he would recommend me for a research degree. I was very flattered and promptly accepted the invitation.

In order that I could inoculate animals, Sir William Osler, Regius Professor of Medicine at Oxford, Sir Charles Sherrington, Professor of Physiology, and Sir Frederick Taylor, President of the Royal College of Surgeons, had to recommend me, a Rhodes Scholar medical student, to the British Home Office for a certificate and then a license. On the 19th of July, 1915, I was admitted as a "student for the degree of Bachelor of Science to enter on a course of research entitled 'An Inquiry into Certain Features of Immunity in Normal and Inoculated Individuals' under the Supervision of Dr. E. W. Ainley Walker." He and Dr. A. Duncan Gardner, later Regius Professor of Medicine at Oxford, helped me make the vaccines. However, it was not until the 23rd of November, 1915, five months later, that Sir John, later Viscount Simon, "one of his Majesty's principal Secretaries of State," issued me an Amended Licence to inoculate animals.

While waiting for the animal license, I asked the Oxford medical students and Rhodes Scholars, medical and otherwise, for volunteers for the inoculations and bleedings, because human beings did not require a license. All of them volunteered, including the other four medical Rhodes Scholars, Wilder Penfield, later Professor of Neurosurgery at McGill, Emile Holman, later Professor of Surgery at Stanford, Eustace H. Cluver, later Director of the South-African Institute for Medical Research, and C. F. Krige, later Senior Lecturer and Clinical Tutor of the Medical School of the University of Witwatersrand (as well as Senior Golf Champion of South Africa). I later was made a member of the Walter Reed Society for these experiments on myself. After innumerable inoculations and bleedings, the agglutination tests showed that triple vaccine would not interfere with the protection against typhoid; in fact, it actually increased the immunity, as Dreyer had predicted. Sir William Leishman then approved the inoculation of the British Army with triple typhoid-paratyphoid A and B vaccine, and the incidence of paratyphoid A or B fever was greatly reduced. I wrote a thesis on the subject, and Dreyer recommended me for a B.Sc. degree which I received on the 11th of May, 1916.

Oxford degrees, except honorary ones, are conferred with less ceremony than in the States. After examinations are passed or theses accepted, the university issues a certificate enabling the holder to obtain his degree whenever it is convenient for him. They are awarded three or four times annually. The individual's servant or scout also attends and is given a traditional tip of one pound. Four years after receiving a B.A. degree, an M.A. may be had for an additional fee. I was very much embarrassed when I applied for my first Oxford degree as I had to prove that I was a graduate of an

American university. I sent in a diploma signed by Woodrow Wilson and received a note from the registrar that Oxford did not recognize Whig Hall as an institution of learning. I had sent in my debating society certificate instead of a Princeton diploma. The error was soon corrected.

The following year, I returned to the United States to get my M.D. degree and was requested to write a report on triple typhoid-paratyphoid vaccine for the National Research Council. When we entered the War on the 6th of April, 1917, this triple vaccine became compulsory for the American Army. I became a medical officer on the 7th of April, 1917, and in spite of twenty experimental inoculations with triple vaccine and its components, I had to take the required three U.S. Army doses.

I had heard that the College of Physicians of Philadelphia offered the Alvarenga prize of $250 for unpublished research work, so I submitted my thesis. I did not hear anything more about the award until I phoned the College of Physicians on the 14th of July, 1917, while in Philadelphia en route from Washington to New York for overseas duty. To my delight, I learned that the decision had been made that day and that I was the winner. The check was sent to me in New York a few days before I sailed for France but it didn't do me much good for one of my fellow officers who had married the night before borrowed the money. A year later when he repaid the loan, I invested the whole amount in a French war bond which after the collapse of the franc was finally redeemed for $25.

In spite of the legal restrictions, Osler, Dreyer, and Sherrington constantly stimulated their students to undertake part-time research problems. I shall never forget Sherrington's dramatic description of his early experiments with diphtheria antitoxin. He had obtained some diphtheria toxin from von Behring in 1893 and had immunized a horse with it. Before he could test its efficacy, Lord Lister, who had heard of his work, called on him late one night and begged him to try the serum on his grandchild who was dying of diphtheria. Sherrington explained that it might be dangerous to use this untested horse serum, but Lord Lister insisted so they went to the stable and while Lord Lister held a kerosene lamp, Sherrington bled the horse and separated the serum. The child lived.

Sherrington offered me a laboratory with my own key, a notable event, so that I could study the effect of intravenous fat on recovery from anesthesia. The experiments didn't prove anything but the experience of working with Sir Charles was invaluable, even more than I realized at the time, because he wrote a very helpful letter about me to Lewis Weed in 1916.

Sherrington also recommended me for a Senior Demyship at Magdalen College and to my surprise I was elected the first American to be a Senior Demy. The honorarium was 100 pounds annually if unmarried. Osler gave me a well deserved reprimand when I delayed accepting the Senior Demyship, because I was waiting to hear from my application to a Beit Fellowship which carried a higher stipend. He quietly but firmly made me realize the embarrassment I had caused to those who had obtained the Demyship for me.

Osler was very keen that his students publish clinical papers, and he and Dreyer persuaded me to write a description of Dreyer's quantitative agglutination method for differentiating typhoid and paratyphoid fevers for the *JAMA*. The paper was promptly refused but Osler wrote the editor a note, and the paper was then immediately accepted.

When Mr. Dodds-Parker, a surgeon at Oxford, devised a frame for the suspension of fractures, Osler suggested that a description of it should be published in one of the American medical journals in order that American surgeons who soon would be in the war could become familiar with it. Everyone else was too busy to write the paper so I undertook it. I started to make the necessary drawings and measurements of the apparatus and wasn't making much headway but fortunately the patient who was suspended in the frame was an Australian architect in civilian life and offered to make the sketches. They were the best thing in the paper. I later found that something like this so-called Balkan frame had been described in the *Southern Medical and Surgical Journal* in 1836 by Milton Antony of Georgia.

The French and British were using the Carrel-Dakin method of sterilizing infected wounds and again Osler wanted a description of it published in the States, so another paper was born.

RADCLIFFE INTERNSHIP

While carrying out the experiments with triple vaccine, I learned that the Radcliffe Infirmary, the 200-bed hospital in Oxford, needed an intern so I applied, and because of the shortage of physicians I was appointed although still a third-year medical student. The work was fascinating, and there was plenty of it for the hospital had only three on the resident staff, or rather two and a half, as MacDonald, the resident surgeon, and Dr. Mosse, the resident physician, put it. I had the title of Casualty House Officer, which means man of all work, and the nickname of "Jumbo," in addition to that of "Davers" and "Five" because I rowed the No. 5 oar on the Merton Eight. I took the patients' histories, gave anesthetics, assisted at operations, and best of all wrote the notes dictated by Osler and other members of the visiting staff. It was good experience, though probably too early in my medical training to be of lasting value. A third-year medical student doing hernia and appendix operations, tonsillectomies and circumcisions soon acquires over-confidence and other bad habits which are difficult to eradicate later. Fortunately, no children were killed by the guillotine tonsil knife which occasionally snipped off the patient's uvula or the end of my fingers. Because we had many burned patients who required skin grafting, all of the foreskins in the circumcision clinic were saved, and occasionally they were successfully used.

Sir William Osler, in addition to being the Regius Professor of Medicine, was the physician-in-chief of the Radcliffe Infirmary. We always affectionately referred to him as Father William. He visited the Radcliffe Infirmary daily except Mondays and Fridays. I greatly enjoyed these ward rounds for his comments on the patients always were amusing as well as instructive. The patients adored him. Cases which seemed very complicated were soon simplified after a consultation with him. He spent much of his time on the children's ward, and my interest in pediatrics probably started there although I was not conscious of it until I met John Howland the following year. On Mondays, Osler, who was a Lt. Colonel in the Canadian Army Medical Corps, visited the Duchess of Connaught Hospital on the Astor estate at Cliveden. As he needed someone to take his notes and collect blood specimens for study, he took me along. Needless to say, I enjoyed the forty-mile automobile trips with the Chief although Lady Osler soon labelled me "Jonah" because of frequent motor and tire trouble whenever I rode in the Osler's Renault, in spite of Mr. Morris', later Viscount Nuffield's, efforts to keep the car repaired. Perhaps he developed his philanthropic interest in medical education and hospitals through his many Oslerian motor conferences.

Sir William would start the Cliveden journeys by stacking ten or fifteen medical journals which had arrived during the preceding week on the car seat between us and would read one after another, "dog-earing" the articles which he recommended for my reading. He could read and digest medical literature more rapidly than anyone I have ever met; at the end of the two-hour ride he would have completed a survey of all the journals. It took me the rest of the week to cover the material he had suggested. The hospital at Cliveden was Canadian, both the staff and patients, and was exceedingly well run. Mrs., later Lady Astor, took a great interest in it and always had Sir William, as well as me, for lunch on our trips. She always called me "Mr. Richardson" for some unknown reason.

The Canadian staff who, like me, worshipped Osler assumed that I must know something because I always accompanied the Chief. Although I explained that the only reason for my presence was that he had no one else available, they would ask me innumerable questions which I could not answer, but I usually would get the information for them from Osler on the return trip. The following incident convinced them that I was overmodest, a trait of which I had never been accused. One of the Canadian shell-shocked patients could not speak, a fairly common neurosis. I was asked what to do. Fortunately, I remembered a similar patient who had been silent for months until he got drunk while on leave, literally roaring drunk, and had no difficulty in talking thereafter as his inhibitions had been broken. I suggested alcohol for the Canadian patient but it was no use, drinking was forbidden in the hospital. Finally, someone recalled that ether acted like alcohol, so the patient was anesthetized. Within a few minutes I was called to the Cliveden operating room to suggest a means of quieting the patient as he had become so ribaldly garrulous under the influence of ether that the nurses had to leave.

Osler was a very keen diagnostician. He was sure that one of the Canadians had typhoid fever, but the staff would not agree because the patient had been inoculated with typhoid vaccine and up to that date no one had seen typhoid in vaccinated individuals. Osler assigned me to this patient with instructions to find out if he had really been inoculated. Just before he died, the Canadian confided that he had faked his record.

Another patient's face was tightly contracted after a head wound, and Osler spotted him as a case of Rose's head tetanus. He had never seen one but that morning driving down from Oxford had shown me an article by Rose on the subject.

On Fridays, Sir William visited Mount Vernon, the Army heart hospital at Hampstead, and often took me with him. His ward rounds there with Sir Thomas Lewis were fascinating, and I have been interested in heart disease ever since.

Osler was a magnificent teacher and made everyone with whom he came in contact feel that he was primarily and genuinely interested in that individual. I have since met hundreds of his former students in America and England who shared that belief. For example, Thomas B. Futcher, who was supposed to give me an examination in medicine when I transferred to The Hopkins in 1916, happily chatted about the Chief for an hour and then gave me a good grade. John Musser did the same thing when I took the National Boards in 1919. In fact, passing examinations seemed more dependent on knowing Osler than on a knowledge of medicine; perhaps they are synonymous.

In addition to medicine and pediatrics, the Casualty House Officer was on call for emergency surgery. One of the Zeppelin raids had a comic-tragic side for I was summoned to the outpatient department in the middle of the night to take care of a casualty. The poor man had started for the cellar when the sirens blew but had tripped and struck his head on a fire bucket at the foot of the stairs. The edge of the bucket had completely peeled his scalp off his head onto his face so that I couldn't tell which was front and back. Fortunately, it was not infected so I replaced the scalp like a sock and after twenty stitches, it healed.

In addition to the Radcliffe Infirmary, Oxford had a large military hospital with several hundred patients, and I was allowed to help with the laboratory and ward work. I became greatly interested in orthopaedics which forms the bulk of war surgery and decided to enter the field when I was graduated. My most amusing orthopaedic experience was in London. Osler had suggested that Wilder Penfield and I should attend Sir Arbuthnot Lane's clinic at Guy's Hospital and gave us a letter of introduction to him. We arrived after Sir Arbuthnot had started operating so we donned white gowns and masks and were given seats in the operating room. Lane was applying his steel plates to a patient's broken leg and making very rude remarks about Americans in general and Fred F. Albee in particular. We gathered from Lane's complaints that Albee had spoken at the Royal Society of Medicine on the preceding evening about his autogenous bone grafts and had said that they were superior to Lane's steel plates which acted as foreign bodies and would bend.

63

After he had finished operating, he pointed to me and said, "You look strong, just try and bend one of my plates." Naturally, I had been annoyed by Lane's diatribe against my country so I did my best to bend his plate and succeeded. After all, I had been rowing for six years and had fairly strong hands and shoulders. Sir Arbuthnot's astonished face as I handed him the bent plate was purple. He called his assistant and bawled him out for not having the plate properly tempered. Lane selected a stronger plate and sarcastically said to me, "Try and bend that one." I did, so he asked my name apparently expecting it to be Sandow. I handed him Osler's note of introduction, and Sir Arbuthnot's belligerent manner immediately changed. He spent the rest of the day with Penfield and me trying to atone for his rudeness, took us all over Guy's Hospital and drove us to the American Embassy in his car. The sequel to this episode came two years later at the Inter-Allied Surgical Conference in Paris at which I was one of the American representatives. Sir Arbuthnot, now a Major General, was one of the British delegation. I asked him if he remembered me. Judging by his expression, he obviously did but very pompously said he had never seen me. Otherwise, this surgical conference was interesting and mutually profitable to the Allies. I was especially glad to have the opportunity of meeting Aldo Castellani, one of the Italian representatives and a great authority on tropical and fungus diseases. (I visited his original laboratory in Colombo, Ceylon, in 1954.)

DUBLIN

I was anxious to obtain more training in obstetrics, or mid-wifery as it is called in England, so Osler arranged a month for me at the Rotunda Hospital in Dublin (28 December, 1915 to 28 January, 1916) in spite of the anti-Catholic and anti-Irish feeling in England and the anti-English activities in Ireland. The crop of Dublin babies was prodigious as birth control was taboo. In order to prevent the eternal damnation which was believed to be the fate of unchristened babies we were instructed not to tell the mothers if their infants were born dead but to christen them immediately and then report their demise. The subterfuge was harmless and was a source of great comfort to the poor mothers. I delivered thirty-five babies in the hospital and district and decided that though obstetrics was a necessary specialty, I would rather do something else. However, it was a grand experience, for Sir William had given me letters of introduction to several professors who were very hospitable. Sir John Moore, the professor of medicine, and Sir William Smiley, the professor of midwifery, could not have been kinder. The former took me sightseeing, showing me the ancient books in Trinity College, even climbing up to the organ loft of St. Patrick's cathedral with me, and then saw me off at the station. The Irish are delightful people though they woke me up every morning drilling in the street under my window in preparation for the Easter rebellion in 1916.

The medical school at Oxford in 1915 was very shorthanded, so I was invited to be a tutor in physiology and an instructor in pathology and bacteriology. Both jobs were instructive to me, but I doubt whether my students, including four of my fellow Rhodes Scholars, learned very much.

RETURN

By the summer of 1916, it was obvious that America would soon enter the War so Osler suggested that I return to the United States to get my medical degree. It would have taken too long in England. Besides, I wanted to go to The Johns Hopkins Medical School because Atala was now a first-year student there. I applied for admission to the third-year class, but Osler said that I ought to know enough by this time to enter the senior class. Because the double schedule I carried or was registered to carry at Oxford would fulfill the required courses for the first two years and my service with the American Ambulance Hospital in France, the experience during the typhus epidemic in Serbia in 1914 to 1915, and my internship at the Radcliffe Infirmary had more or less covered the third year subjects. At any rate, Sir William wrote asking Dr. J. Whitridge Williams, the Hopkins dean, to admit me to the senior class. As a result, my application to the third-year class was ignored and on the 21st of June, 1916, I was admitted as a senior. I had been previously notified that I was eligible for the senior year at the Harvard Medical School.

The Oxford term ends in June, but Lord Milner, a Rhodes Trustee, had given me permission to remain until August, so that I could receive the scholarship stipend I had missed while in France and Serbia. It was hard to leave Oxford. Although I was working seven days a week from six in the morning to midnight, I loved the place and my associates. The most difficult part was leaving the Oslers to whom I was devoted. Just before I sailed, Sir William called Wilder

With friends and teammates during Oxford days

Penfield and me into his study and told us that when he was a young man, old Dr. Henry I. Bowditch, of Boston, had told him that the regret of his life was that he had not saved reprints of everything he had written. Osler said that he was now as old as Bowditch and had saved reprints of all of his writings but the regret of his life was that he had written so much. He invited us to select copies of all of his reprints and then had them bound in three volumes for us. These books are Penfield's and my most cherished possessions. I sailed for home on the *Grampian*, a Canadian steamer, on the 28th of July, 1916. The voyage was uneventful except for dodging mine fields and submarines north of Scotland and icebergs at the mouth of the St. Lawrence. When I arrived in Quebec, the customs officer was not very keen about passing my Zeiss microscope until he learned that I had been in Serbia. He then stamped all my baggage without opening it.

CHAPTER IV

THE JOHNS HOPKINS UNIVERSITY MEDICAL SCHOOL (1916-1917)

WHEN I reached New York, I found that a poliomyelitis epidemic was raging. I had intended spending August on a vacation with Atala but either from a "call" to be of service or a desire for more experience and training (the two usually are confused in every medical student's and physician's mind), I worked at the New York Board of Health and the Willard Parker Hospital where most of the polio patients were being treated. It was interesting, though we had, as in the typhus epidemic in Serbia, a sense of futility. No treatment was efficacious and as soon as all of the susceptible individuals had acquired the disease and recovered or died, the outbreak ceased.

I had a few days of vacation with Atala in September and then we went to Baltimore to medical school, Atala to start her second year there and I to try the senior class. All of my previous records had to be signed by the Hopkins faculty and all were, but I inadvertently annoyed Dr. Thomas S. Cullen, Professor of Gynecology. When he saw Osler's signature on my records he said it was extraordinary how many famous medical men were preacher's sons. He mentioned Osler, Finney, and himself as examples but didn't think it funny when I said my father also was a preacher. Dr. Cullen had written a book on omphalitis, or diseases of the umbilicus, and Osler had told me to be sure to tell him that he had neglected one of the most important features of omphalitis, namely, that many people's lives revolved around their umbilicus and that if they did not have three meals and one bowel movement daily, they were very unhappy. I did not deliver the message.

At first, except for the joy of seeing Atala every day, the Hopkins medical school was a disappointment. After being responsible for a hundred patients in addition to research and teaching, it was a bore to have only six patients on whom to take histories and do blood counts. It took me two months to realize that I was learning more by doing many things for a few patients than I did by trying merely to cover the necessities for a large number. Wilder Penfield also returned from Oxford so we roomed together in one of the white-stooped, old dirty houses at 923 Broadway which were responsible for the high tuberculosis rate among the Hopkins students. We joined the Pithotomy Club in which several of our Princeton classmates were members. The name, Pithotomy, means operation upon a keg, a rite which was celebrated annually in spite of prohibition.

Pediatric clinics by John Howland soon reconciled me to the Hopkins. After the second one, I decided to become a pediatrician and applied for an internship in the Harriet Lane Home, as the pediatrics department of the Hopkins Hospital was called. Dr. Howland gave me the appointment, largely because I had known his sister, Miss Frances Howland, who had been one of the Aides Voluntaires at the American Ambulance Hospital at Neuilly. This changing of my mind from one specialty to another is characteristic of medical students, who rarely end up in the field they had originally chosen. The factors which cause these shifts often are trivial, but the effect is lasting. Because of a fascinating talk on brain surgery by Allen Starr at the Princeton Premedical Club, I had intended to be a neurosurgeon when I entered medical school. Then came the war with its mass of traumatic surgery so I decided that I must be an orthopaedist and even wrote two papers on the subject. Then, after seeing in the Serbian typhus epidemic what preventive medicine could do, or rather what it might have done, I agreed with Osler that preventive medicine and public health had the brightest future of all the medical fields. Osler even wrote William Welch to take me into the new Hopkins School of Public Health after I received my medical degree. But finally, after learning the effects of politics on public health and especially after meeting John Howland, I could not see anything except pediatrics. Years later, I became enamored with administrative work and became a combined office boy and pediatrician. As a matter of fact, pediatrics through natural evolution has now become a branch of preventive medicine, so I did follow Osler's advice though I didn't realize it for twenty years.

My only surgical work at the Hopkins was attending one of Dr. William S. Halsted's clinics. He taught by presenting a patient in the amphitheatre and then calling down six students from the benches in alphabetical rotation for quizzing. The day Halsted was due to reach the "Ds," I naturally was present; students didn't attend surgical clinics unnecessarily. That day, the patient being demonstrated had a hernia which had been operated upon. I was at the end of the line and was greatly perturbed by the questions Halsted asked the students ahead of me and by their erudite answers. They knew the history of hernia operations and the names and techniques of all of them. I had operated upon many hernias, most of them successfully, while I was an intern at Oxford, but I didn't know the names of the methods and still don't for that matter. Fortunately, before Halsted reached me, he switched his questions to wound infections. The other Hopkins students were horrified, first because they had never heard of wound infections (surgeons usually don't admit having them), and second, it seemed sacrilegious even to mention infections in the Hopkins Hospital. Nevertheless, Halsted persisted in his questions as this hernia patient had quite a serious secondary infection. When Halsted asked me at the end of the line how I would treat this infection, I went into reams of detail about the Carrel-Dakin treatment, as the paper I had written on the subject while at Oxford had just been published. Fortunately, Halsted had not read that medical journal and so was amazed at my glib familiarity with techniques of which he had only heard rumors. He dismissed the other students, and I held the balance of the clinic. When it was over, Halsted, in his courtly way, asked my name (he never knew one student from another) and offered me an internship in surgery. I thanked him and had sense enough never to attend another surgical clinic. It was another example of Osler's help, because he had urged me to write the paper on the Carrel-Dakin therapy.

Dr. Halsted was such a dignified man that few students suspected that he had played on the first Yale football team against Princeton in the seventies. His ward rounds were so quiet that the students referred to them as "shifting dullness." The only humor encountered was when a country patient called Dr. Halsted, "Doc." He quietly answered, "I prefer to be called William." However, I have since learned in North Carolina that "Doc" is a very friendly term and unlike Dr. Halsted, I am keen about it.

Dr. Halsted's affection for and later marriage to Miss Hampton, his chief nurse at the Hopkins, are good examples of serendipity. Miss Hampton's hands were sensitive to the antiseptics used in surgery in the late eighties, so Dr. Halsted invented thin rubber gloves to protect them. The earlier rubber gloves had been heavy like those used in modern dish-washing. We wore them at the Radcliffe Infirmary in 1915 because the phenol which was sprayed into the air with a flit gun and which was sloshed all over the floor of the operating room soon made our hands peel. We also wore rubber boots. It seems amazing that I was asked by one of the younger staff at the Canadian War Hospital in 1915 to plead with Osler to persuade the chief surgeon to wear modern thin rubber gloves, because he insisted on operating barehandedly, saying that he could not feel anything with the heavy rubber gloves.

The second example of serendipity was of great benefit to Duke. Mrs. Halsted was the daughter of Colonel Frank Hampton and the niece of General Wade Hampton, the Confederate hero. The Hamptons were large landowners in North and South Carolina, and Miss Hampton inherited a thousand acres of beautiful mountain scenery at High Hampton, North Carolina. At her death, this land was given to The Johns Hopkins Hospital, whose superintendent, without even looking at it, sold it for $10,000. The purchaser soon sold half of it for $100,000.

When Dr. Robert S. Carroll, the founder and owner of Highland Hospital, Asheville, North Carolina, heard of this mismanagement in handling bequests, he notified Raymond S. Crispell, who was in charge of psychiatry at Duke, Dr. Robert L. Flowers, the Duke treasurer, and me, that instead of leaving the Highland Hospital to the Hopkins as he had intended, he would leave it to Duke and in 1938, he did. Under the able management of the late Charman Carroll, with the assistance of Sol Brower, Highland Hospital has continued the splendid reputation and service which Dr. Robert S. Carroll had established.

The Hopkins Medical School encourages students to carry on research, so Howland asked Atala and me to investigate the organism which was causing an atypical case of meningitis. It was fun working together. We soon learned that the organism was a new one which had never been described, and we named it *Micrococcus florens* because it grew so luxuriantly. We also studied its effect in animals and found that it produced meningitis in monkeys and rabbits.

I realized very early that medical meetings are the mainstay of a physician's continuous education. Osler had taken me to several while I was in England, but the grand initiation came in 1917. Welch passed me in the Hopkins corridor one day and casually asked me if I would like to attend the medical meetings at Atlantic City the following week. Of course I wanted to go, and I did. It was one of my most momentous and rewarding early experiences. Welch and I sat on the back row of the meeting room, and he pointed out all the celebrities of whom I had read. I thanked my good luck for being there and also for my memory for faces and names. I have since come to know most of the physicians whom Welch pointed out that day. The climax to the expedition was lunch with Welch, Solomon Solis Cohen, and Abraham Jacobi. They asked me to order the meal and then proceeded to discuss medicine from Hippocrates to Flexner. I sat open-mouthed in adoration, except while eating my favorite veal and ham pie.

By March, 1917, it was obvious that we would soon be in the War so Howland sent me to Washington to explain Dreyer's laboratory methods and triple typhoid-paratyphoid vaccines to Colonel F. F. Russell and Admiral E. R. Stitt, who were in charge of the laboratory services of the Army and Navy. They were very kind, and it was a profitable trip for me. The former made it possible for me to go to France with the first American Expeditionary Force and the latter gave me a very high mark in bacteriology when he examined me for the National Boards after the war, and, incidentally, he remembered the fact in 1943 when I asked him to lecture on tropical medicine at Jefferson. On April 6th, 1917, it was rumored that we would declare war so Atala and I went to Washington to see the excitement. The communists had threatened a demonstration, and the streets were filled with firemen. War was declared that night, and the next morning I called on Colonel R. E. Noble, the personnel officer in the Surgeon General's office, and General W. C. Gorgos and applied for a commission. Colonel Noble said that I lacked two months of being graduated but that if Dr. Welch would phone him that I could be graduated early he would give me a commission. Dr. Welch did, saying that as I was not doing very much class work, the sooner I entered the Army the better, and that my diploma would be sent to me later. I didn't receive it until I had been in France several months. Colonel Noble said he would send me a commission within a few days so I tried to join Base Hospital 18, the Hopkins unit, and also one of the New York units, but they were filled. I immediately resigned my pediatric internship for 1917 before it started and also my Senior Demyship at Oxford for I hoped to be married. I bought my uniform, but nothing else happened in spite of numerous trips to Washington. Finally, I was told to go to the Rockefeller Institute for a course in laboratory methods and that my commission would soon arrive. The work at the Rockefeller was interesting though Lundsgaard nearly killed me. He was studying the effect of atropine on the pulse and when he learned that I had a very slow rate he invited me to be his guinea pig. I, innocently, agreed, but either his dose was too large, or else I am sensitive to atropine, for I stayed several hours in a state of collapse.

I had been trying for several months to persuade Atala to marry me and she finally agreed, probably against her better judgment. I have been very happy ever since, and I hope she has. The wedding was on June 2, 1917, the day before her twenty-fifth birthday. We spent our honeymoon at Montauk Point where we had first met. One of the best wedding presents was the following letter from Lady Osler:

> July 19, 1917.
> 13, Norham Gardens,
> Oxford.

Dear Mr. Jonah:

I am perfectly delighted to hear you are married and I wish you both every possible joy. Of course, we will know at once when you reach England and you must bring your wife to us for a weekend. Isn't it splendid that America has come in? We have been very busy lately with all the units that have come over and, of course, the men dash down to see their "Chief." Revere is in Belgium in the midst of this awful offensive that is just coming off and one is worried to death. The motor is still going to Cliveden and *no more accidents*. Mr. Macdonald & Dr. Mosse are going to Egypt. They are having the R.A.M.C. training now.

With all good wishes believe me,

> Cordially,
> Grace R. Osler

On our return from our honeymoon, my commission still had not arrived so I made another trip to Washington. Fortunately, I saw Colonel F. F. Russell, who took me into his office in a fatherly way and told me that he had hid my commission as 1st Lieutenant, Medical Reserve Corps dated the 19th of May, 1917, in his desk so that I would not be ordered to camp as he wanted me go to France with Major Henry J. Nichols and Army Laboratory No. 1. I was delighted with the opportunity. Within a few days I received the commission and was ordered to report to the Army Medical School in Washington for three weeks of indoctrination and immunization.

CHAPTER V

MARRIAGE AND THE FIRST WAR
(THE A.E.F., 1917-1919)

I REPORTED in New York on the 13th of July, 1917, for duty overseas with the first contingent of the American Expeditionary Force (A.E.F.).* I was told that we were to sail on the *Philadelphia.* There was little secrecy about sailing then. I went to the steamship office to inquire whether my wife could go with me. Fortunately, the clerk was a romantic soul and when he learned that we had just been married, he gave us the bridal suite on the ship. We sailed on the 26th of July, 1917. It was delightful, but my commanding officer was irked at sleeping in the crowded hold while his lieutenant had two rooms and a bath. The voyage was uneventful until a few miles from Ireland. Then, a periscope was sighted, and although the naval guns barked, the submarine loosed a torpedo. Our ship was zig-zagging, and the "tin fish" missed the stern by twenty feet. The naval lookout was so excited that instead of using his telephone to notify the gunners, he jumped from the crow's nest to the deck and broke his leg, our only casualty. The gunners claimed to have sunk the sub, but I doubted it. In response to the ship's radio, two destroyers appeared and convoyed us the rest of the voyage to Liverpool. The British transport officer at Liverpool at first refused to allow Atala to board the troop train to Southampton but Major Nichols finally persuaded him that she was an Army nurse who had been added to the unit too late to be included in the orders.

I had hoped that I might see the Oslers while we crossed England, but we arrived in Southampton late at night and had to cross the channel early the next morning. However, I was able to talk to them over the phone that night. A few days later in France, I received the following characteristic, cheery, Oslerian letter:

13, Norham Gardens, Oxford.
Dear Davison,

We were so disappointed not to see you. Congratulations on the Alvarenga prize. So glad. That is a good bit of work. Let me know if there

---

* The British claimed it stood for "After Everything's Finished." The Yank reply was that it meant "After England Failed."

74

The young officer during World War I

is any literature I can send. The R.S.* in Wimpole Street has arranged to send books & papers. So glad that the L. of your L.† came over. Revere keeps well — says he cannot even get P.U.O.‡ after 4 days & nights of soaking wet in the last offensive. Dreyer is away. Ainslie Walker lost his wife the other day — an obscure complication of Graves disease. I have been in Wales for a week — Welsh Commission business. Hospitals filling up, after a quiet period.

Sincerely yours,
Wm. Osler

The French raised considerable difficulty about Atala's crossing the Channel but romantically succumbed when I told the officer in charge that we had just been married. The arrival of our unit in Paris was really comic. The French laughed heartily as our medical enlisted men marched through the streets wearing murderous-looking Philippine machetes at their belts in accordance with Army regulations and carrying peaceful-looking cages of white mice to meet our needs for the laboratory diagnosis of pneumonia. We also had a good laugh at the expense of our commander officer. Soliciting prostitutes fell upon our detachment but we assured them in French, which the C.O. did not understand, that he was the only one interested. Two husky girls promptly carried him loudly protesting up a side street.

At first the French, who thrive on red tape, required each arriving American officer to carry an Identity Card like any other foreigner. Mine was No. 101. They soon gave up the practice when our troops began to pour into France.

At Neufchateau in the Vosges Mountains we established Army Laboratory No. 1. The First Division had just moved into that area. I was terribly disappointed that Atala was not allowed to accompany me for although we could hear the rumble of the guns thirty miles away at the front, our town was as peaceful as Durham. Paris, where she was a bacteriologist in a Red Cross Hospital, was much more dangerous because it was shelled daily by the German "Big Bertha."

As the youngest officer, I was named mess officer which meant I had to buy the food from the quartermaster, collect the mess bills, and absorb all complaints. I tried to keep the costs down in many ways. For example, one day botulism (food poisoning) killed several members of the 101st Machine Gun Company who had eaten cold

---

* Royal Society of Medicine; † Light of your Life (Atala); ‡ Pyrexia of Unknown Origin (undiagnosed fever; also called G.O.K. [God Only Knows] until forbidden by army orders).

Davison in Army Laboratory No. 1 at Neufchateau

corned beef hash while on maneuvers. We had to test the corned beef so it was fed to guinea pigs. They died, and a carload of corned beef hash was condemned. I persuaded the quartermaster to give it to me and instructed our cook to heat it thoroughly before serving it at our mess. The officers who had condemned this food, unknowingly ate it all winter. I later learned that any meat is fatal to guinea pigs so our test had been valueless. I nearly acquired a carload of soda crackers which had been condemned by the quartermaster because they were moldy. Unfortunately, he asked me what I intended doing with them. When he learned that they would be brushed off, heated, and fed to our mess, he decided to keep them and do his cleaning.

With the rapid shifting of troops, it was a wonder that anyone received his mail, but the Army Post Office did an excellent job and few letters were lost. Packages were another matter as they were badly battered with illegible names and addresses by the time they reached Neufchateau. At Christmas, I received innumerable cakes and puddings which had not been sent to me. The APO apparently gave me any package with a name beginning with "D," and I didn't object as the food was a welcome addition to our mess.

Mess supplies were a perpetual problem. One day the officer in charge of the huge army bakery came into the "Club Lafayette" complaining about the flour which the quartermaster was sending him, saying he couldn't make bread with it. The next day, one of the surgeons at the Base Hospital said the army talcum powder became doughy and caked whenever it was wet. The surgeon and baker later exchanged their barrels.

As soon as the laboratory was organized, we received orders to analyze the water supplies of all of the villages which were to be taken over by the American Army. As I was the youngest officer and always got the "scut jobs," I was given the assignment in spite of my protests that I hadn't the faintest idea of water analysis. Fortunately, Larry A. Kohn whom I had known at the New York Board of Health during the 1916 polio epidemic was in our outfit. By some good luck, Larry had brought a copy of the American Public Health Association's *Standard Methods for the Examination of Water and Sewage* so he and I in a Model T Ford which we had wangled from the French, visited the villages, collected water samples, and wrote reports. We were never sure of our results so to be safe we condemned all of them. At first, wood signs "Forbidden to Drink;

Defense de Boire" were placed on all of the pumps and wells. The next day they were gone, as the French needed wood, and they were insulted by the signs. Paper notices were then printed and pasted on with bill-poster glue so that they could not be removed. The water for the troops was sterilized in Lister bags by the addition of hypochlorite. If it couldn't be tasted, the amount of hypochlorite was too small and if it could, the water was undrinkable. The trick was to keep the concentration of hypochlorite midway between these extremes.

Unfortunately, we condemned the water supply at Vittel, a famous French resort whose waters are bottled and sold all over France. I was summoned to General Headquarters at Chaumont for a reprimand but as we had done a complete analysis of the water and could prove it was bad, nothing more was done to me. A few months later when Lt. Col. Edward Bartow, a real water expert, was assigned to the job he also found that all of the water supplies in our area were bad. Apparently, most of the underlying rock in Lorraine is limestone with huge cracks which allow the surface filth to permeate all of the water strata.

In Gondrecourt where the 1st Division was stationed, the mayor complained that since the American troops had arrived, all of their water supplies had a queer taste. An investigation was ordered, and it was found that the water smelled like chlorine. No one tasted it because everyone surmised that the chlorine came from the slaked lime which had been dumped into the Army latrines to prevent flies. To prove the source of this contamination, a few gallons of methylene blue were poured into the latrines. The next day, the French mayor really was furious for the town water supply was blue, and he accused the American Army of trying to poison the village. Explanations were useless so no more slaked lime was used in the latrines, and the French could then drink their sewage without any disinfectant. As a matter of fact, there weren't many flies, and the French don't drink much water anyway so everyone was satisfied.

The French in a neighboring town also complained that the American troops were polluting the stream in which the women did their laundry. On investigation it was found that they expected our men to use the stream as a latrine but they did object to the wads of toilet paper which floated down.

Another source of water contamination in rural France was the custom of heaping fresh manure around the village pump — the manure kept the pump from freezing in the winter, and the village could guard the manure as it was the most prized possession in that part of France. Efforts to stop the practice were unsuccessful, even though squads of Marines were sent to clean up the mess. One of the most comic sights I saw in France was an irate French woman in sabots keeping six husky Marines at bay with a pitchfork.

The main task of our laboratory was to try to stop epidemics, especially diphtheria and meningitis. We heard of several cases of the former in the 42nd (Rainbow) Division but doubted the diagnosis because the 42nd did not have a laboratory. I was sent to investigate and found that the division medical officer, Herbert C. Knapp, had wangled some throat swabs, diphtheria culture tubes, and a microscope from the French. He could not get an incubator so he placed the inoculated tubes in a GI bucket under a stolen hen, which made a perfect automatic incubator. His diagnoses were correct, and my report may have been helpful in Knapp's promotion.

Whenever diphtheria or meningitis occurred in our area of the American Expeditionary Force, I had to culture the throats not only of the contacts but usually the whole company and in one instance half of a division. The usual assignment was 1,500 cultures. The only break I had in the carrier load was when I was ordered to culture the throats of 15,000 men because of one case of meningitis. I protested to the division surgeon that the task was physically impossible. Needless to say, I was assured in no uncertain terms that the regulations must be obeyed and was ordered to proceed at once. I started with the division surgeon and was able to quarantine him the next morning. His throat culture did contain meningococci, but my friends suspected that he would have been quarantined anyway. The immured Colonel quickly countermanded that carrier hunt. I later learned that Capt. Harry Truman (later President) had been an officer at that camp but whether he was a meningococcus carrier, I do not know. We had to keep these carriers in quarantine until two successive throat cultures were negative, and we frequently had 300 of them behind barbed wire.

One of the British laboratory officers, Colonel A. W. M. Ellis (later the Regius Professor of Medicine at Oxford), told me that he handled his carrier orders in a way which I envied but did not dare copy because I was only a lieutenant. Ellis said that he dipped all

Medical staff with convalescent patients at French hospital, World War I. Davison, first on right, second row.

throat swabs in carbolic before plating them and he always was able to report negative cultures.

When meningitis was reported in the camps near St. Nazaire, I was sent there. It was out of the military zone, so Atala was also transferred there as a Red Cross bacteriologist, and we started housekeeping.

One of my Princeton classmates, Varse Williams, had been assigned to St. Nazaire and soon became bored with unloading ships.

One of the most interesting trips from Neufchateau was a visit to Domremy, the birthplace of Jeanne d'Arc. It seemed strange that this tiny village could have produced such an historic character. Another interesting event at Neufchateau was inspecting Zeppelin No. 54 which had been blown off its course and captured by a farmer with a pitchfork after it had descended when the fuel supply was exhausted. Mechanically, it was a beautiful ship, and it was difficult to see why zeppelins had not done more damage to us.

The happiest parts of the Neufchateau period were occasional weekends in Paris with Atala. She had several apartments in succession trying to get a well-heated one because fuel was scarce.

Being a dysentery patient in a military hospital was an interesting experience. The staff and nurses were my former associates at the Hopkins. The only drawback of the hospital was the cold. One of the orderlies told me that the Russians had used this barracks the previous winter, and several had frozen to death in bed. We had one wood stove, but the Colonels, Majors, and Captains had their beds arranged near it in that order. Little warmth reached the Lieutenants.

William S. Baer, who was in charge of orthopaedics in Base Hospital 18 as well as at the Hopkins Medical School, always made ward rounds followed by a chow dog in spite of the efforts of the commanding officer to discipline him for this unmilitary procedure. Baer's love for chow dogs also got him in trouble with the censor. Mrs. Baer, who maintained a chow kennel in Baltimore, wrote her husband for advice about buying some champion chows from a dealer. Baer cabled her the list of dogs he wanted but as they all had Chinese names the censor accused him of attempting to send code messages and was very doubtful of the truth of his explanation. What infuriated Baer though was that the censor's refusal to send the cable lost him the chance to buy some dogs he had wanted for a long time.

Reading matter was scarce, but fortunately, the Masons sent all their members a pocket Bible. I read it from cover to cover and found it very interesting; there were many juicy bits that I had not read in Sunday school.

Regular A.E.F. officers were promoted faster, regardless of age, than the Reserves, and they received increased pay from the date of their promotion while the Reserves were paid only from the date they received their notice of promotion, which might be several months later. I had been recommended for promotion several times, but it was held up because I was under the required age and when my Captaincy came through I didn't learn of it for two months after I was honorably discharged. When I tried to collect the back pay, I not only was informed that I was ineligible but to add insult to injury, the Army revoked my promotion as I had been discharged as a 1st Lieutenant. It was restored on the 29th of May, 1952, when I was retired after my sixtieth birthday as a Colonel, Medical Corps, United States Army Reserve, and Captain, United States Army.

Absence of rank also had its embarrassing side. At one time as a 1st Lieutenant, I was in charge of a Major and two Captains because I had been in France longer than most officers. My Colonel told me he would help me if I had any difficulty. I didn't. The British and French avoid that situation by using temporary or brevet rank appropriate to the assignment. The French were annoyed with the A.E.F. for sending me, a Lieutenant, to Allied conferences at which the other delegates were Colonels and Generals and listed me as a Lieutenant Colonel to salve their pride.

One of the queerest jobs assigned to the laboratory was to decide whether a girl had been raped. Her father had accused six of the enlisted men of a regiment stationed in the town and offered her drawers as evidence. The Colonel sent the garment to us for an opinion. We were stumped until our Sergeant made the brilliant suggestion of shaking the drawers in a flask of water to see if any spermatozoa could be found. The test worked; not only were many spermatozoa found but also a number of gonococci. When the Colonel received the report he sent for the girl to pick out her assailants. None of them had gonorrhea, and the charge was dropped.

The French were mighty hunters and took the sport very seriously, especially during the wild boar season. While I was in Neufchateau, my landlord, the Major, took me out into the hills where we stood motionless for hours waiting for a beast to appear.

None did. We had better luck on the trip with Major Georges Elbot who was in charge of the French laboratory in St. Nazaire. He had persuaded a French major, Prince de Joinville, to invite Dick Taylor, my C.O., and me to the Joinville estate. Taylor and I had heard that the Major had a sister so we took presents with us. He spent a large part of his pay check for a huge box of chocolates while I invested ten cents in two loaves of quartermaster bread. Taylor was politely thanked for his candy, but much to his annoyance the family went into ecstasy over my loaves, the first white bread they had seen in three years. The Joinville chateau was huge, but the family lived in a few rooms because of the fuel shortage. The Major's great-grandfather had brought Napoleon's body back from St. Helena so the salons were filled with mementoes of the Emperor.

My greatest hazard in France was riding a motorcycle. Automobiles were becoming too scarce for Lieutenants and as I had to have transportation to chase epidemics, I was asked if I would ride a motorcycle. As I had had one years before, I gladly accepted. However, motorcycles had gained in power and speed, so my first trip resulted in a torn uniform and scraped knees. The machine had gotten out of control among a collection of artillery caissons and I ricocheted back and forth until I fell off. The next episode was more serious. My dog, Chienne, was in heat, and one of the French officers down the coast suggested that I bring her down to be bred with his male dog. Army vehicles can't be used for personal business, but my C.O. was away so I took the motorcycle with Chienne in the sidecar. Everything went well until making a fast downhill turn on the way back to St. Nazaire. I forgot that Chienne's weight was insufficient to hold down the sidecar. The first thing I knew I was sailing through the air toward a stone wall. Fortunately, there was a hole in it and I went through it unhurt, but the motorcycle was a complete wreck. Chienne had been thrown over the wall. A peasant ran out and kept asking where my soldier companion was as she had seen a khaki colored blur sailing through the air. A passing truck took the wrecked motorcycle to an army repair shop where a friendly sergeant marked it "wrecked in line of duty" and issued me another one. Chienne never had any puppies.

When I returned from one of my trips to Camp Coetquidon, I found that Chienne had disappeared. As she had become a great nuisance to our enlisted men by sleeping in their bunks, I assumed that someone had shot her and that it was no use making a fuss about it. I did not learn her fate until two years later when one of our sergeants came to the Hopkins Hospital as an agent for an instrument firm. I took him to lunch and as we were now civilians, I pumped him about the dog. He finally admitted that they hated the beast and while I was away had sold her to a certain American sergeant in a neighboring unit. I then wrote to the Adjutant General's office in Washington for the man's address and learned that he lived in the Bronx. The next time I was in New York, I went to the address but was told that he had moved. However, the present tenant told me that the man's girl friend lived across the street. I called on her and casually inquired about the possibility that her friend had brought a police dog from France. She said that he had and that the two of them often went to Westchester where an aunt was taking care of the animal.

I departed for Westchester and whistled as I passed the house which the girl had described. Immediately Chienne leaped across the fence into my arms. The next problem was to get the dog back. I called on the aunt and explained the situation. She told me that she had no doubts about my owning the dog (its behavior proved that), but she didn't want to give her to me until she had communicated with her nephew. She gave me his present address and I phoned him to meet me in New York. He was very recalcitrant and refused to return the dog unless I paid him $100 for the expenses he had incurred in bringing her home. Fortunately, the bonus bill was up in Congress, and I suggested that he might lose his share if the Army authorities were informed that he had stolen a dog from an officer in France. He quickly settled for two dollars, the cost of the dog collar. The sad part of the story was that I could not take Chienne to Baltimore as we were living in an apartment so I boarded her on Long Island for a few months. When we acquired our house at Riderwood, a Baltimore suburb, I sent for my dog only to learn that she had died the previous week.

After the Armistice, I was ordered to take over the laboratory of Base Hospital 33 at Plymouth, England. When I reached London, I found that Base Hospital 33 was at Portsmouth and not at Plymouth and that someone had made a mistake in my orders. The war being over, I saw no reason why I should not take advantage of the error, so I decided to go AWOL at Oxford until the Army caught up with me. I went straight to the Oslers. Their home lived up to its reputation as the "Open Arms," and I was asked to stay until I was found by the military police. Sir William and Lady Osler were then making a brave fight against the terrible loss of Revere who had been killed on the 18th of February, 1918, but their interest in former students was unabated. Seeing them again was like coming home, and I felt what a great contrast my devotion was to the awe and timidity with which I had rung that bell in 1913. After four days of bliss, Osler came in laughing and said that the Army Headquarters in London had phoned that I had been located, that my orders had been corrected, and that I must go to Portsmouth at once.

A few days later, we had orders to send all of the Portsmouth patients home. In forty-eight hours the hospital was empty, and we had nothing to do while awaiting transportation home. I must have been born to work, for those three months of enforced idleness were terrible except for an occasional weekend at Oxford with the Oslers.

The only recreation in Portsmouth was to visit the Navy Yard. German U-boat, U258, had been surrendered after the Armistice and was one of the main attractions. It was eerie in 1919 to look through a modern periscope at the wooden flagship, *Victory*, which was also anchored in Portsmouth Harbor, and to realize that Lord Nelson had been killed aboard her at the battle of Trafalgar on the 21st of October, 1805.

Another happy interlude during the long wait for transportation was spending Boxing Day in London with Ken Waters who was on leave from the British Navy. Boxing Day is the day after Christmas on which all servants expect a gift or box. Boxing Day in 1918, however, was a great occasion because President and Mrs. Woodrow Wilson were met at the Railway Station by King George and Queen Mary, and the four of them were driven in an open state coach through cheering crowds to Buckingham Palace.

Finally on the 12th of February, 1919, we were ordered to return to the States on the S.S. *Olympic*.

CHAPTER VI

THE HARRIET LANE HOME
PEDIATRIC TRAINING (1919-1927)

A TALA and my family met me in New York, and I certainly was
glad to be home. Except for two brief visits and six months at
the Hopkins, I had been abroad for nearly six years. Our outfit was
first ordered to Camp Merritt in New Jersey to be deloused and
inspected and then transferred to Camp Upton on Long Island for
demobilization. Everyone was discharged but me. As I was the
Adjutant (now called Executive Officer who gets all the dirty jobs), I
was responsible for all of the property of Base Hospital 33, about
$100,000 worth. Everything was accounted for except 300 blankets
which had disappeared between Camp Merritt and Camp Upton. It
was no use arguing with the quartermasters, and I was stumped until
my Sergeant came in with my release. I didn't ask any questions
until I was discharged and then learned that the wily Sergeant and
his squad had made up our loss by stealing 300 blankets from another
outfit. He said it was only justice as some other unit must have stolen
our blankets. As I thanked and parted from him, he pressed a small
package into my hand. It was a dark field adaptor for a microscope
and he stopped my protests by saying "I knew you always wanted it
and if you report it now, both of us will get into trouble." What could
I do? At any rate, that instrument served the country for eight years
at the Hopkins and is still being used at Duke!

I reached Baltimore on the 4th of March, 1919, just in time to
receive the fourth and last of John Howland's pediatric appointments. Another fifteen applicants who arrived later remained as
observers, a very unfair arrangement, and I hope that we did a
better job for the medical officers who returned to Duke from the
Second World War and the Korean crisis. My job as instructor in
pediatrics consisted of working in the wards and outpatient department half of the day, supervising the laboratory work of the house
staff and students in the basement of the Harriet Lane, doing the
bacteriology and some research during the remainder of the day in a
laboratory on the fifth floor of the old pathology building, adjoining
those of Stanhope Bayne-Jones and Tom M. Rivers.

My original plan for pediatrics if I survived the war was to obtain a few years of training at the Harriet Lane and then to obtain a part-time teaching job at the Long Island Medical College in Brooklyn and to go into practice there. However, Atala advised continuing in full-time pediatrics so I decided to try it, with the resolve that if I did not receive a professorship by the age of thirty-five, I should go to Brooklyn.

Howland always gave the members of his staff their choice of research problems so I decided to study the infant or summer diarrheas, which exacted such a high annual mortality, by using the same bacteriologic methods which I had employed in the dysentery epidemic among the troops in the A.E.F. during 1918. After a few months' work, it was obvious that the majority of these infants were dying of dysentery and that fly control, lactic acid milk, and clean hands would prevent its spread and reduce its incidence. Howland seemed pleased at the results so he sent Harold L. Higgins and me to study the infant diarrheas which were reported to be causing many deaths in Birmingham, Alabama. We soon found that these also were cases of dysentery. We were quite elated but before the results were published, I found by digging through the pediatric literature that two medical students (C. W. Duval and W. H. Bassett) had made similar studies twenty years before but that no one had paid any attention to their paper. There is nothing new!

Studying bacillary dysentery gave me an interest in other types of infantile diarrhea. It had been known that dogs died of diarrhea if their pancreases were removed, so I started to study gastric and duodenal enzymes, a subject which had hardly been touched in the United States since William Beaumont.

I had become so interested in clinical pediatrics that I persuaded Howland to let me return to the Harriet Lane Home as an assistant resident instead of an instructor. As married house officers were taboo at that time, Atala had to live in Bermuda with an aunt for six months.

On her return, Bill, our first child, was born (5th of May, 1921), and we rented the upper half of one of the old Baltimore houses near the Hopkins Hospital. Two years later, we bought a house in Riderwood in the Green Spring Valley, ten miles from Baltimore, and named it Fyvie for the birthplace of Ethel Gregg, our Scotch governness.

So that I could practice in any state to which I might be fortunate enough to be invited and because I had had only one examination in my whole irregular medical course, namely physiology at Oxford, I prepared for State Board Examinations in June of 1919. I found that if I passed the New Jersey and Maryland "Boards," their reciprocities would give me a license in most of the other states. Howland also urged me to take the National Boards which had been established three years previously. I was not very keen on the Nationals as I understood them to be difficult. Finally, Howland dared me to take them. It was hard work but to my surprise, I passed all three sets of examinations, of which the Nationals were the fairest though hardest.

PROHIBITION

Prohibition, which became a law on the 1st of January, 1920, did more harm than good. Every intern and medical student was using his spare time in fermentation experiments, and the results were nauseating. Laboratory alcohol and even the alcohol in which pathology specimens were preserved disappeared unless it was kept in a safe or was "doctored" by adding chemicals to it which would cause diarrhea and vomiting. Even ether, which acts like alcohol, was "sniffed." Patients would be brought in blinded by wood alcohol. During prohibition, some of the Baltimore ward leaders ran saloons just as openly as those in the Bowery during Boss Croker's day in the early 1900's. In fact, one could often find more policemen in the bars than on the precinct beats. At the saloon patronized by the Hopkins house staff, the barkeeper said that even before prohibition he had not used regular gin so he continued to use the bathtub variety made with juniper berries, glycerin, and industrial alcohol. I wanted to vote for a Princeton graduate who was running for mayor on the Democratic ticket, so I went to see the ward boss who kept a saloon near the Hospital. He was quite sympathetic to my request for a vote but assured me that nothing could be done as two years of residence were required for voting and although I had registered in 1916 when I was a student and though Army service counted as residence, my original registration had been lost. As I left, I said that it was a pity to lose votes as my friend, the Democratic candidate for mayor, certainly needed them. The boss shouted in astonishment, "Hell, why didn't you tell me you were a Democrat, of course you can vote. I thought you were a Yankee Republican." He took me in his car to the City Hall and saw that I was allowed to vote "regular."

One Saturday night, in January, 1920, as Atala and I were walking home from the theatre to save carfare, as well as for exercise, we noticed that the sky over the Hopkins Hospital was lurid with flames. We ran the rest of the way and found that the pathology building was being gutted. Apparently the fire started on the fifth floor from a home-made temperature regulator on an incubator. Atala and I helped salvage the contents of the first two floors, but my laboratory on the fifth floor was a total loss so that I had to move my research to a small dark storeroom in the Harriet Lane basement, which had only one window. Like a mine mule, I commenced to go blind. My chief regret was the destruction of all of the dysentery cultures which I had brought home from France as well as those I had collected in Birmingham, Alabama. Six years later, a new laboratory was added to the Harriet Lane Home, and I came back to daylight.

Atala was graduated from the Hopkins in June, 1920, and she decided to spend the summer with her parents in Chocorua, New Hampshire. To be near her, and also because I realized that I was not learning very much clinical pediatrics, I obtained a summer residency on the old Boston Floating Hospital.

In spite of the Boston faith in milk percentages, woman's milk was fed to any infant who was very ill, so several wet nurses were employed. They stripped their breasts every morning and evening, and the Floating Hospital always had a few gallons on hand. Although most of us were raised on mother's milk, the thought of drinking it in adult life seems to be nauseating. At any rate, it had that effect on the ship captain who always tried to kibitz Joe Palmer's and my nightly bridge game. One evening, seeing a pitcher of milk on a shelf, he helped himself to a glass and was smacking his lips until we told him that he had just drunk breast milk. He promptly vomited it over the side of the ship and never bothered us again.

McKim Marriott, a North Carolinian and one of Howland's associates and my instructor at the Hopkins, finally simplified the infant feeding problem for pediatricians as well as for mothers by introducing evaporated milk to which lactic acid had been added. The mixture has many advantages.

Kenneth B. Rothey, while a student at Duke, demonstrated that dysentery and typhoid bacilli when added in large amounts to lactic acid milk are rapidly destroyed. H. Grant Taylor and R. Winston Roberts, also Duke students, demonstrated that lactic acid milk could be kept unspoiled in open dishes at room temperature for

90

three days, so refrigeration is unnecessary. Lactic acid evaporated milk is cheaper than all other feedings except breast milk, if it is assumed that breast milk does not cost anything, a premise with which no mother would agree.

Lactic acid evaporated milk is obtainable everywhere, while in some areas good dairy milk cannot be purchased. Raw milk, whether or not certified or grade A, should not be drunk, as it can spread disease. Two children were once brought to Duke Hospital because of brucellosis. Their family cow had passed the government test, but Mary Poston milked the cow and demonstrated *Bruccela abortus* in the milk. The farmer told me "that lady bacteriologist might be a good doctor but she was a very poor milker." Under the law, the health officer could not condemn and shoot the cow and pay the owner the state indemnity of $30 because she had passed the government tests. However, he was very cooperative and agreed to retest the cow two weeks later. In the meantime, Mary Poston injected the cow with a vaccine which reversed the tests so when the health officer retested the animal, she did not pass the government tests and the cow was shot and the family received the $30, all in accordance with the law.

In addition to my other duties at the Hopkins, Francis R. Dieuaide, who was in charge of the adult heart service, and I ran a pediatric heart clinic, although Howland was very much opposed to special clinics. At any rate, I learned a fair amount about pediatric cardiology, but the Hopkins pediatric heart clinic did not become famous until first Helen Taussig and later Al Blalook took charge after I had gone to Duke.

Dr. Sidney V. Haas of New York had published an article on the value of a banana diet in celiac disease, and the Baltimore manager of the United Fruit Company phoned that he would be glad to furnish the Harriet Lane Home with all of the bananas we could use. I suggested ten dozen bananas per week, but he sent ten stalks, each containing a hundred or more bananas, so the house staff and nurses as well as our two celiac patients, ate bananas *ad nauseum*. We still use banana diets for celiac diseases, but most of us at the Hopkins feel like one of the Durham celiac patients who suddenly and forcibly stated "I'll not eat one more God-damned banana." She didn't, and she died.

RESEARCH

Research was an essential part of the Harriet Lane Home training. Not only were we encouraged to publish numerous papers, but it was generally understood that unless we did we might not be reappointed. Part of that policy, the encouragement of research, is excellent, but the implied necessity for frequent publication at the Hopkins and other institutions including Duke has filled our medical journals with too much claptrap. It was a common saying at the Rockefeller Institute when I was there in 1917 under Simon Flexner that "a paper a day keeps Simon away." Not only are the medical journals full of inconsequential papers but men were and are appointed on the basis of their literary productivity instead of their teaching ability. The first question asked about a candidate for an appointment is usually "What has he published?"

One of John Howland's great contributions to research was his allergy to technicians. I never had one, nor had anyone else in the Harriet Lane, though an occasional postgraduate physician and a series of medical students usually worked with me. Research Fellows and Ph.D. candidates had not yet invaded medical research to substitute volume for quality.

I may have, inadvertently, been responsible for increasing the number of Ph.D.'s because, while I was in Oxford on my way home from the war, Sir Charles Sherrington asked me why so few graduate students came to Oxford and Cambridge and so many went to Germany. I explained that a Ph.D. was a necessity like a union card for a teacher and that the German universities gave them for a program similar to my B.Sc. At any rate, Oxford soon established the degree of D.Phil. for the former B.Sc. requirements but did not make it retroactive for me.

When Ben Kramer and I visited the laboratories in the Harriet Lane a few years ago and found it filled with technicians, we both exclaimed about what Dr. Howland would have said if he had seen this perversion. He believed, and I think correctly, that research work was a great deal better without the technicians because at least one had to think one's way through the problems instead of telling someone to do the work.

I was as bad, if not worse than my colleagues, for as Howland candidly told me no one could write more fluently or worse than I did. He probably had read Sheridan's couplet:

> You write with ease to show your breeding
> But easy writing's curst hard reading.

Keeping the two acres of lawn cut at Fyvie was a problem, so I bought two lambs to eat and also to fertilize the grass. They were quite successful until they were killed by dogs. However, we benefited from the tragedy because we butchered the animals and hung the seventy pounds of lamb in the Hopkins pathology morgue until we could consume it. The original cost of the two lambs was $7, and the retail price of the salvaged meat was $28! I then sold the two hides for $2. A few days later, a farmer neighbor told me that the county commissioners would reimburse me for the cost of the lambs out of the dog tax fund, so the meat was now all profit. Most of us, including the dogs' owner, knew that the lamb killers were some thoroughbred Airedales belonging to my nearest neighbor. Neither of us mentioned the matter as there wasn't much that could be said without starting a row. However, a few months later, I found one of the Airedale puppies which had escaped from the kennel. I phoned the owner to come and get it, but he embarrassedly forced me to keep the puppy as a present, thereby clearing his conscience and rewarding me for not complaining. At any rate, the pup was worth $150, and I do not see why sheep farmers do not become wealthy as my total profit on two lambs was $180!

Jeana, our daughter, arrived on the 9th of March, 1923. We had planned to name her Atala Jane after her mother and great-aunt, and, in fact, she was christened Atala Jane Scudder Davison, but Bill, who was two, kept calling her Jeana, and the name has persisted.

In June, 1923, I returned to Princeton for my tenth reunion. It started as a gay occasion, for many of us had not seen each other since we were graduated in 1913. I was talking to Paul Myers, a lawyer classmate, about one of his cases in which an insurance company had contested a death claim because the man had died two months after taking out a large policy. I was assuring Paul that that might happen to any of us when there was a loud roar and a ball of fire burst between my knees. I thought some drunk had thrown a fire cracker at me and as I looked around to bawl him out, I saw that Bob Patterson, who had been standing near me, was flat on the ground. Apparently, a bolt of lightning had struck in our midst, but my rubber-soled shoes had protected me. We used artificial respiration on Bob for several hours but could not resuscitate him.

One of my most embarrassing experiences was due to the Hopkins rule that all nurses and interns must be re-vaccinated whenever a suspected smallpox patient was admitted. One of the women interns

93

dashed into my laboratory and demanded that she be vaccinated in some place which would be covered by her bathing suit. She promptly put her foot on my desk and suggested that the internal aspect of her thich as close as possible to the perineum was the best area. I vaccinated her but was fearful that students would drop in during the procedure. I never checked her to see if she had a "take."

Atala, the children, and I usually went to Europe every other summer. They stayed in England or Scotland while I visited pediatric clinics in London, Paris, Stockholm, Copenhagen, and Glasgow. One summer I visited as many German clinics as possible in order to see at first-hand whether they were as good as the older generation claimed or as bad as they were reported.

I started from Strasbourg in France, zig-zagging across Germany visiting the pediatric clinics of Freiburg, Heidelberg, Frankfurt, Wurzburg, Jena, Berlin, Dresden, Leipzig, Breslau, Prague (Czechoslovakia), Vienna (Austria), Budapest (Hungary), Munich, Bonn, Cologne, and Dusseldorf. None of them was as good as the better American pediatric clinics. Their professors, except Finkelstein, Czerny, Bessan, and Bokay, were complacently practicing prewar pediatrics, and only their assistants, many of whom are now refugees in this country, seemed to have any modern ideas. Even they had rarely read American medical literature and did not pay much attention to it, which is probably one of the reasons that many of them are now having difficulty in adapting themselves to the more advanced American medicine. There are, of course, some exceptions, like Paul Gyorgy, who was in charge of the children's clinic at Heidelberg and who is now teaching at the Pennsylvania Medical School. When I first met him at Heidelberg, he asked my opinion of a certain American pediatrician and when I said I did not like his work, Gyorgy was so delighted that he invited me to dinner that evening at his home. My German is not too fluent, but a glass or two of Kummel improved it, and Paul, Mrs. Gyorgy, and I have been friends ever since. I did not have time to visit the other pediatric clinics at Gratz (Austria), Halle, Hamburg, Gottingen, Kiel, Magdeburg, Marburg, and Munster, but I was told that they were very similar to those I saw. It was the hardest work I have ever done, riding trains without sleepers at night and going ward rounds in the hospitals by day. With two other physicians, I repeated this survey in 1945 for the American Army but in greater comfort, traveling by planes and staff cars. All of the medical schools we saw in 1945 were in ruins, but the Germans refused our offer to rehabilitate medical education on the ground that they knew more about it than we did. Only one German, old Professor Volhard in Frankfurt, realized that our help was needed.

After one of our European trips we came home on the *Aquitania*. The second day out the Ship's Surgeon told me that one of the passengers had died and that his family wanted the body embalmed. He didn't know how to do it and asked me to help him. I had never embalmed a body though I had often seen it done. I agreed to help but soon found that I had to do the whole job. The body had been stored in ice and was frozen solid. I remembered vaguely that embalming consisted of the intravenous injection of formalin, but I had no idea of the quantity required. My first task was to melt an arm so that I could insert a needle into a vein. I then poured in hot formalin solution until the body became thawed and the fluid oozed out of the toes. I used six gallons of formalin. I have since learned that a half pint of formalin with three ounces each of glycerin and alcohol in four quarts of water are all that is necessary. I expect that my man is still preserved like Lenin. I was completely exhausted by working for two hours in the hold in an atmosphere saturated with formalin. In addition, there was a storm running. The final straw which broke my back came the next day when one of the passengers asked me for a contribution to help pay the Ship's Surgeon his fee of fifty dollars for embalming.

In 1922, Oscar M. Schloss, the new Professor of Pediatrics at Harvard, offered James L. Gamble and me appointments as Assistant Professors. Jim accepted, but Howland persuaded me to stay by raising my rank and salary and giving me ward privileges as an attending pediatrician. However, they were only paper privileges because, except in the summer, when Dr. Howland was away, no one did anything that Dr. Howland and the resident had not approved.

I also received an invitation to Louisville, and when Atala and I went there to inspect and be inspected, I was very much tempted to accept because John W. Moore, with whom I had served at Base Hospital 34 in France, and other friends of mine were on the faculty. If John had taken me sailing on the wide Ohio River instead of showing me the Churchill Downs race track, I might now be there because I love to swim and sail, and since Serbia, I have disliked horses.

During the same year, I was asked to go to Peiping Union Medical College in China for three years to train a Chinese to head the pediatric department. I had always wanted to see China (an ambition I realized in 1949), but I was doubtful about the possibility of a good appointment on my return. Welch told me that he would see that I found a job on my return but as he was seventy-five at the time, I wasn't sure that he would survive three years. He assured me that he would live to the age of eighty-four like his father. He said that his mother died young, but heredity was only in the male line. As a matter of fact, Welch did live to the age of eighty-four and would have lived longer except for a prostatic carcinoma. I finally told the China Medical Board that I would go for two years with the privilege of returning or remaining permanently, a proposition which was unacceptable to the Director.

In the spring of 1924, J. Whitridge Williams resigned as Dean, and Lewis H. Weed, Professor of Anatomy, was importuned to succeed him. He said he would accept if he could have me as Assistant Dean to do the scut work. I wondered why Weed wanted me because we scarcely knew each other, until he showed me the following quotation from a 28th of March, 1916, letter from Sir Charles Sherrington, Professor of Physiology at Oxford, with whom both Weed and I had worked:

> One of our men, Davison (Princeton and Oxford) has got entrance to J. H. Clinic for, I think, July next. He is a very capital man, a senior research student at Magdalen College here, and obtained an excellent first class Honours in Physiology last July.

Howland tried to persuade me to take the job, but I hesitated because I was very happy in the work which I was doing. However, no one else seemed to be available, and Howland persisted. Finally, on the 23rd of May, 1924, he used the successful argument that it was better to have two strings to my medical school bow and that some position might arise in which double training, administrative and pediatric, might be needed. It turned out to be sound advice because I later was considered for the deanship at Duke on that basis. As it turned out, I enjoyed working with Weed. Until his death on the 21st of December, 1952, he was the keenest man in medical education and took the leadership which Welch held for so many years.

At first, I didn't like Weed. He was too sarcastic and couldn't tolerate a joke at his expense. For example, when I first met him in

1916 when I returned from Oxford, I told him what I thought was a humorous story, namely Sir Charles Sherrington's comment on Lew's and Harvey Cushing's scientific research on the "cerebellar position sense of cats" which always enabled them to land on their feet. Sir Charles had said jokingly "what a waste of time, someone in the 18th century had proven that cats always land on their feet because of their belly fat and low center of gravity."

In addition to entirely too many papers, I published *Pediatric Notes* in 1925. It was an amplification of the Harriet Lane notebook which all of us had compiled. It proved to be more useful than I had anticipated, and for the next nine years it was used by medical students and physicians as far away as China and India.

The second book, *Enzymes,* was much more difficult. I had been studying digestive enzymes in infants for two years and was asked in 1926 to collaborate on a book on enzymes with Selman A. Waksman, an authority in this field and later a Nobel Prize recipient for the discovery of streptomycin. We sent each other our manuscripts for revision and visited each other for the final corrections, Waksman at Rutgers and I at the Hopkins. After six months of hard work, the book was published and apparently filled a need, for it was the only American book on enzymes for the next fifteen years. As a matter of fact, it was the first book on enzymes in English since William Beaumont's study in 1833 of the gastric juice of Alexis St. Martin who had a stomach fistula from an abdominal wound.

If we had recognized the action of the enzymes of *Penicillin camemberti* in the ripening of cheese as an "antiseptic," as well as a "preservative," antibiotics would have been born fifteen years earlier. Our observations were correct, but our semantics were at fault. It was the wrong choice of a word.

In February, 1926, Howland started hiccoughing and became so exhausted and weak that he went abroad on the 31st of March, 1926, for a rest and a holiday. At his request, the Hopkins Trustees appointed me acting head of the department of pediatrics and acting pediatrician in charge of the hospital. While abroad, he suddenly became worse and died on the 20th of June, 1926, at the age of fifty-three from cirrhosis of the liver which had been caused by two bouts of infectious hepatitis several years previously.

Howland died before the ninth edition of his *Diseases of Infancy and Childhood* was ready, and the publisher asked me to complete the revision. All of Howland's friends helped, but the amount of labor required was prodigious, as extensive changes were necessary because of the advances in pediatrics. One of the most difficult jobs was trying to interpret Howland's notes. One, for example, was "write a section on Pfeiffer's disease." I could not find anyone who had ever heard of Pfeiffer's disease. Finally, an old medical dictionary was found which referred to Pfeiffer's disease as glandular fever. After some investigation, it was found that glandular fever was infectious mononucleosis, and so the section on Pfeiffer's disease was written. After the job was finished, I took a boat to Havana and slept soundly for three days and nights.

I had read in the newspapers that James B. Duke had signed the Indenture of the Duke Endowment on the 11th of December, 1924, and that a new medical school and hospital would be established in Durham, North Carolina. I was very much interested because I had roomed for a year in the Harriet Lane Home with George L. Carrington, whose home was in Durham and later in Burlington, North Carolina, and had listened to his glowing accounts of that growing state. Second, I thought with envy that the new Duke University would need a dean and professor of pediatrics but that as I was only thirty-two years of age, I would not be considered for the position. My envy became worse when I saw the architect's sketches of the Duke buildings in the *New York Times*. My interest was greatly increased fifteen months later when Weed showed me the following long-hand letter:

807 St. Paul Street, Baltimore
28 Feb., 1926

Dear Weed,

I have two letters from Wickliffe Rose about the dinner to President Few of Duke University. He says next Wednesday, third March, will be convenient, so I have telegraphed Pres. Few that we shall expect him to dine with us on that date at seven-thirty at the Maryland Club. The bill for the dinner will be paid by the General Education Board.

Rose says that a principal purpose at present is to get the best man available to take charge of the development of the medical plans, selection of faculty, etc.

I will engage the room and order the dinner, but I hope that you through your secretary will issue the invitations. I have jotted down on accompanying sheet a suggested form of invitation, which may be signed either by you or by Pres. Goodnow. Of course Pres. Goodnow should preside at the dinner.

I have also written on an accompanying sheet names of those which occur to me to be invited. Use your own discretion about deletions and additions.

As the time is so short probably the telephone should be used in reaching those to be invited, but I think the written explanatory note should also be sent so that all will understand the purpose of the dinner.

If, as seems likely, Dr. Few wishes to be shown around, can you not put him in charge of Davison. Of course Davison would be the best man for him to secure to develop the school, but I imagine he might hesitate to take on such a job.

I think Ames should be included, as an important matter in the relation of the medical school to the rest of the University.

Pearl is always full of ideas on every subject. Davison, Bloomfield, Rich are possible material for the future school.

Sorry to put all this on you, but there seems no other way.

Sincerely yours,
William H. Welch

I was, of course, very flattered that Welch had recommended me but still felt that my age would debar me from consideration so I was not embarrassed by meeting William Preston Few, the President of Duke University, and thoroughly enjoyed Welch's dinner at the Maryland Club on the 3rd of March, 1926. Several of the guests made speeches giving varied advice to Few on how to organize a medical school. Howard A. Kelly suggested that Duke's greatest contribution would be the establishment of a museum of natural history and especially should have a collection of snakes! Dr. Few thanked the group for the suggestions and described the architect's plans which were being made and the stone with its seven colors which was to be used. The next day, I drove Dr. Few to Homewood, and then Harold L. Amoss and I lunched with him at the Belvedere Hotel. He was the quietest man I had ever met; he rarely talked but when he did he said something worth hearing, and always with a twinkle in his eye. Someone asked him who did the talking when he had an interview with President Coolidge. He replied, "Coolidge." I liked Dr. Few immediately, an affection and admiration that increased with the years that followed.

President Few did not indicate whether he was interested in me but as I had not expected him to be, I was not disappointed. In the summer of 1926, I sent Dr. Few a copy of *Enzymes* which Selman A. Waksman and I had just written. The letter of acknowledgment contained a cryptic sentence which I did not understand: "I hope Dr. Howland's death will not change your plans." The next contact I had with Duke was indirect. Beaumont S. Cornell of Toronto came into my laboratory in the Harriet Lane Home in the summer of 1926 and told me that he had been working on pernicious anemia and since Mr. Duke was believed to have died of pernicious anemia, the Duke Endowment had given him the opportunity of studying it. Judging from a letter from Dr. George Minot to Dr. Fred Hanes, which I saw several years later, Mr. Duke probably had not had pernicious anemia. I was able to arrange laboratory facilities for Dr. Cornell who spent the following year at the Hopkins and wrote an excellent summary of the research done on pernicious anemia.

The only other association that I had with Duke was meeting Dr. Watson S. Rankin at the meeting of the Southern Medical Association at Atlanta in November, 1926. He and I were on the program on different days and each of us had gone to hear the other. I had known of Dr. Rankin as one of the outstanding health officers in the country and had heard Welch speak glowingly of him many times. Mr. Duke, before his death in 1924, had invited Dr. Rankin to undertake the organization and administration of the hospital section of the Duke Endowment. I thoroughly enjoyed my conversation with Dr. Rankin, for our views on medical education, hospitals, and preventive medicine were identical. The friendship which started at that meeting became firmly established during the following years. Dr. Rankin's and my careers are founded on the hookworm. He was a great authority on the subject, and as I learned later, Dr. Wickliffe Rose who had continued Dr. Rankin's campaign against hookworm had recommended that Dr. Few see Dr. Welch about a medical dean for Duke.

Needless to say, I was surprised when Weed phoned me on the 19th of January, 1927, that Few was in his office and wanted to see me. The ensuing conversation with Dr. Few was characteristic of both of us; Few rarely going into details and I making rapid decisions. Few greeted me with, "I have come for you, are you ready?" I replied, "Yes, sir." He then named the salary, the amount for building and for the endowment and asked whether they were satisfactory. I replied, "Yes, sir." Few asked if I could start in September and again I replied, "Yes, sir." He said he would ask the Executive Committee of the Duke University Trustees to confirm the appointment and that was the end of the interview. Two days later (21st of January, 1927), I received a laconic telegram:

You have been elected. Delighted with prospect of working with you.
W. P. Few

My reply was:

Delighted with honor. Wish to express to you my great appreciation.
W. C. Davison

To those who insist on contracts and written terms this informality
may seem amazing, but I found they were superfluous when dealing
with the administration of Duke University. I wondered whether
Few remembered the salary mentioned, but, when the first salary
check arrived in September, it was for the correct figure. Among the
letters of congratulation and surprise which I received, I treasured
most those from Dr. Welch and Lady Osler:

The Baltimore Club,
Baltimore, Md.

Dear Davison,

You know that you have all my best wishes and warm regards. Association with you during your connection with the Johns Hopkins, which
owes you much and, I hope, has given you something by way of inspiration, stimulus and experience for your future important work, has been a
source of great pleasure to me.

William H. Welch

May 17, 1927

13 Norham Gardens,
Oxford, 3rd June, 1927

Dear Jonah,

I am greatly interested in this new scheme of life & future that you
have taken on and send my most affectionate & sincere congratulations,
for it means of course reward for your hard work here and at the Hopkins.
Dr. MacCallum was here and told me much of the plans for the new
university. I hope you will not find the place too isolated. I would like to
ask so many questions, but cannot on paper. Dr. Welch is in London and
will come here next week and he will be able to tell one everything. You
and Atala must be thrilled with thoughts of what a great work is before
you. I hope you will be coming over here before you settle down.

Eights Week is just over, the weather has been perfect, almost too cool
for thin dresses, but the cheeks and lips gave coloring. Christ Church
kept head of the river. Oxford has been more beautiful than ever, masses
of bloom everywhere. Tennis is in full swing everywhere.

My love to you both,

Afftly,
Grace R. Osler

Soon after my appointment, Frank Brown of the building committee at Duke came to Baltimore with the architect's proposed plans

for the new medical school and hospital. A lasting friendship started during the strenuous months which followed. The first necessity was to arrange the location of the various preclinical and clinical departments to obtain the greatest efficiency of operation. Winford Smith, the consulting medical architect, was helpful in the arrangements of the out-patient department.

Sandy, our third and last child, arrived on the 2nd of March, 1927.

CHAPTER VII

DUKE UNIVERSITY MEDICAL CENTER
(1927-1942)

D UKE UNIVERSITY originally was the Union Institute, which was founded in 1838 in Randolph County, North Carolina, by Methodists and Quakers. It became the Normal College in 1850 and Trinity, a Methodist College, in 1859, and was moved to Durham in 1892. On the 29th of December, 1924, the name was changed to Duke University to integrate it with a program of humanitarian effort outlined in The Indenture of James B. Duke. Trinity College became the undergraduate college for men and in 1930 was housed in new Gothic buildings on the West Campus. The buildings formerly occupied by Trinity College on the East Campus, as well as many new Georgian brick dormitories, classrooms, laboratories, and an auditorium, became the Woman's College of Duke University.

THE DUKE ENDOWMENT

The purpose of James B. Duke can best be told by quotations from his Indenture transferring a fortune (now worth a half billion dollars) to a board of fifteen trustees on the 11th of December, 1924:

> For many years I have been engaged in the development of water powers in North and South Carolina. In my study of this subject, I have observed how such utilization of a natural resource, which otherwise would run in waste to the sea and not remain and increase as a forest, both gives impetus to industrial life and provides a safe and enduring investment for capital. My ambition is that the revenues of such developments shall administer to the social welfare as the operation of such developments is administering to the economic welfare of the communities which they serve. I have selected Duke University as one of the principal objects of this trust because I recognize that education is next to religion the greatest civilizing influence.
>
> I have selected hospitals as another of the principal objects of this trust because I recognize that they have become indispensable institutions, not only by way of ministering to the comfort of the sick, but in increasing the efficiency of mankind and prolonging human life. . . . I hope that the people will see to it that adequate and convenient hospitals are assured in their respective communities. . . . It is to these rural districts that we are

to look in large measure for the bone and sinew of our country.

There is bequeathed to The Duke Endowment the sum of Ten Million Dollars and the Trustees shall use not exceeding Four Million Dollars in erecting and equipping at Duke University a Medical School, Hospital and Nurses Home.

Dr. William Preston Few, ever since his election to the presidency of Trinity College in 1910, had dreamed of and worked for the establishment of a four-year medical school in Durham. His first plan in 1923 was a joint project of Trinity, the University of North Carolina, and the Watts Hospital with money furnished by the Rockefeller Foundation and the State of North Carolina. Governor Angus McLean, President Harry Woodburn Chase of the University of North Carolina, John Sprunt Hill, the Watts Hospital Board, and Abraham Flexner of the Rockefeller Foundation had agreed on the program. Then, many of the Chapel Hill alumni objected, some who wanted the new school in Charlotte, others who believed that it should be at Chapel Hill, which already had a two-year school, and others who objected to any church affiliation because Trinity was a Methodist College.

Dr. Few had many discussions on the subject with James B. Duke and also had asked Dr. Watson S. Rankin, the State Health Officer for suggestions. The latter sent Dr. Few a splendid report on the advantages of a four-year medical school and the need for rural hospitals based on his study of the Saskatchewan program. Dr. Few again approached Mr. Duke who asked Alexander H. Sands, Jr., to survey the situation for him. Mr. Duke also sounded out many leaders in Charlotte on the subject.

It is said that Mr. Duke's interest in doing something for medicine may have started with an encounter with a small boy. The youngster saw Mr. Duke watching one of his power projects being built and followed him around, listening to his questions, his orders, his decisions. And, finally, the boy asked his own question. "Mister," he asked, "can you cure fits?" The engineers and secretaries thought it was an amusing joke. But Mr. Duke was irritated with them and was interested in the child. He questioned the boy and learned that the child's father was subject to fits. There and then, Mr. Duke gave orders that attention be given to the boy's father. Jonathan Daniels published this story on the 14th of September, 1947, and it was reproduced in papers all over the country. Duke Hospital was flooded for the next month with the same question, "Can you cure fits?" Fortunately, now, many types of epilepsy can be controlled, and some even cured.

His medical interest also may have started with his attack of erysipelas, which, according to local stories, was responsible for increasing his original tobacco fortune many-fold. At the time of this illness, Dr. W. Gill Wylie, Mr. Duke's old friend, who was attending him, described the hydro-electric plant that W. S. Lee, a South Carolina engineer, had built on Dr. Wylie's plantation. Dr. Wylie also said that Mr. Lee had told him that if anyone had the foresight to purchase the water-rights on the long North and South Carolina rivers and build power plants, factories would spring up throughout the two states. Mr. Duke became interested and sent for W. S. Lee, gave him a check for $100,000, and told him to start the project, which became the Southern and later the Duke Power Company.

The Duke University Medical Center building was started on the 1st of September, 1927, and was completed on the 1st of July, 1930. The collegiate Gothic architecture of the Duke Medical Center is beautiful to behold but difficult to adapt for a hospital. The late Frank C. Brown, chairman of the building committee, and I did the best we could and finally persuaded Horace Trumbauer, the architect, and Carl Lee, the builder, to widen medieval windows and to add third and fourth stories to what would have been two-storied buildings in the fourteenth-century style. Our worst error was in having interior courtyards which in the Durham summers before air conditioning were a foretaste of Hades. Hospital and medical schools should be built so that structural changes can easily be made. The only rooms in the Duke Medical Center which serve their original purposes are the toilets and amphitheatres which are too solid to move. I have had six different offices between 1927 and 1959. Regardless of climate, every area should be air-conditioned.

The impact of the Duke Endowment on medicine and hospitalization has been felt not only in the Carolinas but throughout the South, and even the world. From the establishment of the Trust on December 11, 1924, to December 31, 1962, the Hospital Section of the Duke Endowment under the direction of Dr. Watson S. Rankin, Marshall I. Pickens, and George P. Harris, has contributed $39,436,970.00 to assist the hospitals in the Carolinas, including Duke Hospital, in meeting their operating, building, and equipment expenses. Through its contributions to the Duke Hospital, as well as to Duke University, and its financial help to community

105

Duke Hospital under construction, 1928

hospitals over a period of thirty-eight years, the Duke Endowment has directly assisted a large segment of the population of North and South Carolina. These contributions by the Duke Endowment have supplemented tax funds in the operation, building and equipping of 259 hospitals in 125 of the 146 counties in North and South Carolina, thereby relieving the taxpayers of this additional burden. When the Duke Endowment commenced its operations in North and South Carolina in 1925, the two states had 6,184 general hospital beds, 3,598 physicians, one four-year medical school in South Carolina, and two two-year schools in North Carolina. On December 31, 1962, these two states had 23,236 general hospital beds, approximately 6,255 physicians, and four four-year medical schools.

DURHAM

On the 14th of March, 1927, I went to Durham for my first visit. Dr. and Mrs. Few, Dr. and Mrs. Flowers, Dr. and Mrs. Brown, and Dr. and Mrs. Rankin made my trip very delightful. The history of Durham is interesting. On the 17th of April, 1865, when General Johnston surrendered to General Sherman at the Bennett place near Durham, the town was just a hamlet of less than 100 inhabitants with a post office known as Durham's Station because Dr. Bartlett Durham had donated the land on which the railroad station was built. Because of the political confusion in Washington (General Lee had surrendered at Appomattox on the 9th of April, 1865, and President Lincoln had been assassinated on the 14th of April, 1865), the Johnston-Sherman peace terms were not confirmed for several weeks, and the two armies remained in camp. The soldiers liked the local tobacco and "appropriated" all they could find. After they were demobilized they would write back from Wisconsin, Alabama, etc., for more of the weed they had smoked during the Armistice. As a result, Durham tobacco within a few months had a national market. When Washington Duke returned to Durham (he had been captured after the fall of Richmond), he found some tobacco still stored in his barns which had not been raided. He collected his two sons, Benjamin H. and James B., who had been staying with relatives during the war and started filling the tobacco orders that were coming in from the demobilized armies. The industry grew rapidly and the town mushroomed with it. The population of Durham in 1885 was 5,000, 45,600 in 1927, 52,037 in 1930 and 78,302 in 1960.

After this first visit to Durham, Dr. Rankin and I drove to

Pinehurst to speak at a meeting of northern capitalists who spend the winters there and who were considering the organization of a community hospital. A $150,000 hospital was decided upon and Dr. Rankin said the Duke Endowment would consider a request for $50,000, if $100,000 were raised locally. Ten of the men at the meeting immediately subscribed $10,000 apiece. I had never seen so much wealth assembled at one time. That night as I was going to bed I read a notice on my door that the price of the room was $25. I spent a sleepless night as I had only $20 with me. I felt like the young British officer who was in a similar predicament in a Park Avenue hotel because he had neglected to ask in advance about the room rate. When he paid his bill he suggested to the manager that the sign in his room "Have you left anything?" should be changed to "Have you anything left?" To my amazement when I timidly asked for my bill the next morning I was told I was a guest of the management because of attending the hospital meeting. It was a great relief but it was too late to sleep the night over again. It was a good example of Montaigne's precept that "he grieves more than he need who grieves before he needs" or of Lowell's brief that "the misfortunes hardest to bear are those that never happen." However, I have since made all of my hotel arrangements in advance.

After Pinehurst, I spent a few days in Dr. Rankin's home and during the next thirty-five years it became a second home to me. Dr. and Mrs. Rankin and their son, Jess, and his wife, Ruth, have been closer to me than my parents and sisters. Whenever I became too frustrated with university officials or some of the "grant grabbers" and "empire builders" I would spend a day or two at 2049 Briarwood Road, Charlotte, pour out my troubles, sleep like a babe from 10:30 PM to 7:30 AM instead of 5 AM and go back to Durham to collect more headaches.

One of the greatest assets of Durham was Josh Turnage's barbecue cabin. Josh had a farm near Durham and served barbecue for his friends on Thursdays, the cook's usual night out, but his friends became so numerous that he had to expand. Visitors from this country and abroad frequently are more impressed with Turnage's barbecue than with some of our other activities. Josh picked up the garbage from Duke to feed his pigs, and we frequently commented on the fact that we were re-eating Duke Hospital food. The most amusing episode occurred when the School of Religion objected to the noise of the dogs in the medical school tower, and we arranged

In the kitchen at Josh Turnage's

Dinner at Turnage's in the later years

with Josh Turnage to have a kennel on his land near his old cabin. We always suspected that whenever one of these dogs was killed during fights, which were frequent, we might have had barbecued dog instead of barbecued pig. Regardless of whether it was dog or pig, I always enjoyed it. Jim Warren continued this activity after Josh's death except that he bought his pigs from Iowa. Josh's farm became a real estate development for younger faculty members. Josh's has been an important factor in good student-faculty relations because of the many happy and warm occasions there.

RECRUITMENT OF THE MEDICAL FACULTY

As the caliber of a medical school depends primarily on the ability of the faculty and students and the type of instruction and only secondarily on the buildings and equipment, the country was combed for a faculty as soon as the building was under way. The first question to be answered was "Should the professors be men of established reputation who had 'arrived,' or, should the university gamble on promising younger men with a future?" Fortunately, I had heard Osler discuss this question several times and though most people thought of the original "Four Doctors" of the Hopkins as great men, and they were when we knew them after they had made their reputations and that of the Hopkins, they were comparative youngsters when originally appointed by President Daniel Coit Gilman: Osler was 39, Halsted 37, Welch 34, and Kelly 31, an average age of 35 years.

Duke might not be able to find the equals of those Hopkins pioneers of modern medicine (fortunately no one will know until after we are dead), but our best chance was men under forty years of age. At any rate, that explains why the average age of the original Duke medical faculty also was 35 years. The better part of two years was spent collecting suggestions for a medical faculty and interviewing those who had been recommended. The first appointment was that of Harold L. Amoss as professor of medicine on the 10th of February, 1929.

The chief nurse is the most important person in any hospital and enquiries for candidates were made throughout the country. Everyone agreed that Duke should try to get Miss Bessie Baker, who had been chief nurse of Base Hospital #18, the Hopkins Unit at Bazoilles-sur-Meuse (pronounced "balls on the moose") while I was a patient there in 1917. She had a grand sense of humor and did not

111

report the enlisted men (Hopkins medical school seniors) when they moved a latrine in which she was sitting. After the war, she went to Columbia for the degree which nurses think they should have, and then became chief nurse of the Miller Hospital in St. Paul, Minnesota. Dr. Rankin and I arranged to meet her at the Mayo Clinic in Rochester, Minnesota, and liked her so much that we invited her to Durham. Fortunately, her visit was in March and the jasmine, forsythia, and daffodils were in bloom. Miss Bessie said, "I left six feet of snow in St. Paul and I don't care what your salary is, I want the job!"

She was responsible for the excellent standards of patient care at Duke and for starting the School of Nursing on a sound basis. The staff and patients adored her. She was only ruffled once when she started to sit down and her stiffly starched skirt sent a light aluminum chair skidding away from her and she sat down hard on the floor. She always blamed Vernon Altvater for buying aluminum chairs.

In 1938, severe shingles caused her retirement to Baltimore, but when the Second World War started, she worked with the Red Cross. On the 23rd of June, 1943, she was struck by an Army car. Just before she became unconscious and died, she humorously said, "I am glad that the driver was a Major and not a private."

Miss Bessie, Atala, and I thought it would be very fitting if all of the furniture, draperies, linens, and even the china, were North Carolina products. Most of the furniture, monk's cloth curtains, sheets, towels, etc., were made in the state, but North Carolina pottery could not withstand modern dish-washing machines. Furthermore, if a tea pot were broken, its lid, being hand-made, would not fit another tea pot.

When Duke Hospital was opened in 1930, the academic deans at Duke and Chapel Hill were each asked to recommend their keenest student in business administration to start a program of hospital administration internships as suggested by Michael Davis. F. Vernon Altvater represented Duke and F. Ross Porter came from Carolina. Both made outstanding records in hospital administration and were responsible for the first course in this field. By 1962, Duke had furnished over one hundred hospital superintendents from Medellin, Colombia, to Taiwan.

In order that the new School should be of the most use to the two-year medical schools at Chapel Hill and Wake Forest, it had been contemplated that for the first few years at least, clinical instruction only would be given at Duke, similar to the programs at St. Bartholomew's and Guy's Hospitals in London and the Massachusetts General and Boston City Hospitals which provide clinical training for the students who have had their preclinical years at Oxford, Cambridge, and Harvard. Many authorities felt, however, that the School should begin by admitting first- as well as third-year students. The Rockefeller Foundation granted $300,000 over a five-year period to help cover the high costs of the initial years. The Council on Medical Education and Hospitals of the American Medical Association, on the recommendation of Ray Lyman Wilbur, the chairman, gave the School Class A approval in 1929 before the faculty and building were completed. Notices of the entrance requirements were placed in college papers and soon the admission committee was inundated with applications and has remained so ever since. The keenest premedical students were sought, not necessarily those with "As" but with adequate records and recommendations which indicated that they would not fail and with interviews which showed that they were men and women of "determination and ambition," as Mr. Duke stated in his Indenture.

A pamphlet about the Duke Hospital and Outpatient Department, which had been approved by the medical society, was mailed to the medical profession in the two Carolinas. The members of the staff of Duke Hospital also were encouraged to speak at county, state, and national medical meetings on subjects with which they were familiar ranging from accidents to yellow fever. As a result of these pamphlets and the talks, patients came to Duke Hospital in increasing numbers. Almost all of them were satisfied with their hospital care, and they sent other patients.

OTHER NORTH CAROLINA MEDICAL SCHOOLS

Before the Flexner Report on medical education, there were three four-year medical schools in North Carolina, i.e., the University of North Carolina (1902-10) and Leonard Medical School of Shaw University (1882-1914) at Raleigh, and the North Carolina Medical College (1907-18) at Charlotte, and a two-year school at Wake Forest of which Dr. W. S. Rankin was Dean and Professor of Pathology from 1903 to 1909. Earlier, there had been five other medical schools in the State, a two-year school at Davidson (1887-1907), Edenborough (1866-82), Wilmington (College of Physicians

113

and Surgeons), and two at Jamestown. The last three died at birth or shortly thereafter. The American Medical Association lists another school at Arlington, North Carolina, but even Carl Goerch, a prominent Carolina historian, never heard of it. In 1914, the Shaw School at Raleigh, and in 1918, the North Carolina Medical College in Charlotte, closed. In 1910, UNC closed the clinical department in Raleigh but continued the two-year school at Chapel Hill which had been in existence since 1889. When Duke was opened in 1930, it was listed by the American Medical Association as the seventh North Carolina school. In 1940, the Wake Forest two-year school became the Bowman Gray School of Medicine and moved to Winston-Salem. Ten years later, Chapel Hill opened a four-year school.

DURHAM HOSPITALS

The city had three hospitals before Duke was built. The pioneer work for a hospital was started in 1888 by Dr. Albert G. Carr and was carried to fruition by George W. Watts who built Watts Hospital in 1895. This was the sixth general hospital in North Carolina and the first one in the state to be approved as Class A by the American Medical Association. The location of this hospital was an example of careful planning: bacteriologic plates were exposed in different parts of Durham, and the site with the fewest germs was selected. It had two hundred beds in 1941. The McPherson Hospital with thirty beds for eye, ear, nose and throat patients was built in 1926 and is approved for residents. The Lincoln Hospital for Negroes was established in Durham in 1901 through the efforts of Dr. Aaron M. Moore and the money of Washington, Benjamin N., and James B. Duke "in grateful appreciation and loving remembrance of the fidelity and faithfulness of the Negro slaves to the mothers and daughters of the Confederacy during the Civil War."

In September, 1927, Dr. Rankin invited William A. Pusey, former president of the A.M.A., Charles O'H. Laughinghouse, the North Carolina health officer, Frank E. Chapman, director of the University Hospitals at Cleveland, and me to spend a week visiting the hospitals in western North and South Carolina, which were being assisted by the Duke Endowment. The purpose of the trip was to study the effect which these hospitals were having in improving the medical care of the surrounding population and in attracting young physicians to settle in these localities. We spent our first night at the Elkin Hotel, and I remarked at breakfast the next morning that I had one of my best nights of sleep. Chapman told me that the reason was that I slept on an innerspring mattress for the first time. Like most people, I was ignorant of mattresses and enquired why similar ones could not be used in hospitals instead of the usual board-like variety. Chapman said he was sure that they could stand hospital wear but that no one had courage enough to invest the money to test them. We had both courage and money, so Duke Hospital was the first to be equipped with innerspring mattresses. They have survived years of hard service with only one accident and that was amusing: one night one of the cloth bands which hold the springs in these mattresses in check broke, and the released spring gently popped a patient's rear anatomy in much the same way as the spears of Scipio's men had prodded Hannibal's elephants.

On that trip we also called on Fred and Betty Hanes who had a cottage at Roaring Gap, North Carolina, a summer resort on a 3,500-foot mountain, 146 miles from Durham. I have spent my summer weekends there ever since, usually taking several students and interns with me. My clinical work is with children and as their worst season is in warm weather, I cannot take a full summer vacation, but I could leave Duke Hospital at five on Friday afternoon and be in the cool mountains at eight, and by leaving Roaring Gap at six on Monday morning, be back at work at nine, giving me three nights under blankets. For the first few years, I stayed at Graystone Inn or with Fred and Betty Hanes, while my family spent their summers in Europe or New Hampshire. Finally, in 1937, we rented a cottage at Roaring Gap and that winter bought one. We added a five-bed dormitory to it so that members of the hospital staff could stay with us. Sailing and swimming supplied mild exercise and detective stories and "horse opera" movies at nearby Sparta were recreation. The remainder of the time we ate and slept.

For many years, Fred Hanes and I were the only physicians on the mountain so we had an unavoidably busy general practice which finally became such a load that we persuaded Walter and Edna Bovard of the Graystone Inn to pay externs to answer the calls, give "shots," etc., and to call Fred and me only if they needed help. Until the Second World War, those externs were Duke interns but for the past few years they have been rising seniors who have profited from this preceptership experience in general practice and community medicine as well as enjoying an excellent summer resort themselves and allowing Fred Hanes and me to have quiet vacations.

In 1957, Atala and I bought Colonel Maurice Day's five-room

cottage and sold our larger one. Since my retirement in 1961, we spend March to November at Roaring Gap and December to February in the Caribbean. When we returned to Roaring Gap two years ago, the television had been moved to another room, some of the canned goods and a few of my clothes and shoes had disappeared, and a pair of prison boots were found. The mystery was solved when we discovered the following entry in our guest book. "7th of April, 1960, Gerald Rex Sanford from Largo, Florida chain gang. I run off. Ha Ha Kiks."

When I first came to Durham, several of the younger members of the faculty consulted me on the assumption that because I had just come from the Hopkins, I must know all about the newer methods of birth control. In order to live up to this false reputation, I visited Dr. Margaret Sanger's Birth Control Clinic in New York and was amazed at the splendid work being done. The woman physician in charge embarrassed me by remarking that she had personally tested all of the various methods on herself and preferred diaphragms. I learned later that she was married. I purchased a set of the Sanger equipment and gave it to Daddy (R. A.) Ross, a keen obstetrician and gynecologist in Durham, who started the first North Carolina birth control clinic. During the Depression, Governor O. Max Gardner called a meeting of several of us for advice about meeting the situation. I suggested that a birth control program should be started to stem the very high birth rate. The Governor thought well of the idea and passed it on to Dr. George Cooper of the North Carolina Board of Health, and with Clarence Gamble's money and advice, the program was started, and clinics have been established all over the state. At first, some of the clergy were opposed to the movement. One preacher complained to me about the Duke Clinic on the ground that a knowledge of birth control increased promiscuity. I pointed out to him that these clinics were giving the same information to poor people which the wealthier obtained from their physicians. He also intimated that birth control was immoral. I knew that he had been married ten years and had only two children so I asked him why he wanted to deny birth control to others when he obviously had used it himself. He was very honest and promptly withdrew his opposition, saying, "We apparently have not been practicing the same morality in the bedroom as we have been preaching in the pulpit." However, there is still opposition to birth control elsewhere. A few years ago, Doris Duke, who had been contributing to the birth control clinics in New York, told me that

116

she would support one in Puerto Rico where the high birth-rate has an appalling effect on the infant mortality, but permission could not be obtained. Birth control, also, had its amusing side. When a Negro who had had ten children was referred to the birth control clinic by a social service worker, she replied: "Missy, I don't need it, I am married."

The North Carolina sterilization laws now are models for other states, but, in 1932, Nick (Bayard) Carter and I nearly were jailed. The welfare officer of Orange County phoned me that a mentally retarded girl had been impregnated by her feeble-minded brother and would Nick please sterilize her. Nick agreed if I could get a legal permit. I was astounded to learn from Raleigh that if the girl were sterilized and the community spared from having another unwanted child, the County Welfare Officer, Nick, and I would be sentenced to prison. I phoned the Welfare Officer about the verdict, but he was undaunted because he knew of another North Carolina law which would permit cutting off anything except the patient's head if four Superior Court Judges signed the order. He obtained these signatures. Nick sterilized the girl, and democracy was saved. On another occasion, a priest brought a wildly demented child to be castrated. Ed Alyea, the Duke urologist, asked, "Why?" The priest replied that castration quiets tom cats, and it might do the same for the boy.

The Negroes of Durham, who comprise 35 per cent of the population, have made great contributions to its progress. The Royal Knights of King David, a fraternal insurance society organized in Durham in 1883 by the Reverend Morris, a Negro preacher from Georgia, has been developed into a very prosperous business by John Merrick, John Wright, W. A. Day, J. D. Morgan, T. J. Jones, and W. G. Pearson. In 1898, John Merrick, Aaron M. Moore, W. G. Pearson, and C. C. Spaulding started the North Carolina Mutual and Provident Association. According to local gossip, it made so much money that the organizers asked Washington Duke how they could eliminate the other stockholders and corner all the profits. Mr. Duke suggested to John Merrick, his barber, that a meeting of the shareholders should be held and that one of the directors should paint a gloomy picture of the association's finances. Another of the directors should then offer to buy the stock of the disappointed investors. In any case, the organizers soon had control of the business and by rigid economy, indefatigable energy, and close cooperation, they made considerable fortunes. In 1907, R. B. Fitzgerald, W. G. Pearson, John Merrick, J. E. Shepard, J. A.

Davison with Doris Duke and Dean Wanamaker

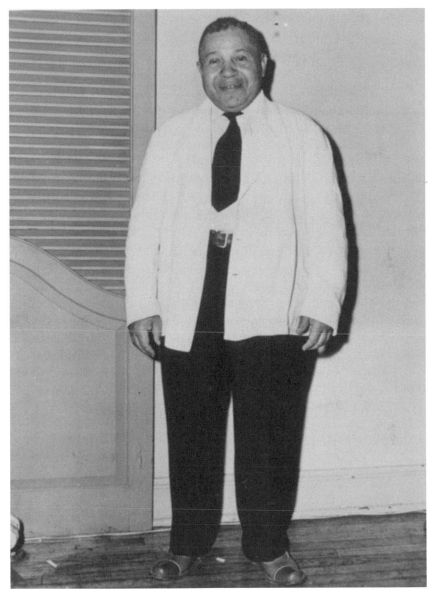

Carl Rogers, known fondly to generations of Duke medical students as the "Assistant Dean"

Dodson, and S. L. Warren established the Mechanics and Farmers Bank. In addition to the Lincoln Hospital, a public library, and the insurance and banking enterprises, the Durham Negroes founded the North Carolina College, with J. E. Shepard as President. State support was obtained in 1925.

Although exceptions occur, the relations between the two races have been very friendly. Certainly, no one could have been kinder to me and to our Medical Center than the faculty of the North Carolina College and the staff of the Lincoln Hospital. The Negro nurses and social workers as well as all other employees at Duke Hospital have contributed greatly to its progress. The expression, "loving," is often loosely used, but not in the case of the Davisons and the Negroes who worked for them. Certainly no one could be closer to our hearts and affections than Sallie, James, Savannah, and Charlie Davis, James Allen, Rosetta Cobb, Rebecca King, Jesse Ferrell, and last, but not least, Carl Rogers, a jovial and stout colored man, who was known affectionately by the faculty and students as the assistant dean. I could stay away for a month or two and the office proceeded smoothly but if Carl were away for a day, everything seemed to bog down. When Carl learned that I was going to Germany in 1945, he asked for his vacation before my departure, stating that "both of us couldn't be away at the same time."

When Grant Taylor accepted the official assistant deanship in 1946 on his return from the war, Carl was promoted to associate dean. Carl believed in communal property, everything I had he could use and vice versa. On my return from Japan in 1949, Carl announced that he planned to get married and that we should build a house. I asked who "we" were, and he replied, "You and I." We did; I advancing the money for material, and Carl and his other friends building the house. On another occasion, while I was abroad, he asked Mona Morgan, my secretary who can cash checks on my bank account, to loan him $500 so that "we" could buy a car. She did, and before he died, he repaid every penny. His sudden death on the 10th of February, 1956, brought letters of sorrow from our graduates all over the country. Mona Morgan was invited by Carl's widow to represent the Medical Center at the funeral, and her warm tribute to him expressed the deep feelings of all of us at Duke Hospital.

HUNTING

Hunting was a universal North Carolina pastime which I enjoyed

120

talking about more than in its performance. I occasionally succumbed though I usually regretted it. Bing (English) Bagby, my
Princeton classmate and best man at our wedding, was now a professor at the University of North Carolina at Chapel Hill and a mighty
Nimrod. He once persuaded me to go squirrel hunting in Orange
County before daylight. He placed me under some large oaks and
said I would see plenty of squirrels as soon as the sun arose. I
promptly went to sleep and awoke just before Bing returned. He
had shot a dozen squirrels and was amazed that I hadn't seen any as
my location was ideal for them. I hadn't the heart to explain the
situation, for, in his enthusiasm for hunting, he would never have
understood my sloth. The same thing happened during duck hunting on Currituck Sound with Fred M. Hanes. We were placed in a
duck blind before sunrise, and I had a splendid nap and no ducks.
Quail shooting was another matter, one had to walk for hours, except
when visiting Walker P. Inman, Mrs. J. B. Duke's son. At his
preserve near his Greenfield Plantation at Georgetown, South
Carolina, horses were furnished and I really enjoyed it, except for
mounting, the horse seemed to get taller each time. I am a very bad
shot and only once got my limit of game. That was when hunting
with Dr. W. S. Rankin at Conway, South Carolina. Every time a
covey arose, Dr. Rankin and I would each kill a bird. It was uncanny
until I realized that a small colored boy whom Dr. James A. Sasser of
Conway had furnished as a guide would shoot his double-barrelled
20-gauge gun at the same time Dr. Rankin and I fired our heavier
guns, which prevented our hearing the guide's gun. At the next
covey, I didn't shoot, but a bird fell as usual in front of me as well as
in front of Dr. Rankin.

Wild turkeys could still be found, but the only one I saw shot was
by a conductor on the slow train from Durham to Lynchburg. He
spotted a turkey, stopped the train, borrowed a shotgun, and got his
bird.

For many years, I have tried to develop a hobby in order to avoid
the boredom in retirement which my father suffered. The most
strenuous, though unsuccessful effort, was trying to raise pigeons,
ducks and chickens. The pigeons flew away, and the ducks created a
horrible stench. Someone asked our daughter, Jeana, what her
parents did for recreation, and she replied, "Mother plants roses and
Dad raises ducks, and they both smell." The chickens were the
worst. I had been advised by a nutrition expert to feed them cod

121

liver oil. Knowing that it was good for infants, I did so, but Atala will never forget the disgust of our guests when we served one of the birds. They tasted like sea gulls, and canned corn beef was hastily substituted. Sandy, who was two and still taking cod liver oil, did not notice the foul taste and had to eat the rest of the flock.

PROHIBITION

North Carolina sheriffs are said to raid only the stills made of zinc because it is injurious to the public. One sheriff, who inadvertently destroyed a copper still, was defeated at the next election.

These stills were made very ingeniously, a long strip of copper would be rolled and soldered into a tube, then filled with hot sand and coiled around a stump to make the "worm." Copper gutters and rain spouts promptly disappeared from Roaring Gap cottage. The stills always were built near a stream or "branch" so that water would be available to cool the worm when distilling. The mash consisted of a mixture of corn and sugar, and the first distillate was known as first-run "likker." Then, additional sugar would be added to the mash for the second and third runs, or "sugar likker," which was cheaper. The product was sold in fruit jars as soon as it was made. I asked one of the moonshiners who was a patient in Duke Hospital why he didn't age his "corn," but he assured me that he had tried keeping it a few days and that he couldn't see that it was any better. The purchaser usually poured the corn into charred kegs and aged it for a year or so, though much of it was lost from evaporation and seepage. The late Haywood Taylor, a Duke biochemist, overcame this shrinkage by aging corn in stoppered gallon glass jugs containing a handful of charred white oak chips. The department of biochemistry was so bothered by requests for the testing of moonshine that Perly (W. A. Perlzweig) issued a mimeographed statement to the faculty that no more analyses would be made. In other localities, rye, wheat, apples, or peaches were used in place of corn. One Virginia moonshiner boasted that he used so many apples in his apple jack that you could belch apples for two days. During World War II, the blockaders were limited by sugar rationing, but some of them substituted sorghum or country molasses for sugar. However, this thick mash did not ferment well because the bubbles could not escape unless it was constantly stirred. The stirrer usually became tight from the fumes, so terrapin turtles were said to be used. They would paddle around and keep it mixed but would slow up and go into a drunken sleep in an hour or two, so turtles had to be added in relays to allow their predecessors time to sober up.

Under the North Carolina Turlington Act, the drinking, owning, and transporting of liquor was prohibited. However, the two representatives in the state legislature from Pasquotank County moved that their county should be exempt from the Turlington Act. As usual with any measure affecting only one county, it was passed without dissent. Later the legislature realized that they had approved of what amounted to secession but the more they thought about it, the better they liked the idea so eventually the representatives of twenty-four other counties, including Durham County, moved that the Pasquotank Act be amended to include their counties. The two representatives from Moore County could not agree on repeal so one of them from Southern Pines moved that his township be attached to Wilson County for the purposes of liquor control. That also was passed. In other words, North Carolina is a bone dry state with twenty-five counties and one township in which state-controlled liquor can be legally purchased. Lawyers seem to be cleverer than physicians in getting around the law.

In the seceding counties, bootlegging practically disappeared. As everyone could purchase liquor at the ABC stores, excessive drinking diminished. No drunks appeared at football games and dances. As one of the officers of a Kansas regiment said in France during World War I, if his men knew that they could buy liquor whenever they wanted it, they did not drink all they had at one time, in fear that it would be confiscated. Durham, as the most western wet county, collected enormous profits from the inhabitants of many dry counties who made their purchases in Durham.

Rivalry between bootleggers was of great help to Duke Hospital on one occasion. A woman, the daughter of a well-known bootlegger, brought suit against the hospital for giving her a poison instead of a drug. The charge was entirely disproved, but we learned later that eleven jurors, knowing that we carried liability insurance, voted to grant her suit. Fortunately, the twelfth juror was also a well-known bootlegger, and he saw no reason to help his rival's daughter, so her suit was lost.

Prohibition, also, was the cause of many alcohol thefts at Duke by employees and students. The former usually sold it, and the latter drank a mixture of alcohol and grape juice called purple Jesus. They also made their own beer. Adding fluorescein to the ward alcohol soon stopped those thefts, but the unadultered pharmacy and pathology alcohol was in constant demand. The Hopkins students even drained it from the museum specimens.

Atala and I had had ponies while we were children, so we, of course, bought them for our children. The first one was a gentle "Banks pony," but he broke into the feed room, ate a barrel of oats, "swolled up," and died. The second one was so vicious that only Atala could ride him, so we packed him in a crate and sent him to Atala's father's farm on Long Island. The express agent fastened the following embarrassing label to the crate, "Judge Townsend Scudder, Glen Head, Long Island — Give him a drink."

Dogs have been a source of grief to me, starting with my German police dog, Chienne, in France during the First World War. My next experience was with a Scotch terrier I had bought at a kennel in New York. Before I took the train south, I realized that many kennel dogs are full of worms so I bought a large bottle of Glover's Worm Cure in the Penn Station. With the help of the porter on the train, we dosed the pup and replaced him in a basket in the upper berth over mine. While going to sleep, I read the list of the contents of the worm cure and when I realized that croton oil was the main ingredient, I hastily shifted the dog's basket to some one else's upper berth. However, nothing happened on the trip, but he later bit Al Shands' ankle and had a bad habit of hiding in the sand trap next to the fourth green and then barking just as a golfer was crouched to putt. I finally gave him to someone who did not live near a golf course.

Our most recent dog was Sandy's Weimaraner, who got loose at a party of twenty people at our home, but the only two who were bitten were Billy Peete and Ken Penrod, my two assistant deans. Sandy gave the dog away because he said that he was afraid that the next time he might bite someone really important.

Soon after we moved into our new Hope Valley home, I received an attractive brass door knocker with the following letter. Needless to say, we greatly prize the knocker, which is now on our Hope Valley front door.

My Dear Dr. Davison,

I am sending this quaint little knocker that my sister, Lady Osler, picked up for you in Durham a year ago last summer. We were visiting the cathedral there soon after she had heard of your appointment to Duke University. You may know the myth of the cathedral being built on a spot where St. Cuthbert was buried — his burial place being ordained by some miraculous message as to a "dun-cow" and that there is a huge knocker at the door like this. I fear I am rather vague as to the tale but at any rate Lady Osler said "I must get one of those for Davison when he goes to his new home in Durham." In the unpacking of her trunk this was mislaid and when I was distributing her things in her room after her death on 31 August 1928, I found it. She really got it as a joke but I am tempted to send it on to you to show you of her thought and hoping you might like it as a memento.

It is very sad to feel that those wonderful days of the "Open Arms" are over, but the influence, therefrom, is spread over the world! Hoping all goes well with you & yours in your tremendous work.

Believe me,
Yours very sincerely,
Susan R. Chapin

23rd March, 1929

On our voyage in 1929, a fellow passenger, Mont Reid who had been one of my instructors at the Hopkins and was then Professor of Surgery at Cincinnati, told me that on the following week he was taking a cruise of the Baltic countries, organized by the International Surgical Congress. I was very keen to go but Mont said the party was limited to members of the International Surgical Congress and as I was only a pediatrician, I couldn't go. However, I learned the name of the secretary of the Congress who lived in Brussels and telegraphed him for information. He replied that I could become a member of the Congress for ten dollars. I had spent several thousand dollars trying to become a pediatrician so I thought, relatively speaking, it was worth ten dollars to become a surgeon and an international one at that. The Baltic cruise was splendid. Clinics and dinners were organized for "us" in Amsterdam, Copenhagen, Riga (Latvia), Helsinki (Helsingfors, Finland), Stockholm, and Visby (Gotland).

Many of the books for the Duke Hospital Library were bought on that trip, especially in Amsterdam. One of the dealers there had a warehouse full of medical books bought from Germans during the crash. I also went book hunting in Leipzig, Berlin, Paris, and London. In Leipzig, I bought an edition of the Leonardo da Vinci anatomical drawings which Osler had shown me in 1913.

Osler stimulated all of his students to take an interest in old medical books so I enjoyed this shopping trip. From Boulanger, I obtained a signed print of the huge mural in the amphitheatre of the

L'École de Médecine, depicting most of the founders of medicine, especially those who were French. I also secured a complete set of Barrier's caricatures of the French medical faculty, several of whom I had met during the war. Boulanger also sold me Laennec's thesis on chest diseases with his notes along the margin. I thought it was genuine until Boulanger, laughingly, told me that he had obtained some old paper and had the thesis, which is in the Bibliotheque Nationale, reproduced so that he could humble people like me who were interested in books.

The Duke Hospital Library had been started two years previously, in fact, the day I was appointed in 1927, because I knew that the library was more important than the buildings, faculty, and students. Mimeographed lists were made of the bound journals in the Hopkins, Rochester, Vanderbilt, and Boston Medical Libraries and were distributed to the medical book dealers throughout the world (fifty-seven of them) with a request that they submit bids on the books, bound and delivered in Durham. Copies of these lists, also, were sent to friends in various fields of medicine asking them to grade them in the margin with "N" for necessary, "O" for optional if the price was low, and "U" for useless. A large grant was obtained from the Duke Endowment, and the offers poured in. Miss Judith Farrar, her mother Mrs. Mildred Farrar, and I decided that three dollars per volume was a fair price for all of the books marked "N" and "O." The dealers wanted more, but they needed money and no other libraries were purchasing bound back numbers. Occasionally, an exception was made up to $50 for some rare book. It was a profitable rule because a man from Texas wrote to me that his father, while a student in Germany, had bought a surgical book by Ambroise Pare, published in 1575. I replied that I knew that the book (*Oeuvres Chirurgicales*) was too valuable for us to buy because $50 was our limit. He wrote, "Please send the $50." George Harrell later found that this volume was one of six copies in the United States and that the last price paid for one was over $1,000. In 1930, Dr. Bassett, the health officer of Savannah, and the daughters of Dr. Arnold asked Richard Shryock and me if Duke would accept the library of the Georgia Medical Society, founded in 1810, which they could no longer afford to maintain. Of course we accepted and received ninety-two cases of books, many of them so rare that the National Library of Medicine does not have copies. In 1950, Mrs. James Semans gave Duke the Trent Collection which she and the late Dr. Josiah C. Trent had collected.

Davison, age 47, in his office at Duke

The meeting of the American Historical Association was held in Durham in 1929, and Dr. Welch came. He had just been appointed the new Hopkins professor of the history of medicine. In spite of his eighty years, he attended every session. After the meeting was over, he asked me to take him to Chapel Hill as he had made the commencement address there twenty years before (1st June, 1909). The first person we met on the "Hill" was Josephus Daniels who told Welch that he had recalled with pleasure his commencement address and especially remembered the story Welch had told at the smoker afterwards "of the old colored man lying asleep under a tree with flies crawling over his bald head until a yellow jacket alighted and stung him. The old Negro then awoke, brushed his head and grumbled 'now all of you will have to get off.'" Welch seemed pleased. We next called on Francis P. Venable who had been president of the University of North Carolina at the time of Welch's visit. Dr. Venable told Welch that he recalled with pleasure his commencement address and especially remembered the story Welch had told at the smoker afterwards "of the old colored man lying asleep under a tree, etc., etc." Welch seemed bored and asked me to take him to call on William deB. MacNider who also told Welch that he had recalled with pleasure his commencement address and especially remembered the story Welch had told at the smoker afterwards "of the old colored man lying asleep under a tree, etc., etc." "Davison," said Welch, "it is time to return to Durham."

The only other time Welch was flustered was after a concert in Baltimore when he, out of scientific curiosity, asked Mary Garden what held her strapless gown up. She instantly replied, "Only your age, Dr. Welch."

I went back to Chapel Hill the next day to see if I could learn the subject of Welch's commencement address, but no one could recall it though several people told me the yellow jacket story again. It took me a year before I found that Welch had spoken on Walter Reed and yellow fever, an address that has now become well known. The Carolina faculty blamed their forgetfulness on the acoustics of the auditorium and claimed that they remembered the story because it was told in another hall in which Welch could be better heard.

The opening of the Duke University Medical Center to the public was on Sunday, the 20th of July, 1930, the hottest day I have ever experienced. I lost six pounds and ruined a white linen suit showing

128

visitors through the building and repairing overloaded elevators. The suit shrank so much that I gave it to a friend half my size. Approximately five thousand visitors from all over North Carolina accepted the invitation to this "Open House" which had been announced in the newspapers. The next day the Hospital was opened for patients. The instruction in hospital administration, dietetics, and medical technology started in August, 1930, and classes of thirty first-year and eighteen third-year medical students were admitted on the 2nd of October, 1930, and twenty-four student nurses on the 2nd of January, 1931.

The other buildings of the West Campus, except the Chapel, the Few Quadrangle, and the Allen Building, also were ready for occupancy in September, 1930. Soon after the Union was built, some of the faculty, chiefly law school, though the medical school was also blamed, held an informal dance in the Union ballroom. Many of the old Trinity College Methodists were indignant and wrote protesting letters to Dr. Few. After the Chapel was built, lightning struck the tower twice, proving that it may strike more than once. One of the Methodist papers commented in a stern editorial that the Chapel tower had been struck as a sign that Heaven disapproved of dancing at Duke. To be on the safe side and still allow dancing, Dr. Few had lightning rods installed on the Chapel tower.

The Dedication of the Duke University Medical Center was held on the 20th of April, 1931. The speakers were Drs. Welch, Weed, Few, Rankin, Elbert Russell, George C. Allen, John Bruton, Thurman D. Kitchin, David L. Edsall, and Governor O. Max Gardner. Welch had promised to write his address in advance so that it could be published, but knowing his ability to procrastinate, I reminded him of his promise every month or two on my visits to Baltimore. He finally made a few pencil notes on an envelope after he had gone on the platform but when he stood up to speak, he put the envelope in his pocket and forgot it. We had prepared for his expected extemporaneous talk by placing three secretaries in different parts of the auditorium to take down his remarks stenographically. Wiley D. Forbus and others then edited them for publication. The result, of course, should have been submitted to Welch before publication, but I knew from experience that he would never read or return the paper. When I told him that his address had been published with the others in the *Southern Medical Journal* (24:1099-1124, Dec. 1931)

At dedication of original Duke Hospital. Far left, William H. Welch, dedication speaker; fourth from left, Davison; sixth from left, William Preston Few.

he was angry, although all he said was "You shouldn't have done it." It was no use telling him that it was the only way his address would have seen the light of day.

In September, 1931, the Hospital and Medical School needed more supervision so I moved into two vacant laboratories in the medical school, using one as a bedroom and the other as a clothes closet. I also rigged up a shower in the laboratory sink. Atala and the children went to Switzerland that year, and the Bayard Carters rented our home in Hope Valley.

On one of my transatlantic voyages, I was greatly amused at the mental confusion and frustration of a well-known Baptist preacher on board. The *Excalibur*'s cabins were arranged in groups of four, all opening on a common veranda. The preacher's wife came to me and told me that the other three cabins were occupied by two young men and a beautiful girl. Each night she said her husband could not sleep until he learned which of the youths slept with the girl. I told her not to worry but to ask the bar steward because each night the two young men cut cards for the privilege. She was shocked, but her husband slept better.

On that trip I visited Rollier's tuberculosis heliotherapy clinic at Leysin. The children there are kept out of doors winter and summer with only a G-string and a hat. The hair on their bodies must have been a half inch long, and it waved in the wind like a wheat field. Although there was deep snow all around, none of the children was cold, confirming the old Indian's reply of "Me all face" when he was asked how he could withstand cold without clothes.

On the 8th of June, 1932, we graduated our first class, the eighteen third-year students who had entered Duke on the 2nd of October, 1930. One of the members of the faculty had written to me while I was in Oxford in May to bring back some cuttings of ivy from the "Open Arms," the Osler home at 13 Norham Gardens, Oxford, so that our first medical commencement could be celebrated on the 22nd of June, 1932, by having William A. Thayer, professor of medicine at the Hopkins, address the graduates and plant the ivy in front of the medical school. It was a very pleasant occasion, but the following week Dr. Few showed me a letter from Secretary Hyde of the United States Department of Agriculture stating that one of our faculty had applied for a permit to import the ivy, which had been refused. Experimental farmers can import plants. I had, carefully, wrapped up the Osler ivy in wax paper and kept it in my pocket on

131

Original Faculty, Duke University School of Medicine

the voyage never knowing that a request for a permit had been made. Dr. Few and I asked our law school to look up the fine so that the man who had made the foolish request for the permit could pay it. Unfortunately, the penalty was a jail sentence which I, and not the requester, must serve. I finally appealed to Senator Josiah Bailey, told him the entire story and also that the ivy had been planted by the west face of the medical school and as result of the glaring sun had died. He told me not to worry about it, and a week later, Dr. Few received a letter from Secretary Hyde stating that the incident was closed. I remembered afterwards that I had given some of those cuttings to my mother on my return through New York in May and that she probably had planted them along with some of my father's and my Princeton Class ivy on my grandfather's grave in the Greenfield Cemetery at Hempstead. However, I did not investigate any further.

AIRPLANES

I have been using commercial planes since 1932 and, occasionally, have had some amusing experiences. On my first flight, I had had no lunch and as the plane was warming up and ready to take off, I asked Vernon Altvater, the superintendent of Duke Hospital, who had driven me to Greensboro to get some sandwiches. It was my first plane ride and though I am rarely seasick, I didn't know how air travel would affect me. I therefore placed my bag of sandwiches on the shelf until I found out whether I should waste them. I soon found that riding in a plane was the thing I did best and reached up for my food bag. I was furious to find only fig newton biscuits, which I loathe. However, I was hungry and so consumed all of them. An hour later, my seat companion reached for a package on the shelf and asked me plaintively, "Are these sandwiches yours?" I replied very apologetically, "Were those fig newtons yours?" However, he didn't mind, so we shared the sandwiches and I forgave Vernon.

On another flight, one of the four motors fell off and the plane fluttered like a wounded bird. I always carry a flask for emergencies and as I was taking a drink, the frightened hostess joined me.

During a flight in a non-pressurized plane, I worked on the material for the third edition of my pediatrics book and was amazed when we landed to find that most of my notes were more senseless than usual. I then learned that we had been flying over 15,000 feet and though I felt no discomfort, my brain was not functioning.

Fortunately, the pilot wore an oxygen mask. On another flight, in a pressurized plane, I had gone to sleep and was very annoyed when Grant Taylor and the hostess woke me up by slapping my face. Apparently, the cabin pressure had fallen, and I had blacked-out. One of the great problems of aviation is to make pilots and passengers use oxygen at altitudes over 10,000 feet unless adequate pressure is maintained because they do not notice the effects of anoxia.

Before starting on a western flight, I sent a card to Paul Rasmussen, a former pediatric resident, who was practicing in Salt Lake City, saying that I should be at the Salt Lake airport the next day. Paul met me all out of breath as I landed and boasted that Salt Lake had the best postmistress in the country. He said she had phoned him a few minutes earlier that a postal card had just arrived saying that a friend of his was coming to town at noon and that he had better hurry to the airport as she hadn't time to deliver the card.

On the 21st of January, 1933, Harold L. Amoss, professor of medicine, resigned, and on the 7th of June, 1933, William deB. MacNider, Visiting Lecturer in Pharmacology, resigned in protest of the acceptance of Amoss' resignation. Ernest M. Poate who had been appointed temporarily by Amoss as assistant professor of psychiatry, was not reappointed in June, 1933.

Fortunately for the Duke University Medical Center, Frederic M. Hanes accepted the Florence K. McAlister Professorship of Medicine on the 1st of May, 1933. He had been our professor of neurology from the beginning and would have been the original Duke Professor of Medicine if his friends hadn't told me that Fred would not be interested in the administration required of the chairman of the department. I was never so greatly misinformed. From the day of his acceptance to his untimely death on the 25th of March, 1946, his and Deryl Hart's leadership were responsible for the progress of the Duke University Medical Center.

On one of my European trips in 1933, I spent the night en route at Vaduz, the capital of the principality of Liechtenstein, and had the fright of my life. I arrived late at night by automobile and asked the first person I saw about a hotel. He became violently excited and kept jumping on and off my running board and talking gibberish which I couldn't understand though I can get along reasonably well in German. He finally guided me to a little inn where an equally wild man seized my baggage and carried it in. I was very puzzled but asked the clerk for a room and found that he also became very excited and unintelligible. As soon as I reached my room, I barricaded the door as I was sure I was in the Liechtenstein asylum for the violently insane. However, just before I undressed, I realized that all three of these queer people might be brothers and be suffering from hereditary spastic paraplegia, a rare condition I had heard of but had never seen. I collected some courage and slipped down to the hotel bar and after a drink told the waitress about my adventures. She laughed and told me that my diagnosis was correct and that many other travelers also had been frightened by the three brothers who were queer but harmless.

On this trip I attended the Third International Congress in London. It was very impressive. The Duke of York, later King George VI, opened it, and I was very much interested in the way he had been taught to overcome his stuttering. Apparently the Duke pronounced each word silently to himself before attempting to speak it. The result was very clear though as staccato as a machine gun. Old Sir Thomas Barlow was present. He was such an authority on scurvy that the Germans call it *Barlowische Krankheit.* I had been invited to discuss the prevention of milk-borne diseases. My contribution to the meeting was quite ludicrous. The other speakers had described elaborate and expensive precautions in handling milk to prevent infections. I had bought a can of evaporated milk, an American one at that, for six pence at a corner grocery, and when my turn came, I held up the can and said the evaporation process completely sterilized the milk, and, by adding a dash of lactic acid in preparing formulas for infants, it could be kept sterile for three days. We had used the method for years on all of the infants in the Duke Hospital with excellent results. George Frederic Still, the Nestor of British pediatricians, who presided, was very intrigued and asked for the can as he had apparently never seen one. I then described the menace of brucellosis or Malta Fever, which the precautions described by the other speakers would not prevent. Several of the participants in the discussion who followed me scornfully said that brucellosis did not occur in Great Britain, Sweden, Germany, etc. I replied that I was sure they were wrong for I had missed many cases until Amoss, Poston, and McBryde at Duke demonstrated the methods by which these cases could be detected. I noticed in reading the medical journals during the next few years that the Europeans started using Duke methods and found brucellosis to be as common as in the States.

In 1933, the American Board of Pediatrics was formed, and I was one of the members. These specialty boards were organized to protect the public against "over-night" specialists. Unfortunately, the public and medical profession have given so much weight to the Boards in pediatrics and other specialties that too many graduates have become specialists, and too few have become family doctors. Before the Second World War, 40 per cent of the Duke graduates were in general practice in contrast to the present 8 per cent.

Specialization has now gone so far that super-specialization or possibly infra-specialization occurs in Boston. While at Hiroshima with the Atomic Bomb Casualty Commission studying a cataract produced by radiation from the bomb (6th of August, 1945), Frank E. Poole, a Duke graduate, noticed something abnormal in the patient's retina and asked the Boston ophthalmology consultant to look at it. The Bostonian proudly stated that he was a specialist in the anterior chamber of the eye and had no use for or interest in the posterior portion. I could not believe it until I was in Boston recently and learned that one of the consultants at the Boston Eye and Ear Infirmary did nothing but repair separated retinas and also had no concern with the anterior portion of the eye.

THE COMPLEAT PEDIATRICIAN

I had been working intermittently on a pediatric book since 1926 when I revised the 9th edition of Holt's and Howland's *Diseases of Infancy and Childhood.* It seemed to me that physicians, when confronted with a child who has certain symptoms, cannot always obtain the necessary help in diagnosis from a systematic textbook like Howland's for often they are unable to interpret the patient's disease from his signs and, consequently, cannot locate the description of the correct disease. I felt that I, and possibly other physicians, needed a book with emphasis on symptoms and signs as clues rather than on description, because a student or physician notices the patient's most obvious symptoms and signs and recalls that they occur in a certain disease, but he frequently forgets that these same symptoms may be present in several diseases. An erroneous diagnosis often is the result.

A. Ashley Weech and I had originally planned to write the book

Frontispiece from The Compleat Pediatrician

together, but Ashley, who left the Hopkins to teach pediatrics at the Peiping Union Medical College, was doubtful about the need for such a book and also was too busy to collaborate, so I carried on alone. Finally, on the 2nd of September, 1934, it was published as *The Compleat Pediatrician*, a title which Atala suggested. It was an amplification of *Pediatric Notes* which I had published in 1926 but with an emphasis on "Diagnostic and Therapeutic Notes" which was its originally intended title. In addition to *The Compleat Angler* by Izaak Walton, there are thirty-five other books using "Compleat" in their titles, ranging alphabetically from *The Compleat Ambassador* in 1655 and *The Compleat Anatomist* in 1956 to the *Compleat View of Manners, Customs, Arms, Habits*, etc., *of the Inhabitants of England in 1775*. I often got letters asking why the Duke Press could not spell "complete."

Thanks to my friends, *The Compleat Pediatrician* reached its 8th and final edition in 1961.* Sixty-five thousand copies have been sold, and several thousand have been given to students and other friends. The profit of about one hundred thousand dollars from these eight editions reminds me of Jim Boyd's comments on Fred Osborne. Both of them were in the Princeton Class of 1910. Jim said that he had difficulty making his living by writing six novels, but that Fred Osborne had made a million dollars on one book. Apparently, Fred Osborne, who became very much interested in the growth of population, decided in 1928 to spend all of his time editing *Heredity and Environment,* so he sold all of his securities and resigned his directorships and spent the next three years compiling this standard work. Then, in 1931, he bought back all of his securities at prices over one million dollars lower than those which he had received in 1928, thereby making a million dollars from one book.

Football provides Duke Hospital with some interesting experiences and problems. A few years ago the president of a college phoned me that his institution was being sued by one of the graduates for injuries incurred in football and that the college records showed that he had been employed to play football and so was entitled to assistance under the Workmen's Compensation Act. The surgical staff at Duke Hospital volunteered to treat the player gratis so that his college would not be involved in any legal responsibility. Another injured player from another college was brought to Duke

* A ninth edition of *The Compleat Pediatrician*, edited by one of the editors (J. M. A.) of this publication, was published by Lea and Febiger in 1969.

Hospital for treatment, with the following story. He had been a husky mill worker in Pennsylvania, and his boss had summoned him to the office one day to meet a man who had enquired about him. The stranger introduced himself as a football coach at a southern college and asked the workman if he wanted to go to college to play football. The reply was favorable, so they immediately left for the south. However, athletics probably are conducted better than they were two generations ago. I remember my father telling me that after Yale had beaten Princeton for two successive years because the Yale right end broke up the Princeton plays, a group of the students employed a professional boxer to enroll at Princeton and play left end. In the next Yale game, the Yale right end was quickly knocked out, and Princeton won.

One of the Duke Latin professors complained that he was being paid a smaller salary than the Duke football coach, and the latter replied that that was as it should be, because regardless of how bad the Latin teacher was, he kept his job, but if the football coach lost a few football games, the alumni soon had him replaced.

When North Carolina changed its method of execution from electrocution to cyanide gas in 1935, some of the newspaper reporters complained to the governor that gas was less humane, so the prison physician at Raleigh invited me to witness the next execution. I protested that I was no authority, but he said he wanted a neutral medical observer. Fred Hanes and I went and if I have to be executed, I should choose cyanide gas as it is quick and painless. Before going to the prison, I asked William Perlzweig, professor of biochemistry at Duke, or Perly as all of us fondly called him, for advice on cyanide poisoning. Although he is violently opposed to capital punishment, his chemical pride made him tell me the best way to generate cyanide gas, information which I passed on to the executioner. The prisoner was seated in an air-tight room. Under his chair was a box of sodium cyanide "eggs" that fell into a bowl of sulfuric acid when the bottom of the box was released by an electric switch outside of the room. Ordinarily, cyanide gas is colorless, but as it was cold that morning, there was a slight cloud of water vapor that rose with the gas. As this cloud reached the height of the man's lips, he gave one gasp and never breathed again. He was dead instantly though his heart beat feebly for a few seconds. After it was over, I detected a slight cloud of smoke behind me and burst out of the jail in record time before I realized that it was cigaret smoke and not a leak from the gas chamber. I hope I am through with executions.

Later in 1935, Perly asked me if I didn't want to be a delegate to the Fifteenth International Physiological Congress in Russia. I had always been keen to visit Russia, and as I had taught physiology at Oxford in 1915, I was eligible. It probably was the best trip I shall ever have. Perly was a delightful traveling companion. We sailed on the *Ile de France* and spent several days in London attending the International Neurological Congress. We then went to Oxford where we lived in Magdalen College like undergraduates. It was like going home, especially when dining with the Wylies and Gardners on Boar's Hill just outside of Oxford. We also spent a night at Cambridge as guests of H. R. Dean, the head of Trinity College, and then crossed the North Sea from Newcastle to Stavenga and disembarked at Bergen on the 2nd of August, 1935. We toured Scandinavia via Oslo, Stockholm, and Helsinki, and finally reached Leningrad. It was wonderful country. The only untoward incident was in Stockholm when the maid carrying a pitcher of hot water came into my room while I was asleep in my usual costume of nothing but a "sleepshade" over my eyes. She shrieked and dropped the pitcher nearly scalding Perly and me.

The U.S.S.R. guards gave me a bad time at the Russian frontier. I had the manuscript for a new edition of *The Compleat Pediatrician* because the first edition had been sold out, much to my and everyone else's surprise. The guards insisted on reading or trying to read every pencilled word, a feat which only my secretaries can do and even they have difficulty. In my pockets, I had two pounds of Edgeworth tobacco which was confiscated and then returned for no reason apparent at the time. I later learned that Comrade Stalin also smoked Edgeworth. I tried Russian tobacco and sympathize with him. I was held up for hours and arrived in Leningrad tired, hungry, and very critical of Russia. To make matters worse, bedbugs descended on me during the first night, and I am very allergic to them. Every bite raises huge welts on me. Perly, on the other hand, was never troubled with them, and this also annoyed me. As he had been born in Russia and spoke Russian fluently, I made him complain to the manager of the hotel. The latter boasted that Russia had no bedbugs and that I must have brought them with me from Finland. I was infuriated as they were "red" and not "white" bedbugs, but I had to grin and put up with them, or rather catch and kill them and

140

scratch the welts. My record was forty casualties in one night at Yalta, three more than Atala and I together had caught at Badejoz, Spain, but, by the time I had been in Russia a week, I had developed good hunting methods. The pests always bit my toes first and as I am tall and fat, it was quite an effort to bend down at each assault. So, I bought some long stockings and a flashlight. In that way, I shortened their field of operations and brought the bites within reach of my hands.

Perly and I spent the first morning in Pavlov's splendid laboratory where one of his assistants demonstrated the salivation reflex by dropping cranberries on a child's tongue. As the laboratory is on the outskirts of Leningrad, Perly had asked one of the technicians, who was a dead ringer for Ben Turpin of the movies, to call a car for us. An hour later, the car had not arrived so I said to Perly in what I thought was a whisper, "Please ask that cross-eyed horse thief to call again for a cab." The Ben Turpin man promptly and angrily replied in English that he had done so. Perly had to spend the next half hour mollifying him by explaining that in the States being called a cross-eyed horse thief was a friendly term like the French *petit chou*. I realized as I have done too many times that it is not safe to assume that foreigners cannot understand English.

I was particularly interested in the Russian plan for medical care, visited hospitals and clinics, and got Perly to question everyone we met about it. Their complete state medicine makes medical service available to all of the people and is, undoubtedly, better than the care which most Russians had had previously. But, its bureaucratic control by officials who were well-meaning but ignorant of medicine has led to some inefficiency and lack of initiative. In addition, the system has the usual difficulties with human nature. It is an old axiom that no one appreciates anything free or compulsory, and it is especially true in medical care. For example, a Russian Intourist chauffeur told Perly and me that he had hoarded his rubles for a year in order that he might consult a private physician, even though he was told before hand and learned afterwards that the peptic ulcer therapy which he received from the state physician could not be improved. He said he felt better satisfied now that he had received a paid opinion. Perly asked the man a lot of details about his treatment, and we learned that it was the same which he would have received at the Mayo Clinic, Hopkins, or Duke.

Except for the soldiers and commissars, most of the people I saw were emaciated and poorly clothed. I was often embarrassed by someone coming up to me on the street and stroking my fat belly and fingering my Chatham homespun clothes and muttering (as Perly translated for me), "Someday, we shall have enough food and will have cloth like that."

The army officers seemed to be selected primarily for "party" reasons, and each regiment had a civilian political commissar who had as much, if not more authority, than the Colonel. I was sure that the Russian army would fold up in six weeks when the Germans attacked in 1941, which indicates how erroneous my inadequate and superficial observations were. In Russia, I had felt the bedbugs and seen the apparently untrained Red Army but had missed the most significant feature of all, the attitude of the people. Everyone with whom we talked said, "We shall do this, our country, our government, our Tovarich (Comrade) Stalin, etc." It was the American spirit of '76, and I had missed it cold. I should have realized the strength and ingenuity of the Russian Air Force, for we attended a gigantic air meet in Moscow at which over a hundred parachutists were in the air at one time. Numerous gliders, also, did intricate maneuvers after they had released their airplane towlines and all landed in formation on a marked-off area fifty-foot square. However, the fact that the failure of one parachute to open drove the unfortunate man several feet into the ground in front of us, throwing dust on us, coupled with the report in the newspaper the next day that no accidents had occurred, made such a great impression on me that I again misjudged Russian efficiency.

In Sevastopol, the capital of the Crimea, Perly and I decided to go swimming so I bought a pair of trunks only to find that I would be ostracized for prudery if I wore them. Everyone goes swimming naked. The women dress on one side of a fence, the men on the other, and then all play and swim together on the beach. Perly was very annoyed, not at this promiscuous bathing, but because he is very near-sighted, while I can read fine print at fifty feet. However, I consoled him that he had not missed any sights for the Russian women, at least those who bathed at Sevastopol, were built for service and were not bathing beauties. The tall, fine-looking aristocrats whom I used to see at the Russian Church in Paris before the First War, apparently, had been liquidated.

Perly and I wished to buy some Russian balalaikas for presents for our children. They were not sold in the Torgain stores and at the

142

official rate of exchange of one ruble per dollar they were fearfully expensive in the Russian shops. We had heard that thirty rubles per dollar could be bought on the black market but that the penalty was imprisonment. Perly, as an ex-Russian, knew that he would be punished worse than I would if we were caught so he insisted that I get the rubles even though I couldn't speak Russian. We were told that the best place to buy black market rubles was in front of one of the Torgain stores because Russians who had accumulated rubles usually wanted to buy dollars or other valuta to purchase the special goods in the Torgains. I therefore walked up and down in front of the Odessa store like a prostitute in Paris until a Russian stealthily tapped me on the shoulder and said something which sounded to me like "paper." He beckoned me to follow him up a dark alley where he carried on a lengthy whispered conversation with someone in a cellarway. I showed him a ten-dollar bill and made finger signs indicating that I wanted three hundred rubles. He nodded, motioned to me to follow him, and dashed off to a saloon. I followed and ordered two beers, using one of my three Russian words. We drank them, and I paid with a few kopeks I had in my pocket. He then crossed the street and sat down on a park bench. I did likewise. After a few minutes, he rose and caught a passing streetcar. I did the same. Thirty minutes later after we had ridden all over Odessa, he nudged me and got off the car. I followed, and we sat again on a park bench. Finally, an old woman joined us, slipped something into my man's hand and then departed. A few minutes later, the man pushed 200 rubles along the bench toward me. I shook my head and twenty more rubles were pushed across. Again I shook my head and twenty more rubles arrived, and so on until the pile reached 300. I then let him have my ten-dollar bill. He immediately bolted like a rabbit. One of my Russian friends told me that I had been cheated, I should have had 350 rubles at the usual black market rate. At any rate, Perly and I had enough for balalaikas and some left over for embroidered peasant dress material for our wives. Atala still uses hers for a table cloth.

While we were in Odessa, most of us acquired dysentery, and as sulfonamide therapy was unknown, we were very unhappy for several days. In addition, several of us caught summer colds. The next morning in Kiev, when I asked Perly why he was busily washing his shorts, he grumbled, "You can't cough when you have dysentery."

We then went to Istanbul through the lovely Bosporus on the

Franz Mehring, a Russian ship. I particularly wanted to see San Sofia because Guy Hughes, an officer on the British submarine, E11, had shown me some photographs he had taken of that mosque through the periscope while they were torpedoing the Turkish battleship, *Barbarossa,* in the Golden Horn Harbor in 1915. That sinking, by the way, was very profitable because the British Navy at that time paid one pound for every enemy sailor killed or drowned. One thousand men and officers went down with the *Barbarossa* so the small E11 crew shared £1,000. I also visited Roberts College on the European side of the Bosporus and Scutari on the Asiatic side where Florence Nightingale during the Crimean War had her hospital. We then returned via Sofia, Beograd, Budapest, Vienna, Zurich, and Paris. The Balkans had progressed tremendously since I was there in 1915.

I also had tobacco trouble on my next trip. At that time, I was a continuous pipe smoker (I stopped in 1948) so I brought three pounds of my favorite Edgeworth tobacco in my pockets when I landed in Italy in 1937, hoping that because my figure was already bulgy the customs officials would not detect any extra swellings. They did, confiscated the tobacco, and made me pay a forty-lira fine. I didn't mind the latter as much as the prospect of two months with the bad Italian tobacco, which I remembered from 1915. Fortunately, that night across the hotel dining room, I recognized Commander J. LeR. Shipley. He was the Medical Officer on the cruiser, *Raleigh,* which had stopped at Naples for fuel during its mission of taking off the American refugees during the Spanish Civil War. I dined with him on the ship the next evening and when I told him of my tobaccoless state, he supplied me with a dozen cans of Prince Albert tobacco from the canteen. The next problem was to get it ashore as no packages were allowed through customs. However, several of the ladies present volunteered to drop one or two cans down their ample bosoms and to disgorge them at my hotel. As this amount of Prince Albert was only a month's supply, I shopped all over Naples to see if I could locate any smokable mixture. To my delight, I found that one brand, Trinciata, was similar to Old Briar so I laid in a supply to take home. I had the same customs difficulty in New York and lost my Trinciata.

Duke Hospital had been approved for internships and residencies by all of the Councils and Boards, except that of Pennsylvania, which required individual inspections. I therefore invited their Board to

144

send an inspector in 1938. Dr. Morgan, the inspector, arrived early in the morning. He was very insistent that faculty and student attendance at autopsies was necessary for approval and asked how the members of the staff were notified when an autopsy was being done. I explained that whenever the telephone operator called Dr. Rokitansky, the name of a famous German pathologist, over the Hospital loud speaker, the staff would assemble in the autopsy room. "Dr. Canfield" was the call for a poker game and, usually, brought a better response because it is difficult to persuade many physicians to attend autopsies, particularly during morning ward rounds. Unfortunately, a few minutes later, "Dr. Rokitansky" came booming over the loud speaker, and the inspector insisted on going to the autopsy. Jim M. Ruegsigger, resident in medicine, was the only one present, and the room looked very empty. I slipped out and phoned Miss Helen I. Stocksdale, my secretary, to corral as many white-coated students and faculty as possible and to herd them to the autopsy room. Within a few minutes, the inspector's eyes gleamed with joy and mine popped with astonishment for about fifty students and physicians poured into the room. Dr. Morgan talked to Buck (W. L.) Thomas and when he learned that he was a gynecologist, at a medical autopsy, he was delighted with this demonstration of scientific interest until he asked him why he had come. "Because I was sent for" was the reply. I thought then that we would not receive Pennsylvania's approval, but I took the inspector, who was an ardent fan, to a Duke-Carolina baseball game that afternoon and when Eric Tipton knocked a home-run with the bases full, our approval was no longer in doubt.

In 1940, the Bowman Gray Fund was used to bring the Wake Forest Medical School to Winston-Salem and to convert it into a four-year school. A good faculty was organized, and the school is a great asset to the state. At the dedication of the new school, I sat next to John R. Cunningham, the president of Davidson College, who was to deliver the prayer. I noticed that he had written it out and was memorizing it. I told him that as a preacher's son, I thought all prayers were extemporaneous. Cunningham replied that too many of them were. I have always felt sorry for college and university presidents. They are expected to make innumerable speeches, to raise money and salaries, and to be constantly on display. Atala said they had a worse time than the men at circus side shows at whose heads the public threw coconuts or baseballs for, in addition, they

145

had the faculty, alumni and parents who kicked them from the rear. Harry Chase, former president of the University of North Carolina, and President Few adequately described the plight of university presidents at a joint alumni banquet. Chase said that if he had his choice of a job, he would like to be the head of an orphanage so that he would not be bothered with parents. Dr. Few countered with, "I should prefer to be in charge of a jail because the alumni would not trouble me."

On October 16, 1940, Duke University lost its president, and our medical school one of its best friends and wisest counselors, William Preston Few. He visited the medical center, which so constantly had occupied his thoughts during the years of its infancy. His loyalty to those to whom he delegated responsibility was comparable only to his courage in dealing with the issues which were his own obligation. When I was appointed, I asked President Few for advice about the type of organization he wished in the medical school. He replied that we should work out salvation on our own responsibility although he would help us whenever asked. His only advice was that "the things you don't say, don't hurt you." As I had stated in the telegram accepting my appointment, working with him was an honor which I greatly appreciated. He helped and facilitated in every conveivable way the founding and progress of the Schools of Medicine, Nursing, and Dietetics, and the Hospital. I never went to him with any problem without receiving a wise and just solution. Dr. Few never issued orders but whenever asked he gave the soundest and friendliest advice. Although many times we deserved criticism, he always aided us by kindly encouragement. I hope that the knowledge of our loyalty and appreciation may in some small measure have recompensed him for all of the help and guidance he gave us. We shall remember Dr. Few as a quiet man of few words, fearless in his encouragement of freedom of opinion and a genuine friend of honest scholarship.

Some of the achievements for which the Duke University Medical Center can take credit are the first course in hospital administration, an "outside" obstetric service in Charlotte, an outside pathological service, flat hospital rates, private diagnostic clinics, an effective vaccine against equine encephalomyelitis, numerous other virus studies, a course for medical record librarians, the ultraviolet sterilization of operating rooms, an intensive nursing service, a cafeteria for ambulatory patients, one of the first hospital blood banks, the organization of the 65th General Hospital, compulsory rooming-in, one of the first Poison Control Centers, the largest number of Markle Scholars selected from its graduates and staff of any medical school, and one of the best medical libraries in the country.

The Medical Center's international influence is illustrated by the 300 or more foreign physicians who have studied at Duke, the staffing of the Atomic Bomb Casualty Commission at Hiroshima and Nagasaki, and the furnishing of consultants to the hospital and medical school in Taiwan (Formosa).

Much of the credit for the present Blue Cross plans should go to the Duke Endowment and the Duke University Medical Center. They were born in 1929 when Dr. Watson S. Rankin, Director of the Hospital Section of the Duke Endowment, saw Dr. Tom W. M. Long's program at the Rosemary Mills at Roanoke Rapids, by which their hospital was financed through voluntary contributions of twenty-five cents per week from each employee. Watts Hill and I formed the Durham Hospital Association along somewhat the same lines and had stamps printed to be pasted in the subscribers' books like the British panel and "penny in the pound" programs. Next came the crash of 1929, and twenty-five cents per week was big money, so, like too many premature babies, the Durham Hospital Association nearly died in infancy. However, in 1933, Dwight Snyder, with a loan of $250 from Watts Hill, resuscitated the baby and christened it the Hospital Care Association. It was the first statewide hospital insurance plan in the world, the first one to provide prepayment coverage for any group to *any* hospital, to enroll groups on waiver basis, and to give family dependents the same coverage as the employed certificate holder. It formed the pattern followed by all present Blue Cross Associations. Up to that time, most hospital prepayment plans were like Dr. Tom Long's program in Roanoke Rapids, which provided coverage for only *one* group in only *one* hospital. There is a record of multi-hospital Blue Cross plans in Sacramento, California, in 1932, and Essex County, New Jersey, followed in 1933 by five other non-profit community group hospitalization programs in St. Paul, Minnesota, San Jose, California, and West Virginia.

After two or three years of financial struggle, with deficits guaranteed by the Watts Hospital and the Duke University Medical Center, F. Vernon Altvater of the Medical Center, Elisha M. Herndon, now Executive Vice-President of the Hospital Care As-

147

sociation, and Sample B. Forbus, Director of the Watts Hospital, placed the Association on a sound basis, and it began to flourish.

Many of the physicians in this and other states were suspicious that socialized medicine was back of the Hospital Care Association, so Dr. Rankin, on the recommendation of Watts Hill and me, persuaded the Duke Endowment to appropriate $25,000 to enable Dr. Isaac H. Manning, the President of the North Carolina Medical Society, and Graham L. Davis, Dr. Rankin's assistant, to go to England and study the British system. Dr. Manning, on his return, started the Hospital Savings Association with the blessing of the North Carolina Medical Society. J. Grayson Brothers has written an interesting account of the progress of Blue Cross in North Carolina.

CHAPTER VIII

THE SECOND WAR (1941-1945)

ALTHOUGH it was obvious to most of us who had served in the First World War that this country must be involved and that the sooner we were in the more quickly it would be over, it was a shock when the news of Pearl Harbor came over the radio on the 7th of December, 1941. I felt as I had in Washington on the 6th of April, 1917. Now, as then, I wanted to get into the Army or Navy Medical Corps as quickly as possible, either in one of the units which were being organized at Duke or in any capacity in which I could be used. Atala and I had decided that we had enough extra capital to maintain our financial obligations on an officer's pay. However, the Surgeon General's Office and Lew Weed advised me that helping to produce more physicians for the Armed Forces was a more useful job for me than being in uniform. It may have been sound advice, but I still regret following it.

After Pearl Harbor, it was obvious that all of us in medicine must double our work and that vacations might be a thing of the past. So, Atala and I decided to fly to Cuba and Yucatan in January, 1942, for a week's prophylactic holiday to get ready for the strenuous days ahead.

I was very much chagrined to find that my daily Linguaphone lessons in Spanish had been in vain. In a cafe in Merida, I ordered a brandy and soda with my carefully but incorrectly pronounced Spanish. The waiter said, "Si, senor," and returned with ham and eggs. I protested that I had not ordered ham and eggs and, painfully, explained that I wanted a brandy and soda. "Si, senor," replied the waiter and brought me a jar of mustard. I gave up and ate my ham and eggs with mustard.

In common with the rest of the nation, the faculty, graduates, and students of the Duke University Medical Center made every effort to help win the war. Our main contribution was three-fold: (1) the adoption of the accelerated teaching program and the training of as many physicians, nurses, and technicians as possible and as quickly as was consistent with good standards, (2) the organization of the 65th General Hospital for overseas duty with the Army and three

149

civilian defense units, and (3) the provision of medical and nursing care for as many patients as was practical during the war shortage of physicians and nurses.

Forty-four per cent of the Duke Medical Faculty, as well as thirty per cent of the physicians throughout the county, were on active military duty. All of the able-bodied medical students were in the Army-Navy Specialized Training Program. Most of the student nurses were in the Cadet Nurse Corps. The campus resembled an armed camp, with 1,000 Navy undergraduates, 600 Marines, 1,100 Army finance officers and candidates, 14 chaplain candidates, 150 Army medical students, and 106 Navy medical students. The war activities of the faculty and students and their casualties and honors are described in my *The First Twenty Years* published in 1951.

The 38th Evacuation Hospital, organized at Charlotte, North Carolina, was largely composed of Duke graduates and former members of the House Staff. This unit in 1943 was stationed near Oran, North Africa. It was a happy coincidence that Atala had a letter from her Bryn Mawr classmate, Jean Sattler, who had married Lieutenant (now Colonel) Jean Marmillot during the First War, telling her that the Colonel had escaped from the Germans and was serving with the Free French at Oran, and that the family had joined him there. As the Marmillots had four daughters, and clothing and food were scarce, several of the Duke graduates in the 38th responded to my request for assistance.

Grant Taylor, a Duke graduate and pediatric resident, had the most difficult time getting into the Armed Services. He had entered medical school at an older age than the average, and when he volunteered for the Navy Medical Corps, he was informed that he was too old at forty to be commissioned as a Lieutenant and too young academically (two years out of medical school) to be a Commander. I took up Grant's application with Jim Magee, the Surgeon General of the Army, who had been in our mess at Neufchateau in the First War. Jim promptly appointed Grant as a Major, and he later was promoted to a Lieutenant Colonel. An example of Grant's ability and of Jim's wisdom in commissioning him was Grant's overcoming the shortage of nurses during the invasion of Okinawa by washing a group of Okinawa women in the surf, redressing them in surgical gowns, and using them to care for our wounded. He was decorated for courage.

Atala realized that the war would produce a shortage of physicians and took a "refresher" course at Duke in the spring of 1942. She then helped with the pediatric teaching, ran school tuberculosis and infant feeding clinics for the Durham Board of Health, and became the school doctor for the Durham city and county schools.

From the physical point of view, during the Second World War, I had many more and much more arduous jobs than I had in the A.E.F. in the First War. I spent at least half of my time traveling. I went to Washington for meetings of the National Research Council, the Advisory Committee on Maternal and Child Health Services of the United States Children's Bureau, the Board of Honorary Consultants to the Army Medical Library, and the Survey Committee and Advisory Board of the American Red Cross; to Atlanta for meetings of the Medical Advisory Committee of Expert Consultants of the Fourth Service Command of the Army and of the Screening Committee of the Medical Deans of the Sixth Naval District of the Army-Navy Specialized Training Program; to Chicago for the annual A.M.A. conferences on medical education; to Panama and Central America to survey tropical disease conditions for the Army; to Haiti to study the treatment of yaws for the Coordinator of the Institute of Inter-American Affairs; to Germany as a member of a team to inspect the medical schools and to advise about their rehabilitation; to Ottawa as American liaison to the Medical Research Committee of Canada, of which Wilder Penfield was a member; and to Fort Knox to see the laboratory of the Armored Vehicle (Tank) Force. Colonel Bill Machle, who was in charge, insisted on my climbing into one of the Sherman tanks. That was easy enough but getting out nearly required obstetric forceps.

I also was President of the North Carolina Conference for Social Service, a member of the Advisory Committee to the Board of Control of the North Carolina Hospitals and of Governor Broughton's Committee on Medical Care, a Consultant to the Institute of Inter-American Affairs and to the Surgeon-General of the Army. When I wrote a paper in 1941 on communicable diseases, in which I recommended that a consulting pediatrician was as essential as a consulting surgeon, I did not expect that I would receive the appointment.

The railroad commuting was the worst feature. I soon qualified for Walter Winchell's definition of a genius in Washington. I developed "an infinite capacity for taking trains." At one time, we had a good plane schedule from Raleigh, but in 1941, the cancellation of the

The Dean trying out tank at laboratory of the Armored Vehicles Force

mail contracts reduced us to one plane a day. The Southern and Seaboard railroads were so rough that sleep was difficult and irregular. Only a capsule of Seconal made the trains endurable. In fact, I could then sleep better than I did at home, but, as the roadbed became worse during the heavy war traffic, I had to increase the dose to three capsules and take a benzedrine pill and numerous Coca-Colas the next day to keep awake. My friends called it my chemical warfare. Seconal also was a very useful drug one night when I missed the sleeper because of a wreck. I finally caught a troop train filled with a very hilarious group of "G.I.'s." Sleep was impossible until I persuaded the men around me to try a capsule. Within thirty minutes our area of the car was a quiet oasis. The trains usually were late so I always carried thermos flasks of coffee, etc. Sleeping on the Pullmans also became increasingly difficult, as the air conditioning apparatus soon ceased to function. However, there always is a bright side to everything. As I slept on my tummy, the jolting of the trains over the rapidly deteriorating roadbed soon massaged off twenty pounds of my weight so, in that sense, I was a war profiteer. I did not regain the twenty pounds until after the war.

Living conditions in Washington were very crowded. I tried, unsuccessfully, to find accommodations in twenty-one apartments and nineteen hotels and finally found a furnished room in the attic of an old tenement house at 1733 F Street, N.W. The cockroaches were numerous, and it was as hot as blazes in the summer but was made sleepable by an exhaust fan which I borrowed from Jack Dann's animal room at Duke. The Washington restaurants were overcrowded. One of them had a sign: "Be kind to the waiters, we have plenty of customers." To solve the meal question, Lew Weed and Dr. George H. Coons, Susan C. Dees' father, nominated me for membership in the Cosmos Club. However, I learned that there were so many nominations for the limited membership that a wait of a year was not unusual. Fortunately, I found that a fellow Rhodes Scholar, Edgar Turlington, was chairman of the admissions committee and phoned for his help. He said that a six-months' wait was the best he could do. I suddenly remembered that he, Tom Means, and I had spent the 1913 Christmas vacation at the Hotel Glacier at Grundewald after the disastrous Oxford-Cambridge hockey match at Murren and that an English widow had decided that she wanted Edgar, who was a very good-looking man. It was a perfectly innocent affair, though the lady's pursuit embarrassed him, but Turlington knew that I could make a good story out of it. At any rate, I asked Turlington that if I didn't call on his wife and tell her the Grundewald story could the waiting period be reduced. He said, "While we have been talking, Davison, I believe that I have found a way to have you elected earlier." I was notified of my election the following week, on the 14th of September, 1942. Blackmail sometimes pays.

The Washington streets were so crowded that the police had to direct pedestrian traffic and fined those who did not obey their directions. I was given a "ticket" because one of the cops said I had not obeyed the traffic lights. I protested that I came from North Carolina where we did not have traffic lights. He replied that he also was from North Carolina and that even his town of Taylorsville had traffic lights. During the argument I told him that I knew the Flowers family of Taylorsville, and he promptly tore up the ticket saying that he would not arrest any friend of the Flowers.

Lew H. Weed, my former chief at the Hopkins, was serving as Chairman of the Division of Medical Sciences of the National Research Council and needed another assistant, as the activities of the Division had been greatly expanded. As Vice-Chairman of the Division during 1942 and 1943, I left Durham every Monday evening and returned Friday or Saturday morning, working an average of four days a week in Washington and doing my Duke dean's job on Saturdays and Sundays. I concentrated all of my week's teaching, ward rounds, and clinics on Mondays.

Frank Swett and Vernon Altvater did much of the Duke work which I should have been doing while I was in Washington and elsewhere. The former's sudden death on the 10th of February, 1943, the advent of the Army and Navy Specialized Training Program in the medical schools, and the fact that the Vice-Chairman of the Division should spend his full time in Washington made it advisable for me to resign on the 30th of June, 1943, but I remained a member of the Division and commuted to Washington every other week instead of weekly. In that way, I could carry more of my share of the Duke load.

Because of the disruption of medical education in Britain during the War, the Rockefeller Foundation provided scholarships for bright British medical students at several American medical schools, including Duke. All of us enjoyed having them. At dinner at our home one of the Scotch students wore his kilt and one of the more unsophisticated American medical students told Atala that it was the

154

first time he had ever seen a man cross his legs for the same reason for which a woman does.

One of my most interesting assignments during 1943 was trying to improve or rather to introduce the teaching of tropical medicine into the eighty-six medical schools because the danger of malaria, yaws and other diseases was greater than that from the Japanese and Germans. I spent two weeks in Central America, a week in Haiti and several weeks persuading our too few authorities on tropical medicine to give lectures at the medical schools. Harold W. Brown, who taught preventive medicine at Duke and Chapel Hill, gave more lectures on tropical diseases at more medical schools than anyone else.

During my Central America trip, we found that Army engineers in the Second War were just as unsanitary as those in World War I. At Las Cañas, Costa Rica they had built their latrines on the top of the hill because the view was better. Their mess shack was half way down, and the well was at the bottom of the hill. Any infection from the latrines would appear in the food and drinking water. In spite of our medical report, they did not change, illustrating the need of the medical corps for more authority.

Also, at Las Cañas, a fiesta bull-fight made us realize how little some people care for life. I dislike Spanish bull-fights because so many horses are gored, but at Las Cañas, my sympathy was for the participating men. The bull-ring consisted of a fenced four-acre field full of bulls and drunk Costa Ricans on horse-back or on foot, all in wild confusion. A man, while fighting one bull, was often gored in the back by a passing stray bull. We saw two men killed, but nobody seemed to mind; they were just pulled off the field, thrown over the fence, and the "fun" continued until sundown.

As typhus and other diseases were tick-borne, a reward was offered for a certain type of Mexican tick which needed study. While taking a shower in Mexico City, I found one of them on my abdomen. I carefully removed it and threw it in the john. Fortunately, before I flushed the john, I remembered the reward, rescued the tick, and received the reward. This tick was later studied at N.Y.U. Medical School by Ed (H. E.) Meleney.

The amount of research work needed in tropical medicine was prodigious. Better means of treating malaria, filariasis, and other diseases were an urgent necessity. Harold Brown had become interested in filariasis because of his love for hunting. As many of the hunting dogs die of heart worm, a form of filariasis, Brown experimented with a variety of drugs and found that anthiomaline, an antimony compound, was effective. At the request of the Navy he used the same method in curing human cases of filariasis in the Virgin Islands. That is, he cured all but one, a girl who told Brown that she could not continue the painful "shots" in her hip as they incapacitated her from making her living as a prostitute. This application of a dog remedy to human disease ought to please dog lovers and antivivisectionists.

YELLOW FEVER

Yellow fever, the worst of the tropical diseases, was reported in Brazil and Kenya, so our troops were immunized. Unfortunately, during the first year, our vaccine caused jaundice in 60,000 of the troops, with sixty deaths. At first it was suspected that these cases were yellow fever due to live virus in the vaccine. Later it was believed that the reason that the American vaccine produced jaundice and British vaccine did not was because the former contained human serum in contrast to saline only in the British vaccine. Finally, one of the members of our National Research Council received the following letter from one of the top British medical officers:

8th August, 1942

Recently, it has been rumoured that serum from a Harvard student was the cause of jaundice in your yellow fever inoculees. A Yale-ite told me that this streak of yellow was not unexpected.

I was assigned the task of locating the individual from whom the serum had been obtained and was greatly chagrined to find that it was a Hopkins student. Thereafter, the vaccine was made without the addition of human serum and, apparently, was just as effective and did not cause jaundice. No one has yet discovered whether the individual whose serum was used in the vaccine had infectious hepatitis or homologous serum jaundice, but, apparently, he must have had.

Germany was my most interesting war assignment. I was invited to spend three months in 1945 as a consultant to the United States Group Control Council surveying the medical schools in the United States Zone of Occupation. En route, I also spent a night at the 65th General Hospital, the Duke Unit, at Botesdale, on an airstrip 80 miles north of London.

156

Colonel Davison in Germany, August, 1945

All of the German universities had been closed since the invasion in April, 1945, and our assignment was to recommend procedures by which those in the United States Zone of Occupation could be purged of Nazism and militarism and then be reopened in accordance with the following directive of the Allied Military Government:

> Germany will not be occupied for the purpose of liberation but as a defeated enemy nation. . . . The principal objective is to prevent Germany from ever again becoming a threat to the peace of the world. Essential steps . . . are the elimination of Nazism and militarism. . . . No attempt should be made to force upon German educational authorities any . . . methods of teaching which are not desired by and do not emanate from the Germans themselves.

The medical schools of Erlangen, Heidelberg, Marburg, and Tubingen had not been damaged, but those at Berlin, Bonn, Frankfurt, Freiburg, Giessen, Gottingen, Cologne, Munich, and Wurzburg were in ruins. After our surveys, we recommended that all Nazi teachers be removed, an adequate faculty obtained, and the number of students admitted should not exceed the facilities for instruction and housing.

Whether our report on the policy to be followed by the German medical schools will make "good" Germans out of Germans remains to be seen. It probably was as ineffective as advice to a Harvard man from a Princeton or Hopkins graduate. The opinion, too often expressed in the States, that there are good Germans in Germany is a masterful over-statement. It is true that we rarely met anyone who admitted having been a Nazi, but after examining their *Fragebogens* and other records, the statement that all men, especially Germans, are liars needs little further proof. One of the German characteristics is the keeping of voluminous personnel records, and when our Armies invaded, the officials could not bear to destroy them. As a result, the Nazi, university, police and other documents were collected and transported to places like the Ministerial Collecting Center at Kassel, where they were studied. The MCC is located in a German TNT factory which occupies twenty-five miles of cellars dug under a pine forest. The chimneys could be telescoped at the approach of hostile aircraft. Our intelligence staff claimed to have known of this arsenal, but it was never bombed. We wanted to check the records of several medical teachers, so we visited Kassel and asked for them. They were promptly delivered for they had been sorted into readily available categories.

In addition to work, all of us had several pleasant parties in Washington. The most amusing one, though embarrassing for me, was the dinner at the Statler given by Morris and Anna Fishbein for Lew Weed, George Lull, and me. The floor show consisted of Don Giovanni, an excellent sleight-of-hand artist. He called up several officers from their tables and while conversing with them, he would present them with their purses and wrist watches which he had removed without their noticing it. He finally called me up, and I concentrated my attention on my purse and my wrist watch during his spiel and was astounded when he asked me if the suspenders (braces) which he held in his hand were mine. Fortunately, I was also wearing a belt so I did not lose my trousers as Senator Pepper of Florida did during the later floor show. I shall never understand how Giovanni removed my suspenders without my feeling him do it.

CHAPTER IX

POSTWAR DUKE (1945-1960)

AFTER my return from Germany in November, 1945, I soon earned the rather doubtful distinction of traveling from the Raleigh-Durham airport more than any one else, with an annual average of thirty out-of-state trips, usually including one or more out of the country, and in some years exceeding 50,000 miles annually. These journeys, usually at the taxpayers' expense, were caused by the splendid cooperation of our government and universities on national and international committees and councils required by the expanded influence of the USA in world affairs.

At present on my working day, half of the senior members of the Duke Medical faculty are in Taiwan, Indonesia, or Cairo, or even more frequently in Washington seeking research grants. Only those interested in teaching and in staying in Durham to "mind the store" should be named chairmen of departments, and they should have research professors under them who can do research or travel. Duke needs defensive and offensive teams as in modern football.

In 1945, our daughter, Jeana, who was a junior medical student at Duke, caught tuberculosis from a non-cooperative patient who carelessly coughed and spit without any precautions. Jeana knew that she had had a negative tuberculin test in her second year so she repeated it and found that it had become positive. She remained in and out of a sanatorium in California for the next two years and completed her medical course at Stanford.

I had tried, unsuccessfully, to persuade our faculty to make BCG vaccination compulsory and after Jeana's illness, I told the students that BCG was still voluntary but that they could not pass pediatrics unless those who had negative tuberculins were vaccinated with BCG. As a result, no other students acquired tuberculosis.

Several hospitals had been having epidemics of diarrhea among the newborn infants in their nurseries, sometimes with fatalities. Duke had been fortunate in not having had one, and in fact, no other nursery troubles, except for a small epidemic of impetigo in 1931 and the addition of too much lactic acid in some infants' feeding mixtures, neither of which, though potentially serious, did any harm. However, by the spring of 1946, Angus McBryde, who was in charge of the Duke nursery, and I decided that our luck might not continue so we abolished the nursery and Duke became the first hospital to require "Rooming-In."

For some queer and unexplained reason, at the age of 54, I became allergic to cold air and rain and had frequent virus respiratory infections. I probably had been too wet and too long in France during the First War. At any rate, whenever the temperature would drop or we would have a shower, I would sneeze and have all of the signs of hay fever and allergic rhinitis. Thinking that the climate of Santiago de Cuba might alleviate my symptoms, I flew there in December of 1946. Santiago had swimming, mountains, and good food, and I love the place and returned to it as often as I could, until prevented by Castro and the Communists in 1960. However, I sneeze as much there as in Boston and Durham.

In the spring of 1947, the medical school and hospital were running smoothly, and I finally became bored with dictating hundreds of useless letters (the average was one hundred and fifty per week), and attending three or more intra- and extra-state medical and committee meetings, so I planned to retire on my sixtieth birthday in 1952. I actually wrote my resignation on the 17th of April, 1947. When Dr. A. Hollis Edens came in 1947 to succeed Dr. Robert L. Flowers' successor as president, he said he had heard that I wished to resign in 1952 but that he hoped that I would stay until I reached the compulsory age of 69 years and at least until I was 65. I said that I should be very happy to do so if he didn't object to my taking long vacations in Cuba and Roaring Gap. He said that he had heard that I had always done so and would probably continue. As a matter of fact, by 1949, the affairs of the Medical Center had become more difficult due to some determined effort to "cut it down to size," and I flattered myself that I was needed. As a result, my boredom disappeared, another good lesson in psychology.

The medical alumni, spear-headed by Grant Taylor and Jay Arena, commissioned Mr. Wayman Adams to paint my portrait in a characteristic pose, half-sitting on a tall stool with five pediatric seniors on camp stools in front of me. Robert A. Gowdy, George Reid Andrews, W. R. Hadley, J. W. Hollingsworth, and Charles G. Gunn, Jr., were the seniors who posed with me daily from the 2nd of August to the 6th of August, 1947. Unfortunately, only the backs of the heads of the first three and none of the other two are shown in the

Portrait of Davison, in typical pose, teaching medical students

portrait. It was presented to President Robert L. Flowers for Duke University on the 17th of October, 1947, by Eleanor B. Easley ('34) and Jay M. Arena ('32), the President and Secretary, respectively, of the Medical Alumni, and was hung in the Medical Amphitheatre.

The Atomic Energy Commission was anxious to explore the medical applications of radioactive material and organized the Oak Ridge Institute of Nuclear Studies (ORINS). I was appointed to the Board of Medical Consultants on the 13th of March, 1948, and was given a "Q" clearance on the 1st of July, 1949. However, by the 18th of May, 1954, I realized that my knowledge of nuclear physics was inadequate, that I was of no help to the Institute, and that I was bored. I had learned during the innumerable conferences of the National Research Council Committees that I had to take benzedrine or caffeine to remain awake. One to three one-grain caffeine tablets usually were sufficient but, if I needed four, I resigned. The meetings of the Oak Ridge Medical Advisory Panel had reached the four-tablet stage.

On returning from one of my Oak Ridge trips, after seeing some advanced cancer patients, I noticed that my tongue was very red and sore. I suspected that my pipe might be causing a mouth cancer because I had smoked fifteen daily, five after each meal, since I quit athletics in 1914. I stopped smoking for a week, and the redness and soreness disappeared. By that time, I had realized that the cause of the condition was not my pipe but some penicillin lozenges which I had been sucking because of a sore throat. I was so chagrined by my wrong diagnosis that I haven't smoked since. The first year of abstinence was the hardest; in fact, I wasn't sure that I could hold out. After the second year, I have had so much smug, self-satisfaction in bragging about my willpower that I haven't missed my pipes for fifteen years.

August, instead of January, must be my month of good resolutions because on the 4th of August, 1962, I stopped taking a drink before meals and at cocktail parties in order to keep my weight under two hundred pounds. I found that I didn't miss it but in order not to develop a permanent distaste and allergy to alcohol, I started on the 4th of April, 1963, to take three to six 2-oz. drinks of bourbon or rum and soda daily, with remissions of abstinence for weeks or months whenever my weight rises.

The Surgeon General of the Army asked us to reorganize the 65th General Hospital, the Duke Unit in the Second War, on a stand-by basis in case of another war. No one seemed to want the job so I was commissioned a Colonel in the Army Medical Reserve on the 13th of May, 1948, and kept up the paper organization until I was retired for age (60 years) on the 29th of May, 1952. As far as I can learn, I am one of the few officers who has a double honorable discharge in two ranks: Colonel, Medical Corps, United States Army Reserve, and Captain, U.S. Army (my final rank in the First War).

On the 19th of November, 1948, Dr. Robert L. Flowers, who had been in poor health, was promoted to Chancellor, and Dr. A. Hollis Edens was elected president by the trustees without referral to the faculty committee appointed by the trustees to help select a president. The first twenty-two years under Dr. Few and Dr. Flowers, which had been like Joseph's years of plenty in Egypt, were followed by eleven lean years until Edens "resigned" on the 19th of February, 1960. Only by the strenuous efforts of the medical faculty and Paul Gross was the medical school able to maintain some of the standards which had been established before Edens' arrival and to prevent *Lux extincta est* (the light has failed), to borrow John Howland's epitaph.

In 1949, Dr. J. Clark Moloney, a psychiatrist, Dr. Dudley R. Smith, a gynecologist, and I were invited by the Army to visit the medical installations in the Far East Command. I also was asked by the American Board for Medical Aid to China (ABMAC) to lecture at the medical schools in Shanghai. (Edens, unsuccessfully, tried to block my visit to China, but I had received authorization from Mr. George J. Allen before Edens' appointment.) The six weeks from the 10th of March to the 21st of April, 1949, which I spent in the Orient were the most interesting and instructive in my life. I went a week earlier than my schedule because a process server for a suit against the Hospital was pursuing me with a subpoena. Fortunately, Mona Morgan, my secretary, recognized him and told him that I had gone to Japan. Grant Taylor held him in conversation while I escaped home to pack. He followed me, but I climbed out of my bedroom window and caught the next plane to Japan and, thereby, made Mona an honest woman. I went by Army planes from San Francisco to Honolulu, Johnson Island, Kwajalein, Guam, Japan, Okinawa, by commercial planes to Shanghai and Manila, and returned by Army planes. Flying as a VIP was often embarrassing because the Officer on Duty at each stop had to meet the Army plane and make arrangements to house and feed us. I told one young ensign who had to

Davison's United States Army Reserve Identification Card

meet me in Honolulu at 3 A.M. that I was sorry that I was a VIP. He said, "I don't believe it, all of you love it," which probably was true.

As VIP's, we stayed at the Imperial Hotel in Tokyo and observed a most amazing optical illusion. For weeks I was convinced that the waitresses at lunch were different from those at dinner. Finally it dawned on me that the difference was only in clothes. At lunch, the girls wore "middy blouses" and skirts, but at night they were arranged in beautiful kimonos and obis.

At dinner, at the home of one of the Tokyo physicians, the hostess noticed that I was not eating raw strawberries and said she was sorry that their flavor was not as good as usual because General MacArthur had made them use artificial fertilizer instead of "night soil." Greatly relieved, I ate the strawberries. I also had to eat raw fish while thinking of all of the fish parasites.

One of the objects of our mission, in addition to inspecting the American medical installations and to raising the morale of the younger medical officers, was to advise the Japanese on medical education. It was a wasted effort. The medical faculties were polite but obdurate. They would accept any materials or fellowships offered but, smilingly, declined any advice on the grounds that their schools were copied from the Germans and could not be improved. Judging by the young Japanese physicians employed by our Army and Atomic Bomb Casualty Commission, Japanese medical education was worse than that in Germany. Keio (in Tokyo) and Nagasaki were the only passable schools, and the bomb destroyed so much of Nagasaki that a new start had to be made with our help.

The flight from Tokyo to Okinawa was the coldest and most uncomfortable of my life. The heater in the plane was broken, and I was trussed into a parachute too small for me. Okinawa was interesting chiefly because of the tombs built to resemble a female perineum so that the dead could re-enter a womb. They made excellent shelters during the 1945 invasion of Okinawa.

To visit Shanghai, which was closed to Americans because of the fighting, permission had to be obtained from the Far Eastern Command, and an answer to my cablegram to Dr. J. Heng Liu in Shanghai did not arrive until the day before I left. The city was fascinating. Any university in this country would be proud of the pediatrics and medical education I observed in the seven Shanghai hospitals and medical schools I visited. The American fellowships and aid had been a good investment. I met several former Hopkins students of mine and was very pleased that they were doing good work. In fact, everyone I met during my stay was doing medical work comparable to that of the better institutions in this country. Although Shanghai was under martial law, there was no panic about the impending occupation by the Reds. As far as I could learn the wealthy people were perturbed about the effect of the Reds, but the hospitals, medical schools, and other activities expected to continue as usual though they anticipated increased taxes and restrictions.

The Reds were shelling the city when I left on the 13th of April, 1949, and the airport loudspeaker announcing that my Northwest Airline flight would depart in a few minutes for Manila, Anchorage, and Milwaukee was very comforting. My pediatric friends who had been so hospitable and from whom I hear indirectly, through Hong Kong, have been rudely awakened by the restrictions and hardships, and, in some cases, prison and death, imposed by the Reds, after Nanking fell on the 24th of April, 1949, and Chiang Kai-shek and his Army left for Taiwan (Formosa).

Drs. Smith and Clark whom I rejoined at Manila (they had flown directly from Okinawa) and I inspected the College of Medicine of the University of the Philippines on the 15th of April, 1949, for the Association of American Medical Colleges. I also had the pleasure of seeing Tarcilla Lapearl, a former Duke medical student, and her husband Dr. Perfecto L. Mendoza, who invited me to return. I did two years later and was royally entertained in Manila and Baguio.

Atala and I spent the 1949-1950 Christmas holidays in Guatemala. My most amusing experience there was at a huge dinner of the Lions Club and their wives. The lady on my left said that she had heard that I was from Duke University and asked if I knew Drs. Hart and Moody and their research on how to have sons or daughters, whichever one desired, as described in the *Ladies Home Journal*, and please would I explain the method because she had seven daughters and wanted a son. All of this was in rapid Spanish, which, bad as my Spanish is, I understood, but I knew that I never could explain the female estrual cycle and the optimal period for fertilization in Spanish in a Catholic country. While trying to think of some way out of the dilemma, the lady on my right said that she had overhead the conversation and was also very interested in the methods because she had seven sons and wanted a daughter. Some one must have been taking care of me because when I suggested swapping husbands, the ladies were delighted, and I left Guatemala before I learned the results.

While in Europe in 1950, a near-tragedy occurred just over the Belgian frontier. Ken Waters had given me three bottles of Scotch in return for bringing him some Havana cigars and sugar. I had consumed part of one bottle and poured the balance up to the necks of the two remaining bottles so that I could place them in my trouser pockets and evade the Belgian customs. Either the heat of my body or that of the Austin which I was driving expanded the whiskey which burst the bottles, and I had to stand in the road trying to "drip dry." It was before the days of synthetic fabrics so I was thoroughly wet and smelled like a distillery. When we reached Bruges, Atala had to register for both of us and explain my predicament before the hotel would accept me.

While we had been in Europe, the Korean War had started (25 June 1950), and the Red Chinese and North Koreans had driven our Army back to Pusan. A counterattack (November, 1950), MacArthur's amphibious landing above Seoul, and the Marine retreat from the Yalu River had produced a stalemate by January, 1951. I was told that the standby 65th General Hospital of which I was commanding officer might be called to active duty. As my weight had climbed to 256 pounds because of French and Swiss food and as my 1945 uniform was built for 200 pounds, I dieted and lost sixty pounds. Just as I reached a weight of 196 pounds (my 1914 Oxford rowing weight, 14 stone by English standards), I was notified that I had reached the retirement age of sixty and was out of the Army. Nick Nicholson (Lieutenant Colonel) succeeded me as Commanding Officer of the 65th General Hospital, the Duke Unit, but it was not called to duty.

In the spring of 1951, Milton Winternitz, then Chairman of the Division of Medical Sciences of the National Research Committee, asked me to go to Hiroshima and Nagasaki and "phase out the Atomic Bomb Casualty Commission and to close it because no more information was being obtained from the study of the survivors who had been exposed to the uranium bomb dropped on the 6th of August, 1945, on Hiroshima and the plutonium one exploded on the 9th of August, 1945 at Nagasaki." Atala went with me, and her ability to stand the long flights was excellent proof of the Air Force Motion Sickness Remedy. Grant Taylor, who was on leave of absence as Assistant Dean of the Duke Medical Center and who was in charge

168

of the ABCC in Japan met us at the Tokyo airport and conducted us by train to Hiroshima, a twelve-hour journey in comfortable, but short, sleeping compartments. Mrs. Pat Taylor met us at the Hiroshima station and installed us in a beautiful Japanese house at Hiro, twenty miles from Hiroshima, complete with maid, food, and drink. We spent a very happy two months there with side trips to Nagasaki, Osaka, Kyoto, Naha, and Tokyo for inspections, talks at medical societies and sometimes plain, unadulterated sight-seeing. We were introduced to the Emperor at the meeting of the Japanese Medical Society, at which he and I spoke on different days. Several of the members of the ABCC staff were Duke graduates, and they and the others gave us a grand time.

The trip was not all pleasure, and it was obvious, especially after John H. Lawrence and John Bugher arrived, that ABCC not only should not be "phased out" but that its scope should be enlarged. This might be the only large-scale study of the effects of radiation. In addition to twenty per cent of the survivors having cataracts, which had already been reported, John Lawrence, following a tip from one of the Japanese doctors, demonstrated that five per cent of the deaths among exposed people were due to leukemia, in contrast to 0.1 per cent in the Japanese general population. The knowledge of nuclear and atomic physics demonstrated by John Bugher, now Head of the Medical Division of the Rockefeller Foundation, gave me an inferiority complex for several years until in 1958 I discovered that he had taught college physics for two years and naturally knew more about the subject than I did. My ego returned.

We presented a unanimous report to the National Research Council that ABCC should be supported for many years, and it still continues to produce valuable data.

I was getting involved in so many activities inside and outside of the University, and pediatrics was getting so complicated; I can think in terms of mg.%, but millimoles and milliequivalents were getting me down, so I resigned the chairmanship of the pediatric department on the 1st of June, 1954, and named a committee to nominate my successor.

People in the Orient, apparently, respect an old man with white hair because he has been smart or fortunate enough to live that long in an area of high mortality; also, one with a pot-belly because he is rich enough to have plenty of food which the general population lacks, and especially one who has written a book because they revere

169

The Dean in his office at Duke

learning more than we do. As Wiley Forbus and I qualified on all three counts, he was invited in October of 1953 and I in June of 1954 to spend several months helping to reorganize the medical curriculum at the National Taiwan (Formosan) University College of Medicine and Hospital, known as Taita. Mrs. Je Harned Bufkin, the Duke Professor of Hospital Records, also was invited, though she qualified only on the last count, having written a book. She had red instead of white hair, and a good figure instead of Wiley's and my pot-bellies. Ross Porter, the Duke Hospital Superintendent, who was reorganizing the Taiwan hospitals on a two-year leave of absence, probably was responsible for our invitations.

The work in Taiwan was delightful. Everyone was very enthusiastic about improving the medical teaching and service. Our suggestions were not only welcomed but implemented. It was a pleasant contrast to our unsuccessful offers to rehabilitate medical education in Germany in 1945 and in Japan in 1949.

Dr. Chiang Lim Chin, the Associate Professor of Pediatrics, who received his medical degree from Taita, had spent 1950-51 with us at Duke. Dean Huoya Wei, also a pediatrician, had spent a year at Columbia. The probable reason that so many pediatricians are deans is that their clinical interests do not conflict with medicine, surgery, and obstetrics, and their knowledge of child behavior helps their relationships with faculty and students. Everybody we met did everything possible, and very successfully, to make our visit pleasant and interesting. Anyone who has had the privilege of visiting Taiwan looks forward with great pleasure to returning. The names of the island are particularly inviting. Three centuries ago, the Portugese called it Formosa (beautiful), and the Chinese refer to it as Taiwan (the terraced island).

Dr. O. K. Khaw, a Major General in Chiang Kai-shek's Army Medical Corps, was my particular friend. We were of the same age, and he had been at Cambridge at the same time that I had been at Oxford. We both loved to eat strange dishes, and he knew where to find them. I acquired dysentery early in Taipei but did not attempt to cure it so that I could enjoy this exotic diet without gaining weight. I actually lost weight and had no difficulty in curing the dysentery with sulfadiazine when I reached Hong Kong. My only mistake was in trying to race O. K. Khaw up and down the thousand steps (actually there were 1,200 of them) to one of the temples during the feast of the full moon. No harm occurred to us sixty-two-year-old men.

171

Thanks to Ross Porter, I lived comfortably at FCCC (Friends of China Club), visited all of the Taiwan towns, the Pescadores Islands, and attended an aborigine dance. I was worried there when I was asked to drink from their wooden bucket because the aborigines are full of diseases, but after one swallow of the fiery local moonshine, I knew that no germ could survive. Even I, accustomed to North Carolina corn during prohibition, could scarcely swallow the liquor.

While we were in Taiwan a rumor was spread by the Japanese communists that all of the Pacific fish were radioactive and dangerous due to our bomb testing at Bikini and Enewitok. Geiger tests in Japan and Taiwan proved that the fish were safe, but someone in the United States Department of Agriculture banned the importation of Japanese tuna fish into the States. In other words, they were safe for the Japanese and Taiwanese, but not for Americans. As fishing was one of the major industries in Taiwan, a first-class panic and depression were started, and we were blamed. In spite of enquiries, no one in authority in the United States would state that the fish were safe. Finally, I received a cable from a friend at Oak Ridge stating that if he could be sent to Taiwan he would eat all of the radioactive fish on the island. I showed this cable to the Taiwanese, and the radioactive bubble burst. One of the leading fishermen at Kaochung also held a free fish fry and as no one was the worse for it, the catching and eating of fish were resumed.

Dr. Harold W. Brown, head of the Department of Preventive Medicine at Columbia University, while on a recent survey of Taita for the China Medical Board, wrote to Mr. J. L. Brent, Chief of the United States Mutual Security Mission to China: "My return to Taiwan Medical School and Hospital nearly five years after I participated in the plans for their reorganization gives me a good perspective for evaluating progress. The progress that has been made is truly remarkable." Among other comments, he mentioned that we had made Duke University an intellectual second home for many of the Taita faculty.

Keith Cannon, the then Chairman of the Medical Division of the National Research Council, asked me to re-inspect the ABCC program at Hiroshima while I was in Formosa. I wrote him that Margaret Porter and Je Harned Bufkin wanted to go with me and needed permits. He cabled that they could go and that the HRC would pay my expenses but not those of "my women." We flew to Hiroshima via Okinawa, and Bob Holmes, the new ABCC director, Mildred

Sherwood and Marian Batchelder who had been loaned to ABCC, met us at Iwikuna, the nearest airport to Hiroshima. I was tremendously impressed with the progress that had been made since my first visit in 1951, and especially with the transformation of the city which had been in ruins.

I greatly appreciated being appointed on April 15, 1955, by Frank B. Berry, Assistant Secretary of Defense (Health and Medical) as a member of the Department of Defense Civilian Health and Medical Advisory Committee. The Council consists of six members who serve as members for four years and then as alternates. They are invited three or four times a year to visit Army, Navy, Air and Space installations in the United States and Europe. I was reappointed on July 1, 1961, and also named as Chairman of the OSD Planning Group on the Military Medical Requirements in the San Francisco-Oakland area with Colonel Ben C. Liles, USAF, MCS, as Executive Secretary.

My life was threatened by an insane patient so I bought and carried a Colt 38. I unsuccessfully tried to deduct its cost as a medical expense in my income tax return, but the following year the item was allowed as "insurance."

On the 6th of November, 1955, while Jim Cleland was dedicating the bronze memorial tablets to Bessie Baker, Frank Swett, Perly Perlzweig, and Fred Hanes in the lobby of the Medical School, Elizabeth Swett said she had a severe headache, sat down on a chair in my office, and was dead within a minute from a massive cerebral hemorrhage. Her death was one of the greatest losses the Medical School had had. She knew and loved every medical student, quietly helped many of them financially and in many other ways. At her funeral there were Duke Medical alumni from nearly every state in the Union.

On the 10th of February, 1956, Duke suffered another great loss in the death of Carl Rogers, my jovial "associate dean," who had done so much to maintain a friendly spirit in the Medical Center. He managed or helped with almost every student and faculty party. I once remarked to Judy Ruffin that Carl and I seemed to be invited to the best parties. Judy replied that she didn't know about me, but Carl always was included.

On the 10th of March, 1956, I was appointed by the Navy to be one of the consultants to the Naval Medical Research Unit (NAMRU-3) in Cairo. We flew via Casablanca and Tripoli to Cairo.

173

NAMRU-3 had been our typhus laboratory during the Second War and had maintained such useful and friendly relations with the Egyptians that it had been continued in order to study the numerous endemic diseases in that area. We also flew to Beirut to participate in the Middle East Medical Assembly. We returned via Rome, Paris, and London.

One of the nicest things which ever happened to me, aside from marrying Atala Scudder and knowing Osler, was the very happy dinner which Mary Semans, Ross Porter, and some of the Faculty "elders" and their wives had arranged on the 7th of February, 1957, celebrating the thirtieth anniversary of my appointment at Duke. Jim Cleland presided and the following spoke: Hollis Edens, Wiley Forbus, Marshall Pickens, Ross Porter, Watson Rankin, and David Smith. Dr. Rankin, to whom I am more indebted than to anyone else, was particularly gracious. I was especially flattered by his quotation from Osler that the master word of medicine is work, and his reference to me as "Osler's master word made visible and viable." It is true that whatever I have done has been based on work and the utilization of odd times on planes, trains, ships and bars, but it is equally true that I work for the fear of boredom such as I endured for three months in Portsmouth awaiting transportation home after the First War. Perhaps, to quote Rollo May, my perpetual work is a defense against existential anxiety, and "keeping busy" for its own sake is a neurotic activity to allay anxiety. Elon Clark, Bob Blake, and others composed and lettered a magnificent scroll of which I am very proud. Atala was presented with a handsome silver soup tureen, and Jim Cleland reminded her that the Chapel could use it when she relinquished it. I was given the copy of the *Bonetti* of Francesco Redi (1702) which William Osler had inscribed and given to S. Weir Mitchell on the 15th of March, 1912. Naturally, these gifts made Atala and me very happy.

On the 21st of October, 1958, during the meeting of the American Academy of Pediatrics in Chicago, thirty-two of us in the Duke Pediatric Society and Mona Morgan celebrated Sherry's (Mildred M. Sherwood's) thirty-five years of devoted service to children with a dinner and a poem by Dan Pachman. My first contact with Sherry was at the Harriet Lane Home when I invented a machine for making protein milk, a vile concoction then considered necessary for infant diarrhea. All of the nurses, except Sherry, refused to use it because it was a converted Alemite automobile grease gun, even though it saved several hours work a day. Sherry's comment was "it works and I shall use it, and if you will paint it white, the other nurses will not object to it." I persuaded her to take charge of Rowland Ward in 1930 and she did except for two years (1953-55) when she and Butch (Miss Marian Batcheldor) were loaned to the Atomic Bomb Casualty Commission at Hiroshima in 1954 and she found herself in charge of sixty Japanese nurses shorter than she was.

In 1957, Frank Berry, Pat Cushing, and the Civilian Advisory Committee spent two days at West Point, and Frank talked to the cadets on the advantages to the Army as well as to themselves if some of them would study medicine after they were graduated from the Military Academy. Frank cited the career of General Leonard Wood which had been medical as well as military. The following year, Lieutenant John Feagin, a West Point graduate, applied for admission to Duke and was accepted. I told him how pleased I was that he had followed Frank's speech. He said that he had always wanted to study medicine but had not thought it was financially possible until he talked to some of the Duke faculty who were medical consultants at Fort Bragg where he was stationed as a paratrooper. Several other West Pointers have followed Feagin's example at Duke and other medical schools and are now medical officers with a military training.

At the end of January, 1959, I was again invited to be a member of the American-Egyptian Committee of Consultants to the Naval Medical Research Unit (NAMRU-3) in Cairo. Unfortunately, just after we took off in a Navy plane from Washington, the heating system blew out and I have not been so cold since the First War or on the flight from Tokyo to Okinawa in 1949. We landed at the Azores in hopes of getting heating equipment but had no luck and so continued to Naples, also without luck. After trying to warm up for two days in Naples, we flew to Cairo and still couldn't find a heater. To make matters worse, all of us acquired a severe virus infection and spent most of a week in bed. Sweating was the worst symptom, requiring frequent changes of bedclothes. I was too weak to change my clothes so I rang for the maid. When this Cleopatra-like creature arrived, I reached for my dressing gown, only to be deflated by: "Don't bother, I don't even look at the young ones." She stripped and redressed me every hour and hung the clothing on the balcony where it dried in a few minutes in the Egyptian sun, but I was too old and too ill to enjoy the experience.

CHAPTER X

RETIREMENT (1960-   )

A. HOLLIS EDENS announced his retirement on the 19th of February, 1960, following prolonged negotiations. The argument was over the alleged desire of Edens and some of the University trustees to make Duke University independent of The Duke Endowment and to keep it as a small church college, as it was originally, instead of making it a great university, as Mr. Duke intended. All of the medical faculty, and most of the members of the other faculties who were privy to the situation, had struggled hard during the eleven years of Edens' tenure to keep up the standards and to help Duke grow in stature and influence. However, the University trustees were misinformed that the clash was a private quarrel. They have since, privately, acknowledged their mistake. Deryl Hart was then elected president, healed all of the wounds, and Duke began again the progress which had been made under Few and Flowers.

As the Medical School was now safe from presidential attack, there was no need for me. Also, it was obvious to me and to most of the medical faculty that inasmuch as I must retire automatically at the age of 69 in 1961, and as I was becoming increasingly antagonistic to the eager research beavers (and vice versa), a new dean was needed. A committee considered several candidates and recommended the appointment of Barnes Woodhall, professor of neurosurgery. I asked for a sabbatical year from 1960 to 1961 so that I could resign as dean on July 1, 1960, and continue as James B. Duke professor of pediatrics, without any duties, but with full salary until September 1, 1961.

I had virus pneumonia for three successive winters, with the worst as well as the most embarrassing attack in Cairo in 1959, so Atala and I decided to spend the three winter months of 1960-1961 in Puerto Rico. We preferred Santiago, Cuba, but I had been threatened with arrest there in January, 1960. We found that the Hotel El Rosario five miles in the hills from Mayaguez, Puerto Rico, was ideal for bird watching for Atala, and there was an excellent beach nearby for swimming.

In January, 1961, Tom Perkins telephoned me while I was in Rosario, Puerto Rico, asking me to return in February because I had been nominated as a Trustee of The Duke Endowment. I was so delightfully surprised that I asked him to repeat the message because I could hardly believe it. Until Dr. Flowers' death in 1949, I had had unimpeded and welcomed access to the Trustees of The Duke Endowment whenever I needed help, and that was often, and they always gave it. But, for the next eleven years under Edens, visits to the Trustees had to be made surreptitiously. Now, not only to have access to them again, but to be one of them was more than I had ever dreamed.

Because of my Father's example of boredom during his retirement and my failure to develop a hobby and a dislike for golf and all other physical activities except swimming, I adopted a series of activities or goals to keep me amused, interested, and busy during my retirement.

(1) We shall make our headquarters at Roaring Gap from March to November and spend the three winter months in the Caribbean area.

(2) By trying to avoid virus infections, which have plagued me for the past three winters, I shall try to outlive the Davisons. (So far, I have lived two years longer than my Father did.)

(3) I shall try to keep my weight under two hundred pounds, though it means giving up beer or wine for lunch, martinis before dinner, bourbon before retiring, drinking low calorie ginger ale at cocktail parties for months at a time, and going to Josh Turnage's barbecue once a month instead of weekly. (So far, I have been successful.)

(4) I shall try to make rotating internships in the community hospitals in North and South Carolina so attractive educationally and otherwise by the appointment of Directors of Medical Education that Duke and other graduates will apply for them.

(5) I shall ask the Duke Endowment to finance scholarships for junior and senior medical students so that they can become acquainted with community hospitals and general practitioners during the summer or other free time.

(6) I shall try to increase the number of physicians by helping to organize two-year medical schools in North and South Carolina.

(7) Working with SAMA (Student American Medical Association)

177

and the American Academy of General Practice I shall try to recruit more high school boys and girls for the health professions.

(8) I shall encourage more graduates to go into general practice, especially in pairs.

(9) I shall complete the 8th edition of *The Compleat Pediatrician.* (It was published 25 August 1961.) Future editions, if any, will be written by Jay Arena or someone else.

(10) I shall help to expand outpatient departments in the community hospitals in the Carolinas.

(11) I shall try to keep my diary and these reminiscences up to date.

On the 4th to 8th October, 1961, Josh Horne, Don Elias and other Trustees of Duke University and of the Duke Endowment, the faculty of the University and Medical School, especially their wives, Miss Fannie Mitchell and the medical alumni held a Symposium on the Commonwealth of Children. Many illustrious speakers discussed all phases of children's problems, and I was presented with a Lincoln Continental and a check for $7,718. One of the most interesting talks was by Dr. Wiktoria Winnicka, secretary of the infancy and maternity sections of the World Health Organization in Geneva. She said that when they were freezing and starving in Warsaw in 1945 at the end of the war, someone in the States sent her an anonymous package of warm underwear, food, soap, and a copy of *The Compleat Pediatrician.* She said that it took her two years to understand the book but that she still has it and uses it!

Among the highlights of the Symposium were the exhibit of pediatric books from *Hammurabi* to *Gesell* compiled by Mary Semans and Henry Schuman. All of the editions of *The Compleat Pediatrician* were displayed including the one carried by John Bumgarner during the Bataan retreat, as well as the October number of the *North Carolina Medical Journal* containing articles by Duke medical graduates and former house officers, edited by Nick Nicholson.

Paul Gross was the gracious toastmaster at the farewell dinner on the 5th of October. B-J (Stanhope Bayne-Jones), one of my oldest friends of the Hopkins of 1916, Jim Cleland, Watts Hill, Watson Rankin, Yank Coble, Lige Menefee, and Jean Craven were the speakers. When Yank Coble was on the podium to speak for the student body, words would not come forth. After a few painful, silent minutes with the entire audience pulling for him and still

178

At the Commonwealth of Children Symposium, October, 1961

unable to articulate, Paul Gross, mercifully, stood up and said that Mr. Coble was so overcome by the occasion that he was speechless. Mildred Hendrix and Edythe Spekter provided the music. Ted Minah and Bill Jones miraculously fed 994 of us, a feat which I had not thought possible and so had suggested barbecue.

I was not allowed to use my unexpurgated speech, but I cannot miss this opportunity to tell my favorite story about one of the speakers, Jean Craven, who is my favorite resident. She had applied to the Hopkins Medical School from Southern California while I was assistant dean at the Hopkins, and although her scholastic record was perfect, the Hopkins regional representative in Los Angeles would not recommend her admission because of her charm, which he said would lead to early marriage and a waste of a place in the medical school. He did not know that women practice medicine in spite of marriage. At any rate, the Hopkins needed charm; Jean was admitted; she married, was a pediatric intern and resident at Duke, and has practiced pediatrics in Lexington, North Carolina, ever since.

Needless to say, I was delighted to become an owner of a Lincoln Continental and greatly appreciate Lige Menefee's efforts as a fund raiser. Dr. Rankin said that the main reason for electing me a trustee of the Duke Endowment was to enable me to live in style commensurate with so grand a car, with or without a chauffeur's cap.

Nothing could have pleased me more than Yank Coble's and the medical students' establishment of a scholarship for a student to spend a term abroad. Years ago, I wrote a paper on the value of student migration, but I did not know that I would live to see the dream become a reality.

On the 7th of October, at the medical alumni breakfast in the Hospital, the former administrative interns unveiled a splendid bronze plaque commemorating the first training program in hospital administration. It was a very much appreciated surprise which left me speechless for once in my life.

Also, that morning, my family and I were very touched by Deryl Hart's citation, as well as for the honorary degree of LL. D which he conferred on me. I had heard rumors of this degree ceremony, but its reality was wonderful. When Deryl continued speaking after conferring the degree, I assumed that he was making a closing address, and it did not dawn on me that he was naming the medical school building for me. This honor came as a complete surprise. I

180

Davison and the Lincoln Continental

Davison receiving honorary degree

had known that Lenox Baker had suggested it, but remembering the hassles we had had with Edens, in getting the wards named for living individuals, I had assumed that the effort had died aborning.

The Symposium ended on Sunday, the 8th of October, with a magnificent funeral oration on me by Dr. James Cleland. It was wonderful and had everything except flowers, taps and the last volley. In fact, the ceremony was so complete and realistic that Atala had received letters of sympathy on my death, including one from Cairo and another from Brussels.

The whole program was magnificent. All of the references to me were much exaggerated and, therefore, doubly appreciated. We had never realized how many friends we had. We shall always be grateful to all of them. Morris Fishbein sent me the following report on the Symposium from the *Medical World News*.

POMP AND CIRCUMSTANCE FOR A RETIRING DEAN

Dr. "Dave" of Duke gets an array of awards ranging from honorary LL.D. to Lincoln Continental.

A medical educator, last month, was paid a superlative tribute in the style heretofore reserved for movie stars, conquering generals and hard-hitting center fielders.

Honors were heaped on quiet, informal Wilburt Cornell Davison by the fans he had won during the third of a century he was dean of Duke University Medical School. Dr. "Dave," sitting on the platform next to Doris Duke, daughter of the University's principal benefactor, the last James B. Duke, was feted at a king-size testimonial dinner.

A "Duke Blue," air-conditioned, Lincoln Continental was bought for Dr. Davison by alumni and friends.

The student body provided five hundred dollars toward a "Davison Scholarship" that would enable a Duke medical student to spend one semester abroad yearly.

University trustees informed "Dave" of a unanimous vote to have the medical school building bear his name and earlier, an honorary Doctor of Laws degree had been bestowed on the much-honored dean.

Almost embarrassed by riches, those in charge of the ceremonies announced that $7,718 more than the price of the automobile had been received. Dave gave this check to the Duke Chapter of the

Student American Medical Association and the Duke Medical Student Government for student activities.

The gala affair was held in conjunction with a five-day international "Symposium on the Commonwealth of Children," which attracted twenty speakers from five countries. They discussed the future of health, economics, education, and other matters concerning children, with which Dr. Davison has been primarily concerned during his professional life.

When called upon to speak at the dinner by a thunderous ovation from his audience, Dr. Dave gave one clue to his success, concern with the grass roots of medical practice.

He did not belittle the school's national contributions: "Thirteen of our alumni are deans or assistant deans of several medical schools," but he noted that "our greatest accomplishment has been that twenty per cent of our alumni are in the practice of medicine in North Carolina, and that twenty-five per cent of their number are in general practice."

(Quoted from *Medical World News,* p. 62, Nov. 10, 1961)

Three generations of Davisons

Atala and Dave

A moment's reflective pause during "retirement" at Roaring Gap

A resident's caricature of the dean

Wilburt C. Davison in his Oxford robes, 1968.
Artist: George Lynch, Oil on Canvas
31½ x 35½'' McGovern Allergy Clinic, Houston

TRIBUTES

Wilburt Cornell Davison

He Built a Medical School of Stone—
and Left It Marble

Jay M. Arena, MD, Durham, NC

Dr. Wilburt C. Davison, first Dean and Pediatric Chairman of the Duke University School of Medicine, was once described by Sir William Osler as "a new American colt who is wrecking a medical school tradition." Since that memorable day at Oxford University in 1913 and until his retirement in 1960, Dean Davison continued to wreck traditions.

Dr. Davison came to Duke in 1927 when both the hospital and medical school were still only in the idea stage. He shouldered the responsibility of planning, organizing, and directing the medical school and hospital literally from the ground up. As construction progressed he was never without his tape measure or yardstick and on occasion would don overalls and join the labor crew to give a hand as well as direct.

Dean Davison realized from the outset that an efficient faculty would have to be more than a collection of brilliant individuals who might or might not cooperate, so he began by selecting the professor of medicine; then he and the professor jointly selected the professor of surgery. The three of them then chose the next professor and so on down the line, thus assuring them of a cooperative staff. Each department chairman was encouraged to help in planning for the total development of the school so

that, in effect, as one faculty member put it, there were nine deans with Dr. Davison as their Chairman, all but one under 35 years of age and with reputations still to be established. There were disagreements about policies being formulated in such a democratic way, and not infrequently the majority of the department heads would insist on some policy which Dr. Davison did not particularly favor. Nevertheless, he had an extraordinary quality of being objective about each problem as it arose, and seldom held grudges against the chairmen who opposed him.

"Dave," as he is known to his friends and colleagues, was in his prime a bluff, hearty 200-pounder, well over 6 feet tall and always appearing in a hurry. He spoke in a deep resonant voice and would slip from one idea to another, frequently leaving an unwary listener several se-

quences behind. He had an elephantine memory, aided and abetted by a little black notebook carried in his hip pocket.

The secret of his greatness and his success was that he was many things to many men. Never pretentious, he could and did reach people at any level, whether they were kings or serfs, millionaires or paupers, white or black, adults or children, renowned professors or lowly interns. As a matter of record, he was probably more attached to Carl Rogers, a black orderly whom he referred to as the "assistant dean," than anyone else in the entire medical complex.

With his nimble wit and broad sense of humor, he could take a joke as well as tell one. He once was moving down a corridor at a fast clip in a new section of Duke Hospital. Right on his heels were Ross Porter, former superintendent of the hospital, and

Fig 1.—A proud dean with the commanding officers of Duke's 65th General Hospital (1940 to 1945).

Received for publication March 16, 1972; accepted March 30.

From the Department of Pediatrics, Duke University Medical Center, Durham, NC.

Reprint requests to Duke University Medical Center, Box 3024, Durham, NC 27710 (Dr. Arena).

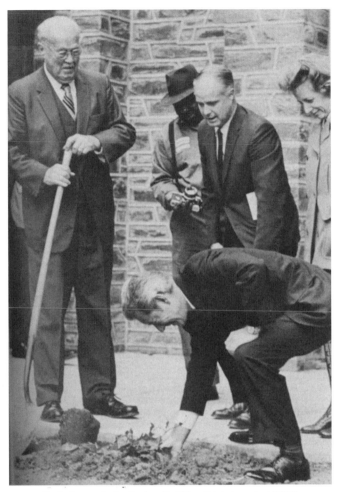

Fig 2.—Dave replanting ivy from Sir William Osler's homestead (1970).

nancial assistance, especially during the depression, when there was dire need.

Formality he detested. He liked to work in a rumpled and inexpensive suit (often purchased at Sears and Roebuck), tieless with collar open, or in his shirt-sleeves and suspenders, with odd neckties handy for an emergency. His office was on one of the busiest corridors in the medical school, with the door open always to students, house officers, personnel, and faculty alike.

A man of tremendous energy and talents, Dean Davison held a host of public service jobs, among them the vice chairmanship of the National Research Council's Division of Medical Sciences, and membership on the National Health Council. He was a consultant to the US Army Surgeon General, a member of the executive committee of the Association of American Medical Colleges, a member of the Executive Reserve in the office of the Assistant Secretary of Defense (Health and Medical).

Abhorrence of idle moments was so ingrained that he filled in otherwise unoccupied time attending portions of movies. He might see part in New York, part in Chicago, and part in San Francisco, and the order did not seem to make any difference to him. Dr. Davison probably had more unfinished parts of more movies floating around in his head than any man in the United States, and he did not jumble them up, either. His criterion for a good movie corresponded to the degree of "fanny fatigue" that developed.

Unoccupied moments also were spent in authorship endeavors. Despite almost countless activities at the national and state levels, Dean Davison found time to write well over 200 scientific papers plus a book, *The Compleat Pediatrician*, which sold approximately 100,000 copies in its eight editions. The book editions were revised, he said, "in otherwise idle minutes on trains, steamers, and planes, in bars on ships and at airports, and at lectures, concerts, and medical

another dignified-looking gentleman. The trio reached the end of the corridor and looked into a room. They turned around quickly, in great confusion, and headed toward another room, still moving along at a fast clip. The doctor poked his head into the second room and whirled around to start off in another direction. Before

he could make up his mind where to go next, a nurse stopped and asked, "Doctor, can I show you anything in the new ward?" "Yes," replied Dr. Davison, "the men's room."

Though frugal, he was generous to a fault, as attested over the years by his students and house officers who received generous nonnegotiable fi-

meetings."

Contents of the Dean's traveling bag included

1 flask of brandy
1 flask of bourbon
1 flask of scotch
1 deflated rubber sitting ring
1 steel container with aspirin, cascara, secobarbital, caffeine, sulfa, and antihistamine drugs
1 copy of *Readers' Digest*
1 copy of "Omnibook"
The Compleat Pediatrician in revision
1 cheese sandwich (for breakfast)
1 thermos of coffee
1 cellophane bag of chocolates and one of varied candies
1 bag of peanuts
1 eye shade and several sets of ear plugs.

These accounted for perhaps half of the contents of the bag. What the rest of it held, I never discovered.

He once became so engrossed in revising some material while sitting through a paper being given by an old crony that he failed to note that the subject had been changed at the last minute. At the conclusion he stood up and congratulated his colleague on a brilliant discussion of a topic which was never delivered.

Dr. Davison kept a tidy tabulation and found that his book's 257 pages plus index required 1,930 hours for compiling and writing "spread over nine months—a normal gestation—in addition to half an hour daily reading and abstracting every year the 6,437 references used and 996 hours of proofreading by my wife, secretaries, and the Duke pediatric house staff and students."

The Compleat Pediatrician was begun in 1919, when Dr. Davison was on the Johns Hopkins pediatric staff, as a notebook record of easily forgotten facts and methods. The 1-lb volume was kept at that weight for ease in carrying and tucking in a satchel. His greatest thrill and satisfaction occurred when he heard that *The Compleat Pediatrician* was the only medical book available after the surrender at Bataan during the Second World War, and that it was used at Cabanatuan to calculate the dietary needs of the 13,000 American prisoners of war. Though stating that this "survived eight editions," he disclaims 100% thoroughness: "This book attempts to present the bare facts . . .; it is like a G-string, in touching the subject without any pretense of covering it, or even more aptly, like a brassiere, in only touching the high spots." The preface refers to the Spanish, Japanese, and Italian translations, and to someone's recommendation that an English version would be an improvement. The dust jacket offered the flexible, bound volume for $4.25 cash or $4.50 on credit; "money back if desired."

The ninth edition of *The Compleat Pediatrician* was expanded and published by Lea & Febiger in 1969. Fifteen Duke associates collaborated in writing this book as a tribute to the man who was an educator, author, administrator, colleague, warm friend, and compleat pediatrician.

Wilburt Davison was born in Grand Rapids, Mich, in 1892, the son of a Methodist minister. Princeton gave him the AB degree in 1913, and thence he went to Oxford University, England, as a Rhodes Scholar. At Oxford he began the business of tradition-breaking by calling on Sir William Osler, dean of the medical school, to request permission to complete the first two years of medical training in one year.

"I was delightfully surprised," Dean Davison recalls, "when a small man came to the door and said cheerily before I could open my mouth, 'I am Sir William and have heard of your request which I think is very foolish but of course you can do anything you please and now let's have tea.' Taking the amazed me by the arm, he propelled me into the drawing room, introducing me to Lady Osler with, 'Grace, here is a new American colt who is wrecking a medical school tradition. Give him some tea.'"

This episode marked the beginning of Dr. Davison's affectionate devotion to Sir William, who profoundly influenced his thinking about many aspects of medical education. Dr. Davison earned the BA and BSc degrees at Oxford, and got his MD from Johns Hopkins. In 1917 he married Atala Thayer Scudder of Glen Head, Long Island, NY, to whom he had become engaged when she was at Bryn Mawr and he was at Princeton. Mrs. Davison, like her husband, is an MD and a pediatrician. The Davisons have three children, two of whom are physicians.

Dean Davison's 34 years at Duke were marked by constant dissatisfaction with the status quo, with his mind always open to new ideas on how to spur the school toward the highest levels of excellence. The movement to train nonmedical men for positions as hospital administrators was inaugurated here. This is one of the few medical schools which includes nursing procedures in the medical curriculum, so that the students can instruct patients and relatives of patients. In accord with a practice of European medical education, Dean Davison encouraged students to spend one or more terms at medical schools other than Duke. He was instrumental in the establishment of loan funds for rural students in medicine—a step toward helping fill the need for physicians in rural areas of the South.

He maintained consistently that while specialization in medicine was necessary, the success of total medical practice must depend upon a substantial proportion of well-rounded generalists. He was continually challenging the students and house officers with the opportunities, satisfactions, and needs of general practice. Running countercurrent to the trend of specialization, he kept utilizing many devices to interest more medical students in family practice.

One of his lesser known contributions to the health and welfare field was that he was one of the pioneers in establishing hospital insurance in the United States. The need for a method of providing medical care for those unable to pay all or a part of the cost first became obvious to him in 1927, shortly after his arrival in Durham from Johns Hopkins. The hospitals

192

in North Carolina, he found, had a steady procession of patients who, although not really indigent, did not have the necessary cash to pay their hospital and doctor bills. Unless hospitals could find an answer to this problem, Dr. Davison reasoned, many of them would not be able to stay in business. Searching for a solution, he heard about a prepayment scheme which had been started by Dr. T. W. M. Long at the Roanoke Rapids Hospital, for employees of textile mills. Under this plan all employees of the mills paid the hospital 25¢ per week, per family, and this entitled them to receive basic minimum care at the Roanoke Rapids Hospital, for both hospital and doctor bills.

With Dr. Watson S. Rankin, director of the Hospital and Orphanage Division of the Duke Endowment, Dr. Davison visited Roanoke Rapids and studied the plan. If such a scheme would work for a single hospital and a single group of mills, they decided, then why not set up a broader plan, on a community-wide basis, with all community hospitals participating?

Dr. Davison began by calling on local businessmen and doctors trying to arouse support for this idea. The response was not encouraging, but he had never been one to discourage easily. The break he needed came when he contacted George Watts Hill, Durham philanthropist and president of the Board of Directors of Watts Hospital. With Hill's enthusiastic backing, interest in the establishment of a community-wide hospital service plan in Durham soon increased.

When Dr. Davison went back to Oxford for the 25th Anniversary of the Rhodes Scholarship Program, in 1929, he learned of the English voluntary contributory prepayment scheme called the "Penny in the Pound Plan." Contributors paid twopence a week into a common fund, which entitled them to receive limited hospital care without additional cost. After studying this system and comparing it with the Roanoke Rapids plan, Dr. Davison evolved his concept of a community-wide program com-

bining the best features of both these plans plus his own and Hill's ideas on the subject. After three years of tedious spadework, the Hospital Care Association was finally organized.

During Dean Davison's administration, the Duke School of Medicine produced some 1,800 physicians and trained a veritable army of workers in fields such as medical technology, hospital administration, physical and occupational therapy, nurse anesthesiology, x-ray technology, medical record librarianship, and hospital dietetics. Postgraduate courses still attract practicing physicians from throughout the nation and foreign countries. Duke Medical School and Hospital often serve as hosts for state, regional, and even national conferences, and meetings of professional medical organizations.

After his 76th birthday he wrote me the following letter.

July, 1968

Dear Jay,

Helen Thomas told me that you wanted me to write you a letter about Atala's and my activities, so here goes.

We live in a five-room cottage at Roaring Gap at an altitude of 3,000 feet from March to December. We then go to Saint Croix in the Virgin Islands for three months.

Thanks to Nick Nicholson, Banks Anderson, Marty Kreshon, Cal Callaway and others I am in good health in spite of having arthritis, glaucoma, lymphocytic leukemia, and old age.

Atala, thanks to Billy Peete who removed a thrombosed vein, is in perfect health.

I see patients on the mountain, except between the hours of one and five when I generally take a nap, though not for the whole period. I believe I am the only physician who has such a rule of having office hours for 20 hours and no patients for four hours. I enclose a copy of the sign on my door* which all of my friends on the mountain respect and observe.

I am still driving the Lincoln Continental which the Alumni and Trustees gave me in 1961 when I retired. It has now gone 69,000 miles and is running better every year.

Our son Bill is practicing orthopedics in Port Huron, Mich; our daughter Jeana is working in the Forrest Laboratory at

Berkeley; and Sandy, our younger son, is practicing forestry up and down North Carolina with headquarters in Hillsborough.

We have nine grandchildren and manage to see all of them at least once a year.

During the nine months at Roaring Gap I go to New York, Washington, Durham, or Charlotte at least every two weeks so that I am traveling about as actively as I did 50 years ago.

I am going back to my 55th Princeton Reunion tomorrow and then to the AMA Meeting in San Francisco and to see my daughter and her three children in Berkeley.

We are thinking of going to Portugal, Madeira, the Canary Islands, Casablanca, and Tangier in August.

W. C. DAVISON

PS: We sold the cottage which you remember in Roaring Gap and bought a small five-room cottage all on one floor a mile and a half away from the other cottage. I reached 76 on April 28 and Atala did likewise on June 3. We had our 51st Wedding Anniversary on June 2.

Although now feeble at the age of 80 years, he is still alert, humorous and very much dedicated to Duke, its alumni and students, and to the world's children.

Today, only 42 years from its beginning, the Duke Medical School and its associated hospital comprise one of America's renowned medical centers. With Dr. Davison's retirement the first great Duke era came to an end, yet with his imprint permanently set upon it. The future developments and further progress of this great medical school, and the passing of time, will never erase the stamp left by its first Dean and organizer. He built a medical school of stone—and left it marble.

---

*SLEEPING (1-5 P. M.)

Don't knock, and don't go away mad, but go away until five and then please return for a drink at the fourth door (toward Sparta). Please leave any messages under this door, but not under the other three doors. *The first door is my study, the second is the kitchen, the third is full of garden tools, and the fourth (nearest Sparta) is the front or hospitality entrance.*

The Davison Medallion

(Remarks Made at the Presentation Ceremony,
Medical Alumni Weekend, November 1969)

John P. McGovern,* MD, Houston

This year of 1969 is a most fortuitous one in which to be able to present the Wilburt Cornell Davison medallion (Figure). This is because it is the year that marks the 50th anniversary of the death of Sir William Osler and the medallion is being presented to Osler's youngest living American student, one who is, in the judgment of many, his greatest.

We at Duke are fortunate indeed to have the "Davison Tradition," molded in Osler's classical humanist-physician tradition but renascent with the unique hallmark upon it of the singular great spirit and personality of our beloved mentor and warm friend.

This man, to whom I must present this medallion with unseemly brevity, was a Rhodes Scholar under Sir William at Oxford. I mention brevity, for although Dean Davison has been my own lifelong hero and benefactor in medicine, and although his accomplishments and honors are of truly promethean proportions, he would be immensely displeased if I tarried too long in introducing him—for brevity

and modesty have been watchwords of his life.

Nevertheless, even though I hope to be brief enough to please him, I cannot be sufficiently modest, for Dean Davison's place is secure among the greatest of American physician-educators.

Eight years ago I asked the Dean if he would send a copy of his curriculum vitae for my Davison Library. The reply I received reflects only a touch of his accomplishments but tells a great deal about the warmth, humanity, and humor of the man himself. It is characteristically succinct and contained what he termed *The High Points of My Life*, briefly stated, which I shall read to you:

Marrying Atala Scudder '17, Rhodes Scholarship '13, Osler's friendship '13-'19; Rankin's friendship '27-, Asst. Dean and Acting Ped. Hd. at JH '23 and '26, Dean and Prof. Ped. Duke '27-'61, James B. Duke Professorship '53-, eight editions CP '34-'61, NRC and Lew Weed '42-'52, stopped smoking '48, Trustee of the Duke Endowment '61.

He concluded by giving his *Daily Routine:*

At Princeton, in my day, it was a disgrace to study excessively and to be a "greasy grind." Princeton, unlike Yale, under Woodrow Wilson was the best country

Received for publication June 5, 1972; accepted June 6.

*Dr. McGovern is president of the Duke Medical Alumni Association.

Reprint requests to McGovern Allergy Clinic, Houston 77025 (Dr. McGovern).

The Wilburt Cornell Davison medallion.

club in America, and studying beyond getting a "third or gentleman's group" wasn't done. However, I wanted to obtain a Phi Beta Kappa Key, and my "P," and a Rhodes Scholarship, as well as to be elected to a club, so I began to get up at five or six o'clock and work until breakfast at eight without anyone, except my roommate, knowing about it. Besides, I was so tired at night after rowing and swimming that I would fall asleep studying in the evening. I have continued this nefarious habit for 54 years, so far. Now from five to 11, I write, dictate or read.

At 11 when in Durham, I go to the hospital and remain until three or four in the afternoon. When at Roaring Gap or Puerto Rico, I swim at 11.

At three or four, or earlier if I can, I take a siesta. At five or six, if the weather is clear, I walk for half-hour to an hour. At 7:30, I go to medical meetings, movies, or in my declining years look at television or read Westerns.

Aside from his professional attainments, it is for Dean Davison's spirit as it has flowed to us that we are most grateful. Sir Berkeley Moynihan has said that men such as this are gratefully remembered not so much for the work of their hands and minds, or for spoken or written words, but for the spiritual legacy bequeathed to those they inspire; this is the true immortality.

In a recent address titled *The Basis of Sir William Osler's Influence on Medicine,* Dean Davison, after stating that "Osler was the most human of human beings I have ever known," listed the seven pillars upon which Osler's fame rested. These were first, as a physician; second, as a teacher; third, as a scientist; fourth, as a medical reformer; fifth, as a medical writer; sixth, as a humanist, and seventh, as a personality. Dr. Davison said of Osler in terms of the seventh pillar—as a personality:

Those who knew him firsthand, and this included all who knew him even briefly, felt the warmth and glow of his presence, and were a devoted, almost an apostolic band. If their zeal was at times overlavish . . . their motivation was honest. Though Osler, unlike Atlas, never stopped to shoulder the world, he always kept his arms around it. He exuded familiarity tempered with reserve. He could take the arm of the most exalted without arousing resentment, but no one took his arm or slapped him on the back. He did what comes naturally, he followed the golden rule, and his creed was to like and sympathize with everyone. He never gave a thought to the length of his own shadow. If he could not see good in people, he saw nothing. In any gathering, he seemed able to address each guest intimately—Tom, Jack, Jim, or whatever familiarity dictated. Osler's wonderful power made every young man he met feel that he was in the presence of one who was taking a personal interest in him. It was a true and natural expression of the overflowing humanity that was part of him. Universal sympathy was the essence of his greatness, a greatness of personality, that characteristic power to perceive and elicit the best in any companion.

These statements succinctly and yet eloquently describe an essential part of the greatness of Sir William Osler. More important to us, however, is that these words were written by Dean Davison to describe his own beloved mentor. Of course, of still greater significance is that if I should substitute the word Davison for Osler and read these sentences back to you in the present tense, they would most accurately describe our own hero, whom we cherish and by whose presence today we are honored. His life and career, with his dear Atala by his side, truly represent a monumental success in the great art of living.

And now, Dean Davison, from all of your friends—those present and those unable to be here—may I present to you, with all of our love and affection and esteem, the Wilburt Cornell Davison Medallion.

195

Wilburt C. Davison and Medical Libraries

Martin M. Cummings, MD,
Bethesda, Md

Knowledge is not wisdom; wisdom is knowledge, when it is tempered by judgement
FRANK E. EGLER, 1970

Wilburt C. Davison stimulated and inspired medical students and faculty colleagues for more than half a century. At 80 years of age, he remains a knowledgeable and wise man.

I was fortunate to be a student at Duke when his powerful influence as Professor of Pediatrics and Dean of the School of Medicine was approaching its zenith. I observed his giant figure and warm personality in the setting of his office, the hospital ward and clinic—as well as in his home. In each of these places he used books and journals to teach the principles of good medicine, scholarship, and humanism. He supported libraries everywhere. He loved the library which he created at Duke. Importantly, he used it frequently and taught others to do the same. Gently, he led students to this source of knowledge,

Received for publication Jan 18, 1972; accepted Jan 26.

From the National Library of Medicine, Bethesda, Md.

Reprint requests to National Library of Medicine, 10 First St SE, Bethesda, Md 20014 (Dr. Cummings).

and for many the library became the place to browse, study, think, and write, even though its chairs were hard, its lighting poor, and its space limited.

It was through Dr. Davison that I became acquainted with the importance of the history of medicine and some of its leaders of the day. As a student, he introduced me to Dr. John F. Fulton, then at Yale, and Dr. Arturo Castiglioni, refugee medical historian driven from Italy by Mussolini.

It is not surprising, therefore, that I should feel pleased and honored to be invited to comment on Davison and medical libraries on this occasion. In my present work, I have learned that Dr. Davison assisted the National Library of Medicine in many important ways. In this sense, he was a disciple of its first Director, Dr. John Shaw Billings, great American bibliographer, medical educator, innovator, and administrator.

The year 1913, which brought to a close the career of Dr. Billings, witnessed the appearance of Dr. Davison on the medical scene, as a Rhodes scholar in medicine at Oxford, where he met Osler and studied under him.

Cushing,[1] describing Osler's life at Oxford during World War I, wrote the following:

... only Rhodes scholars and invalids—in the University; but with the colleges and

196

streets full of soldiers—many of them invalid Tommies in their blue coats and red ties—and with 5000 Derby recruits gathering in the Parks, the city of Oxford was anything but deserted. Of the American Rhodes Scholars, three or four were taking the medical course. One of these, Dr. W. C. Davison, was Secretary of the American Club, an organization which formerly brought together every Saturday night the Americans studying in Oxford. . . .

The influence of Osler upon the life and work of Davison was varied, and I have chosen to cite a few vignettes from Davison's reminiscences to reflect this.[2]

It was Sir William's custom to dash into laboratories and ask amusing and often disconcerting anatomical questions of students who were dissecting, or to look down the microscopes and inspect the slides of those studying pathology and bacteriology. Osler was a magnificent teacher, and made everyone with whom he came in contact feel that he was primarily and genuinely interested in that individual. I have since met hundreds of his former students in America and England who shared that belief. For example, Thomas B. Futcher, who was supposed to give me an examination in medicine when I transferred to the Hopkins in 1916, happily chatted about the Chief for an hour and then gave me a good grade. John Musser did the same thing when I took the National Board in 1919. In fact, passing examinations seemed more dependent on knowing Osler than on a knowledge of medicine—perhaps they are synonymous.

Osler deepened Davison's interest in books and reading.[2]

One of the most delightful features of the medical training at Oxford was Sir William's interest in the history of medicine. At intervals throughout the year he would send six or seven of us one of the following treasured invitations:

From the Regius Professor of Medicine, Oxford,

Dear Davison,

If free dine here please with me Thursday evening, 23rd, 7:30.

Sincerely yours,
Wm. Osler

After dinner, he would bring out many of his precious books, and we would spend hours in pouring over them while he explained the part Avicenna, Paracelsus,

Wilburt C. Davison, MD, presiding as President of the Association of Honorary Consultants to the Armed Forces Medical Library.

Leonardo da Vinci, and others had played in medicine. These evenings gave us a background that was invaluable.

Like Billings and Osler, Davison was born in the North Central region of America, Grand Rapids, Mich. Migrating to the East for educational purposes, he left his mark in the same cities where Osler and Billings also worked, Baltimore, Washington, and Oxford. He extended his frontier southward to influence medical developments in North Carolina and nearby territory.

In his preface to the seventh edition of *The Compleat Pediatrician*,[3] Davison wrote, "This edition required 1,930 hours for compiling and writing the changes spread over nine months—a normal gestation—in addition to a half-hour daily for the past eight years for reading and abstracting the 6,437 references used." It should be noted that this text is orga-

nized and arranged in a fashion which makes it easily adaptable for computer storage and retrieval.

Davison's half-hour daily reading habit, too, is to be traced to the influence of Osler:

On Mondays, Osler, who was a Lt. Colonel in the Canadian Army Medical Corps, visited the Duchess of Connaught Hospital on the Astor estate at Cliveden. As he needed someone to take his notes and collect blood specimens for study, he took me along. Sir William would start the Cliveden journeys by stacking ten or fifteen medical journals, which had arrived during the preceding week, on the car seat between us, and would read one after another, "dog-earing" the articles which he recommended my reading. He could read and digest medical literature more rapidly than anyone I have ever met; at the end of the two hour ride, he would have completed a survey of all the journals. It took me the rest of the week to cover the articles he had suggested, but it started a life-long habit of reading medical journals for at least a

197

half-hour daily.

In 1916 Davison completed his scholarship at Oxford and returned to the United States. Now his life history was to intersect with strands originally woven by Dr. Billings, while yet retaining an interrelationship with Osler and William H. Welch to the first faculty at Johns Hopkins.

He was appointed the first dean of Duke University School of Medicine in 1927 and, for this mark of favor, he thanks Osler because Osler had written to Welch about him, and Welch had recommended him to Duke. He was, as you can see, as pious as Aeneas.

In 1961 Stanhope Bayne-Jones, MD, praised Dr. Davison at a testimonial dinner at Duke on Oct 5, 1961. I am going to quote some thoughts from that delightful talk which bears on my theme.

Osler's influence upon him has been incalculably inspiring, and has been of constant benefit to the school over which he presided for thirty-three years. This influence was by no means limited to ideals of clinical medicine and teaching, and methods of observation, but extended to books, medical history and literature, and the genuine humanism so badly needed in a period becoming ever more strictly scientific.

In his reminiscences of Sir William Osler, Dr. Davison wrote[2]:

One of Osler's most helpful aphorisms was: "To study the phenomena of disease without books is to sail an uncharted sea, while to study patients without books is not to go to sea at all." It made me realize how essential a medical library was to every school, and that although buildings could be built and a staff assembled, a library had to be hunted in the four corners of the earth. As a result, the collecting was started three years before the school opened, and now the Duke Medical Library is among the best ten in the country.

Davison's interest in libraries led to his nomination as an Honorary Consultant to the Army Medical Library in 1943, and we have in our files his letter of acceptance to MG Norman T. Kirk, the Army surgeon general, dated Nov 27, 1943:

Dear General Kirk:

I appreciated very much your letter of 22 November. Needless to say, I shall be very happy to serve as a member of the Board of Honorary Consultants to the Army Medical Library.

It is a field in which I am very much interested, and I feel very honored to be associated with the splendid Army Medical Library.

Thanking you for the invitation, I am

Yours sincerely,
Wilburt C. Davison

From 1950 to 1953 Dr. Davison served as President of the Association of Honorary Consultants from October 1950 until its dissolution in December 1952. During this period he laid the groundwork for its conversion to the National Library of Medicine. The Library files contain a number of photographs showing Dr. Davison active in "Library Hall" of the old building at Seventh Street and Independence Avenue, NW. Except for the furniture, the room had little changed during the years. It still had a Gothic appearance and the tiers and stacks towered massively (indeed, I should say almost menacingly) over the visitors' heads. This is the same room where Osler had worked, and which had known the presence of many of the greatest names in medicine since its opening in 1887 (Figure).

In reading Dr. Davison's many remarks at meetings held at the Library under his presidency, one quickly realizes that he took a genuine interest in this national resource. "The Army Medical Library ... is woven through the lives of all of us in medicine," he remarked. The most important problem facing the Library in the 1950s was that of acquiring a new building and it was to this problem principally that Dr. Davison and his colleagues addressed themselves. "We have been trying for years ... to get a new building, which is perhaps the most essential thing before the Library and before the Association of Honorary Consultants," he pointed out in 1951. Referring to

the Library's building with its leaky roof, at the last meeting of the Consultants, Davison said, "It is the only place that profited from the drought we have had, since the place has been dry during the summer." The building was, in his own words, "a fire-trap and a sieve." Though fire spared the collection, water did not, and through the year, rain and bursted water mains brought hundreds of rare volumes to a useless end.

The second concern of Dr. Davison was to convert the Army Medical Library to the National Library of Medicine in name as well as in fact. New legislation was passed in 1956, creating the National Library of Medicine as the first specialized library with its own Congressional mandate. Dr. Davison remarked, "It took John Shaw Billings twenty-two years to get out of the Ford Theater over here to Independence Avenue, and I hope it does not take us quite as long to get from Independence Avenue to Bethesda. ..." It took a long time, but we finally moved into a new building in 1962.

From time to time we still receive requests for library services from Dr. Davison. They come from Roaring Gap, NC, and reflect that he is still reading at least half an hour a day. It would be indiscreet and improper for me to tell you precisely what kind of requests he makes, but I am sure he would not object to my classifying his subject interests: medical education, history, and humanism. In behalf of medical librarians and libraries everywhere, I salute and thank this lifetime learner. He did more for us than we could have done ourselves.

References

1. Cushing H: *The Life of Sir William Osler*. Oxford, England, Clarendon Press, 1926, vol 2, p 516.
2. Davison WC: Sir William Osler, reminiscences. *Arch Intern Med* 84:110-128, 1949.
3. Davison WC, Levinthal JD; *The Compleat Pediatrician*. Durham, NC, Duke University Press, 1957.

Building a School

Eugene A. Stead, Jr., MD, Durham, NC

The Duke University Medical School is Dr. Davison's School. He was there before the buildings were built, before the books were bought for the library, before an administrative staff was assembled, and before a single faculty appointment was considered. On all of our walls under the paint, one finds inscribed, "Davison was here."

Under Dr. Davison's guidance the Medical School grew into a community of scholars concerned with all phases of knowledge. He concerned himself with the practice of medicine in the state, the South, and the nation. He built an outstanding library. He operated a clinical center which has steadily grown until it has a worldwide reputation. He developed a system of private university clinics which bring a steady flow of visitors to Duke to study their operation. He spread pediatricians far and wide over the land and laid the basis for the development of a children's clinical center at Duke. He recognized the vitalizing impact of research upon the corporate body of the Medical School, but properly pointed to its inordinate demands. There were no slaves or masters on his form sheet.

Dr. Davison had the ability to delegate responsibility to others. He required a high level of performance, demanding of others the same standards of excellence which he had for himself. Under his guidance the school was not paternalistic. If a faculty member failed at Duke, the credit for the failure belonged to him and not to the dean. If a faculty member succeeded at Duke, the dean made it clear that the credit for the success belonged to the faculty member and not to the dean.

Dr. Davison separated his personal feelings from his responsibilities to the school. He did not hesitate to state his own adverse opinion of an individual. If his performance in the school was good, he supported him while disliking him. He was interested in assembling an outstanding faculty rather than a social club.

Dr. Davison operated informally. He was known to the faculty simply as "Dave." He did not depend on props for dignity. Coatless and tieless, he was always the Duke Medical School. He believed that no rules should ever be written down if it were possible to avoid doing so. Why limit the future by the vision of the past?

Dave always knew that good administration required a personal touch. Accomplishments of faculty members, wives, or children were acknowledged by a note from the dean. Every patient with any interest in Duke was visited by him. In truth, the man seemed to have eyes in the back of his head and ears everywhere.

As with all good administrators, his word was his bond. He carried a little notebook attached to his wallet. Once he agreed to a course, it was noted in the book. The matter was then as good as accomplished.

Received for publication May 30, 1972; accepted May 30.

From Duke University School of Medicine, Durham, NC.

Reprint requests to Duke University Medical Center, Durham, NC 27710 (Dr. Stead).

A Few Reminiscences About Dean Davison

GEORGE R. ANDREWS, M.D.
WAUSAU, WISCONSIN

One of the most memorable features of a medical education at Duke from 1930 to 1960 was Dean Wilburt C. Davison. Though it was of necessity rare for organisms orbiting around the transverse colon and the island of Reil to encounter someone who went as casually to Bangkok, Vladivostok, and Sydney as most people did to the A. & P., still Duke students always knew the Dean was there with them and for them.

His secretary might explain that at the moment he was in Washington or Peking, but such reports were never unsettling, however seemingly urgent the errand on which one had come. The image of the Dean winging sedately across the Steppes of Asia, over the oceans and continents, was somehow reassuring. It gave one the feeling that not only the concerns of American medicine, but somehow the ultimate interests of Duke itself stretched to the furthest corners of the planet and were in the best possible hands. While students and faculty were straining together to push back the frontiers, the Dean was out surveying new ones against which future generations could organize alarums and expeditions. He provided a feeling that we were participating with him as he presided over the course of empire and the unfolding of manifest destiny on the most elevated level of medical affairs.

The reason for this sense of close identification with him was the air of warm and hearty interest he always showed to each student who came to see him. It was as true in the years after graduation as before. If you came to lament a low-pass, the Dean was as dismayed as you were at such an obvious miscarriage of justice. If you came to ponder the temptation of internships and residencies which tendered the lures of living wages, he was gently sympathetic but nonetheless judicious in pointing out the large price of a lower quality of training which would most likely have to be paid eventually. For the alumnus

returning to Duke, the feeling on seeing Dean Davison was that of meeting an old friend rather than someone who had once intimidated on the basis of a superior office and the power to control the destiny of the students within his sway.

Someone once defined medical meetings as places where doctors are given the opportunity to act for a few days like the men they once imagined they would be. There are times when, to most students, medical schools seem like places where some physicians are permanently provided such an opportunity. Of course, such cynical critiques need to be softened by acknowledgment of the somewhat paranoid state of mind of the average medical student, who is momentarily expecting disaster, trembling at the shadows of leaves falling past the window in October, and hearing whispers in the night as portents of calamity. In the depths of their being, few of them ever really expect to graduate or become licensed physicians.

In such an atmosphere of highly charged suspense and imminent catastrophe, the sight of Dean Davison was more salutary than two or three years on an analyst's couch would have been. With collar open and loosened tie, he was the picture of ease and common sense. He was an invitation to learning. The omnipresent pipe completed, though nothing could have improved, the picture.

Equally as effective as the sense of existing in a meaningful relationship to the world and its affairs which Dean Davison provided was a historical dimension he gave in which, through a sort of benign "guilt by association," we all could participate.

As a Rhodes scholar he had had firsthand experience of England and its institutions of higher education in a period preceding the first World War. His professional association and friendship with Sir William Osler had a certain magical quality about it. The thought that the Dean had been so closely associated with this legendary figure in medicine was redemptive for young men and women on whose horizons usually loomed only such grave concerns as learning the names of all the femur's tuberosities, or looking up and memorizing every article on ainhum ever written.

The uncounted pictures of athletic teams, military figures, educators, and distinguished colleagues of the past, which took the place of wallpaper in the Dean's office, gave a visitor the feeling of being immersed in the historical process. The fact that he had been a member of the faculty of Johns Hopkins and had led the Duke faculty in creating the Duke Medical School gave a final measure of distinction.

The peripatetic nature of the Dean's Office through the years at times seemed to support rumors periodically circulated that he was voluntarily withdrawing from his headquarters to "make room for mice and seagulls" in the interest of research. The sight of the Dean and his faithful associate, Carl, heading undaunted out to the periphery of the campus in search of a new, more secure base of operations was a familiar and moving one for students through the decades. When at last the final location was once more near the lobby of the medical school, even though on the opposite side of the hall from where it had been for such a long time, there was a sense of fulfillment. There was a rightness about the return which had all the components of the "happy ending." The Dean had come home again where he belonged. The dramatic unities had been fittingly observed.

The Dean's Portrait

Probably every Duke Medical School graduate has some particular memory of the Dean which he particularly cherishes. If I had to choose one, it would be of a singular experience, which several of my classmates and I shared with him. One summer's day I was walking innocently toward Howland Ward when I encountered Dr. Grant Taylor, who was the Assistant Dean at the time. He reached out and beckoned. I paused uneasily, expecting some clap of doom, such as that in 10 minutes I was to present a case in the amphitheatre to the student body, faculty, and visiting luminaries from Harvard, Hopkins, and Aberdeen.

"Get a few of the boys," he said. "They're painting a picture of the Dean, and they need some of you fellows to sit around at his feet like on rounds."

It was at the moment a seemingly obscure assignment, since none of us had ever had any experience along these lines, but it sounded like a splendid opportunity to break the routine. I had no idea how long it took to paint a dean's portrait, but it sounded as though we might get a few days of official leave while interns and residents fumed impotently at our departure from the chores of the lab and the ward. At the particular moment it had not clearly dawned on me what a remarkable enterprise we were embarking upon, nor what a privilege we were being offered.

I mentioned the project to Hank Gowdy, Bill Hadley, and Charles Gunn, who responded with enthusiasm. We drove over to the building on the East campus where we were to meet. We were in the kind of holiday mood students always develop when unexpectedly school lets out, whether because of plagues, wars, natural catastrophes, or some equally providential but much more pleasant reason such as the mission on which we engaged.

It was warm weather, clear and sunny. We were all wearing our white coats, so that we would look like, even if we were not altogether so, authentic students in the painting. The room was a large one on the ground floor, the setting simple and, as I look back on it, similar to the kind of scene we have all observed countless times on our TV screens.

There was a tall wooden stool for the Dean. In front of it were four folding chairs without backs for us. The total effect was quite reminiscent of rounds with Dean Davison on the pediatric ward. The easel was set up at a distance of perhaps 30 feet from the Dean. He faced us and the artist, and we faced the Dean. It gave the artist a fine view of him and of our backs, though there was a third or quarter view of the faces

slight emotional difficulty in getting up on their feet and facing the world, the problem has not been overwhelming. But however great the encouragement to remain dependent throughout eternity, or at least until the amphitheatre collapses, the handicap has been far more than compensated by the uncancellable opportunity of dropping in and seeing captured forever a brief moment out of youth, spent in the company of a singularly knowledgeable and inspiring man whose abilities as a teacher were surpassed only by his capacities as a human being.

Wilburt C. Davison -- The Dean and the Friend

An Appreciation by a Latin American Pediatrician

ERNESTO COFINO, M. D.

GUETEMALA, CENTRAL AMERICA

It would be a big job to relate, even briefly, the scientific trajectory and the magnitude of the work of Dr. Davison, even when we follow him only as a pediatrician, the founder and dean of a medical school, and the author of one of the most original summaries of pediatrics ever written. I am sure that a more complete picture will be developed in this special dedicatory issue, by his intimate colleagues, by his pupils from yesterday and today, and by those who have lived close to him and know of his life of continual movement, his immense spirit of understanding, and his dominant obsession of helping others even before their petitions.

My contribution to this "honor" number will be simple, considering only Dr. Davison's position in international pediatrics, especially in Latin America.

First of all, I want to say that one of the things that have characterized him is his fineness. The generous help he gave was always invisible, so that the people who received it seemed to walk by their own efforts.

Dr. Davison has passionately loved to travel—a characteristic of his constant activity and his interest in all countries and people. He has gone everywhere with his eyes open and with the fervent wish to understand and appreciate all the good, noble, and interesting things that every country offers.

He has been able to accomplish much by a kind of intuition that is an expression of his genuine generosity. To understand the dominant feelings of a country, to capture its virtues, and to excuse its defects is very difficult when the language of the country is well known; but to do this without knowing the language is possible only to men provided with a sixth sense—the sense of love for all the inhabitants of this planet. I really think that if Dr. Davison had the opportunity to travel to other planets, he would know how to interest and understand the inhabitants and to serve them.

How I Met Dr. Davison

In 1944 I accepted the generous invitation of the State Department of the United States to visit representative pediatric clinics in my position as professor of pediatrics in the University of Guatemala. I was anxious to meet personally the North American pediatricians and professors, having followed with interest the notable development of pediatrics in that continent through books, publications, and occasional assemblies. My own training in medicine and pediatrics I owed to France, where I studied in the school of Professor Robert Debré.

I arrived in Washington in June, 1944, and started getting acquainted through the courtesies of Mrs. Elizabeth Shirley Enochs and Professor Henry Helmholz (who died recently). It was my first formal visit to the United States, and I was a little confused, mainly because of my incomplete knowledge of the language. Professor Helmholz discussed several possibilities for permitting me to gain a better understanding of North

of the students on the ends, as the chairs were arranged in a curving line for purposes of composition.

Dean Davison was there talking to the painter. We were introduced to him, and then all of us, feeling remarkably self-conscious, sat down. In a little while we had grown accustomed to the situation, and there began the most remarkable week any of us had known in medical school. Of course, there was no work involved except sitting for a couple of hours, morning and afternoon, on those backless chairs. During the entire time, the Dean reminisced about events in his life with the relaxed, keen sense of humor which is one of his most notable characteristics. He provided us with glimpses of existence at Princeton, in England when he was a Rhodes Scholar, at Hopkins and innumerable places around the world where he had been in his work and travels. He sketched personalities, both distinguished and uncelebrated, that he had dealt with through the years. He spoke of medical schools, his philosophy of education, his views on the microcosm and the macrocosm. There were the highly amusing anecdotes which he always has in such limitless supply.

One of the many that I recall was of a trip he and Dr. Perlzweig, the first chairman of the Department of Biochemistry, made to Russia in the early thirties. Their hosts suggested at one point that they all take a day off at the beach. The two travelers said that unfortunately they hadn't brought bathing suits. This didn't matter, their hosts told them, since it was not the custom to wear anything on the beach in that part of Russia. Somewhat nonplussed, but not wishing to seem unappreciative of the offer, they accepted and went along. As Dean Davison recalled it, he and Dr. Perlzweig both spent a rather amusing day covertly watching each other in the process of trying to act casual and relaxed, though under circumstances which, in at least one respect, were strikingly unfamiliar to them.

"Actually," the Dean told us, "I didn't regret the occasion myself because I had always been curious about how the Russian women were built." He paused and puffed meditatively on his pipe while we waited. He looked at us then with a twinkle in his eye. "Very solidly," he concluded. "Very solidly."

By chance I sat second from the left, with Gowdy on my left, Bill Hadley on my right, and Gunn on Hadley's right. Bob Sheridan, as I recall, replaced Charles after the first day or two because he couldn't return. As it turned out, the man on the extreme right wasn't included in the painting, and only a portion of Gowdy's and Bill's faces showed up. Mine didn't at all, since I had my back to the painter.

The week passed very swiftly, and we were all soon back at our familiar labors. The painting was finished in detail without further help from us. As everyone knows, it now hangs in the amphitheatre at Duke, where countless generations of students have a splendid opportunity to see what the school's first Dean looked like in those days when he ran the institution, traversed the globe, and shepherded the successive bands of aspiring physicians through the innumerable psychic and physical traumata of undergraduate days.

It is just the right sort of portrait to have painted. It catches and preserves faithfully the personality of the Dean, with his warmth, his dislike of pomp and formality. The loosened tie, the open collar, the pipe symbolize perfectly the kind of man and teacher he was and is. Someone once described the ideal school as a log with Mark Hopkins on one end of it and the student on the other. In more modern terms, an ideal medical school might be defined as a half dozen stools with Dean Davison on the highest and the students on the others.

Outside of the fond recollections of that week with the Dean while we were all being painted, the anonymous students who posed with him have had a unique and very interesting little psychologic problem. Whenever they drop by and see the painting, as well as at other times, they realize that it is their singular role to advance backwards upon posterity through the eons, sitting forever at the feet of Dean Davison. While this might have caused some

American pediatrics, allowing me to choose the most convenient method of meeting my needs. We came to the conclusion that the best place to begin was at Duke, under the direction of Professor Wilburt C. Davison.

So I came to Durham at the beginning of July, 1944, finding myself in a very small town, with a university which had been set up by the generosity of one man—an extraordinary university town, in which the contributions of Dr. Davison had been remarkable.

Next day I was in the presence of the Dean in an environment of frankness and simplicity that contrasted with the solemnity and grandeur of the severe English-style buildings. I was introduced immediately to the Dean's office; it was a simple room full of bookcases, pictures, caricatures, and diplomas. Everything was a palpable and graphic representation of Dr. Davison's life, his love of travel, his passion for people, and his vocation.

The Dean's personality was in harmony with his environment: on a revolving chair, behind a simple but ample desk, I saw a man big in his physical dimensions, the only ones I could see then. The same dimensions I afterward saw as small in comparison with his spiritual ones. He received me as he used to when he did not have to submit to rules and protocol—wearing a shirt without a tie, and with a pipe in his mouth. That famous pipe was my nightmare for several months; because of it his words came out of a small space, causing me to exert constant effort in order to understand a little of his speech.

Going to an unknown country, where the culture, customs and way of life are different from one's own, is always most difficult, especially when one does not travel as a tourist with the pockets full and the mind empty. When the wish is to learn and retain what a generous country has to offer, the differences in language and customs are great obstacles. This situation is even harder when one is past his youth and has enjoyed in his native country a satisfactory social, medical, and educational position. It is difficult to become a student again, and terrible in the American sense. For Americans, in order to save time, use a great number of abbreviations, well known to them but absolutely incomprehensible to the poor beginner.

So it is not surprising that my face took on the proper characteristics of an idiot, and that the resident or "boarder boy," not used to dealing with foreign doctors and apparently confusing language difficulties with ignorance, asked, "Who is this Guatemalan professor who does not begin to understand pediatrics?" For the foreign doctor the fight was very hard, because he did not want to develop an inferiority complex.

Great was the confusion and the mental exertion of the "poor foreign professor" after he had been on visits, in discussions, conferences, and conversations in the dining room.

But then Dr. Davison's intervention began to be felt. With the goodness of a friend, the knowledge of an expert, and all the weight of a dean, he smoothed out all the harshness and unpleasantness, and did it all without the visitor's even realizing that someone was trying to help him.

The Magic Touch

Dr. Davison intervenes in everything, but the foreign visitor does not feel his presence. He has the impression that, thanks to his own spirit, his difficulties have become less and his initial inferiority complex is replace by a feeling almost of superiority. He feels that his Latin spirit has given him an extraordinary capacity for adaptation. He feels that doors are opened by a magic eye as soon as he steps near. In every department and office there is someone ready to help, almost guessing his questions. He doesn't realize that this great man, Dr. Davison, who has the virtue of "resting—working," this man who knows how to fill his "leisure" time, is behind all this attention.

This attention is not limited to the medical and technical aspects of the visitor's life, but is in the social atmosphere too, letting him know the way of life in North American homes. To attain these results, Dr. Davison starts inviting the visitor to his house and honoring him with special attention. His colleagues, perfectly trained in

204

his school, follow the Dean who has exhibited such a comprehensive and helpful attitude.

One knows that Dr. Davison wants his department always to be in good harmony. Besides, everybody knows that in him we have the teacher and the friend to solve all our family, economic, and educational difficulties. From him we have learned to follow the precept, "Don't let your left hand know what your right hand does."

It was under these conditions that I stayed at Duke for four months, being forced to leave to complete my program of study.

When I went to Mayo Clinic with Dr. Helmholz, to the University of Minneapolis with Dr. McQuarrie, and afterwards to Chicago, New York, and Richmond, my situation had changed. I was more sure of myself because I had a greater knowledge of the language and had become acquainted with North American medical concepts; but most of all, I had captured the peculiar way that North Americans have of helping others: "Few words and much efficiency."

"A Special Place"

After this trip I had many occasions to meet Dr. Davison—in assemblies, meetings, when he visited my country, and in his home at Duke. Every time I have been able to appreciate his extraordinary qualities. Among all the good people I have been privileged to know, he has a special place. I am sure that this feeling is unanimous among his many friends and admirers in Latin America.

The man who was able to create a medical school in a tobacco field; the man who wrote the most original and useful book on pediatrics that exists; the man who has visited so many places and appreciated all the good in them; the man who knows how to create, just by his presence, an atmosphere of cordiality and human understanding; a man with this moral in this materialistic world—Dr. Davison keeps playing a role of top quality even when regulations impel him to retire from some of his university activities.

His years have been full, and his crop very good. Now that he leaves the routine administrative responsibilities, he will be able to practice even more freely his role of furthering good will among peoples.

CORRESPONDENCE

THERE ARE FEW better ways to portray the man who was Wilburt Davison than through his correspondence, for he was a devoted and dedicated writer of letters, and especially of the meaningful short note, often on a postcard. During his lifetime he wrote thousands of them — to his students, to his house officers, to his faculty, to colleagues all over the world and to his many friends, both in and outside the medical profession. His letters served many functions and revealed much of the character, humor and humanism of the man. He used them most often to congratulate and encourage, and for moral as well as tangible support of the efforts of others; occasionally, to cajole and stimulate, often to seek or to give out information, and not infrequently to fight for those things that were important to him and to Duke (and to change those things which he found deficient). Many served as introductions that opened doorways throughout the world. These notes often expressed his joys, his sorrows (cloaked in dry humor), and sometimes his anger — but the pervasive thread throughout was his affection and enthusiasm and encouragement for those he loved and who loved and, often worshipped him. Davison's correspondence was itself a genuine force for good, creating a vast and diverse network reaching out from Durham, or from Roaring Gap, or wherever he might be in his extended travels. By this means he created a kind of extended family of those dedicated to health care, particularly those who had been associated with Duke. Binding together this network were the intellect and concern, the warmth and good humor, and, finally, the incredible energy and almost photographic memory of the Dean. His detailed recollection of important moments and treasured details in the lives of thousands of his friends and colleagues was a constant source of joy and of amazement to them all. Indeed, for many, he seemed like a member of the family, though one who generally was away on business. But his letters kept bringing him home.

A long-term project is envisioned to collect, catalogue, and perhaps annotate and publish Davison's complete correspondence.

Our purpose here, however, is to present only a representative sampling — a potpourri — of characteristic Davison letters; we have included only a few of these thousands of letters written by the Dean and to him. For ease of access, and because of time constraints, we have selected correspondence primarily from a sampling of the many hundreds of letters written by Davison to the editors, Dr. Grant Taylor (another former student and lifelong friend), and to several other colleagues and friends, as well as a few written to him. Also included are several letters written to the editors about Davison. We hope this limited and highly selective collection will reveal some of the varied talents and characteristics of this unique man, an educator, administrator, author and pediatrician, but most of all a warm, thoughtful, generous, genial and humorous man who liked people, particularly if they were medical graduates or trainees from Duke, and especially if they were pediatricians providing health services and care to children.

JMA
JPM

Durham, North Carolina
April 21, 1952

Dear Grant [Taylor]:

I have been swamped for the past three weeks with several trips to New York and Washington, so this is the first chance I have had of answering your letters of 27 March, 1 April, and 10 April. I shall take them up seriatim, so this will be really a record-breaking long letter for me.

Please thank Dr. Maki for distributing the clothes. I wish that there had been more, but our yard man and the cook at the country club, who are built along my lines, took part of them.

I shall also write Dr. Maki. The microscope which he sent me is also a great success. The duty amounted to $150, making the total cost, delivered to Durham, $503.06. Steve Simmons paid about the same amount.

He wrote me that he also was delighted with his scope.

Steve's wife has been staying in Chapel Hill for the last ten days, visiting her daughter, who is in the Division of Health Education there.

I am sorry to hear about Furth. I asked Wiley Forbus to get some information about Dr. Silverman, who is now in Charlotte. He is a Canadian, and Wiley recommends him very highly. Can I be of any help in approaching Silverman on my next trip to Charlotte?

I am sorry about the confusion in the hastily-called meeting of the CAC, but apparently the budget figures had to be in the hands of the AEC by 1 April. Arrangements for the meeting were made by telephone. All of the committee greatly regretted that it could not be postponed until Jim Neel returned.

I am all for the contingency fund. As you know, for twenty years I have included one in the Duke budget, and each year for twenty years it has been removed. The bequest of Fred Hanes of half of the interest from a million dollars, to be used any way that the Executive Committee wishes for the improvement of teaching and research, has been a godsend as a contingency fund.

I appreciate your suggesting that Jim Neel take me out for an Italian dinner. I am sure that I will be much more amenable to his arguments. He still denies that he has a rubber stamp saying "Property of Jim Neel." I wish you would send me a copy of it. Armed with that, I am sure he would give me two Italian dinners.

Many thanks for the can of Pityrol paste. I am asking Susan to try it, and shall keep you posted. As you know, ACTH and Cortisone have completely changed the problem of the severe eczemas of infancy. Children who come in screaming and scratching are quieted with ACTH and Cortisone almost miraculously. Of course it has to be continued, but it certainly is a wonder drug when it does work. The same is true of asthma. Mrs. Joe Markee is living comfortably and normally as a result of Cortisone now. She had very severe asthma.

I am glad the Wells' baby arrived safely and that Becky Wells and the new daughter are getting along comfortably. I also am very glad that Jack Wood has decided to remain. I was very favorably impressed with him when he was with us, and I think you are fortunate in having him. John Mitchell wrote that he would give permission to Jack and also to Dr. Sutow to take the Board examinations in San Francisco.

I am writing to Charles Harris, and also to Philip Evans, to see if they can communicate with someone so that Lt. J. H. Renwick can be assigned to ABCC.

I am glad that your income tax forms arrived, and also enclose letters from Charles Lowndes and Henry Brandis, who are great tax experts, on the question of your tax responsibility. Mr. Jones concurred in their opinion that if you received federal money you were not exempt, but non-federal money after 18 months you did not have to report as income. Whether money received indirectly from the government, as yours, from NRC via AEC, is taxable I don't know. However, when you return and I flee to the delights of Santiago de Cuba, I shall be tax-free after 18 months. One of the many nice things about Cuba is that only the people pay taxes who want to. In other words, all taxation is by lottery; and if you would like to take a chance on the numbers you pay taxes — if not, you don't.

According to the man in Washington, if I send the journals to you, you and the ABCC must pay freight. But if I send them to Dr. Kusama, they are tax-free. However, I feel sure that if I asked the Washington man to send them to Dr. Shimizu at the Hiroshima Medical College, they would go to him on the same basis that they would to Dr. Kusama. If you could let me know his correct address, I shall ask that the next shipment of books goes directly to Hiroshima. They are mostly back-numbers of the *JAMA*.

John Hubbard sent me a copy of his letter to you about the National Board, and I sent him the information. I was recently invited to become a member of the National Board, but now that I am rapidly approaching the age of sixty, I am acquiring some sense. At any rate, I declined the nomination, because I have so many foreign entanglements at the present time. The tragedy of growing old is that I had lost 36 pounds in order to qualify for active duty this summer at the 65th General Hospital at Fort Bragg. We had orders to report there for 15 days field duty. After I had struggled through this weight loss, I was then notified that inasmuch as I would be sixty years of age on 28 April, my commission would lapse. When I was in Washington last week I learned that the previous age of retirement of 64 years had been reduced to 60 years for brigadier generals and below, and the only way that I could remain in until I was 62 was to be made a major general, which I assume was not being contemplated. Therefore, I have recommended that Bill Nicholson be in charge of the 65th General Hospital and that I go to Fort Bragg this summer merely as a spectator, in spite of my reduced weight.

In connection with the assignment of Lt. J. H. Renwick, would a letter to Major Watt be of any help? He and Warner Wells were very friendly, and I gathered that Major Watt would help the ABCC in any way that he could.

Many thanks for the interesting photographs. The Shirley Temple of Japan was lovely. Lady Mountbatten seems very interested. Her father-in-law, Prince Louis Battenberg as he was called before the royal family changed their name to Windsor, once refereed a water polo game in which I played against Cambridge. Cambridge won 2 to 1. I enjoyed the dinner after the game, at which Prince Louis presided, more than I did the water polo game. I am a much better trencherman than water-poloist.

I also appreciate having the reprints and also "A Study of the Umbilicus."

I was greatly interested in your stateside personnel chart. I believe Ted Johnson is interested in a job with you. He said he had seen the chart, and wondered whether you would not need a replacement as Deputy Director, so that George could remain in Tokyo.

I realize the great difficulties in correlating activities in Hiroshima and in Washington, particularly now before the election.

I note you have taken up the question raised in your letter of April 10 with Det Bronk. Would it be of any help if I urged more speed and firmness in the post-war program? I gathered at the meeting, from Det, that the State Department was doing everything possible to give ABCC everything requested. Needless to say, I want to do everything possible to clarify the situation, so please let me know what you wish me to do.

I was interested to know that Dean Shimizu had retired as dean in favor of Dr. Kawaishi, and that the former is responding well to the rice diet. Someone ought to write a paper on the advantages of a rice diet to a Japanese.

I have had a letter from Jim Neel saying that he stopped a few hours with John Lawrence and learned that the meeting of CAC had been held. Jim and I are to meet in Atlantic City on Sunday, May 4, at Hackney's or at an Italian restaurant in accordance with your suggestion, so we can discuss matters which should be urgently presented to Washington. Jim sent me a copy of your letter of 3 April to Bob Livingston. I hope very much that Det will call a meeting of the CAC in the near future.

I am going to Washington almost every week now, and can go at any time in between regular visits if I can be of any help, so do not hesitate to let me know what I can do.

Atala has tried for three months to persuade some friends of hers,

211

including me, to drive to the West Coast to visit Betty Hanes in Tucson and Atala's sister at Coronado and, of course, Sandy and Mary in Portland. However, none of us could get away, so she departed ten days ago in her Austin by herself and so far has had a very successful trip. She spent one night in Memphis with the Sprunts, another night in Nashville with the Branscombs, another night in Tucson with Betty Hanes, and several days in Coronado, and is now on her way to Portland to see Sandy and Mary. She said that the driving was easy and she was completely enjoying the complete liberty and lack of responsibility of driving by herself.

With love to Pat, Grant Jr., Worth and yourself, I am

Yours sincerely,
Dave

Durham, North Carolina
May 3, 1952

Dear Grant:

Many thanks for your birthday letter. I wish that we could have celebrated it together. Phil Handler organized a surprise birthday lunch, and I certainly was surprised as well as embarrassed and very pleased.

By all means keep the lactic acid and vinegar milk papers. I hope to get around to publishing them in the near future, but with so many meetings turning up this spring I do not know whether I shall get a chance.

I was very interested in the clippings from Japan, and am forwarding them on to Frank Poole and Paul Fillmore.

I am driving to Southern Pines in a few minutes to leave my car there in order to take the train to Atlantic City, so that when I return there for the state meeting I shall have a car. I am looking forward to meeting Jim Neel and my son Bill at the Brighton Bar at 5:30 p.m. on Sunday. Also Doug Sprunt.

Many thanks for sending me a copy of the Neel report. I am looking forward to discussing it with Jim when I see him tomorrow.

With best wishes, I am

Yours sincerely,
Dave

Dear Dr. Davison:

Thank you for your nice letter of 21 April. As you say, it is the longest letter I have ever received from you, but I am putting it in my file of selected Davison letters. We were delighted to learn that both you and Dr. Simmons had received your scopes, but we were a little surprised at the final cost.

Dr. Furth has continued to be a good Samaritan, and continues to send us names of capable young pathologists. Two of these I understand are being interviewed by Carl Harris.

I did not know about the effective use of ACTH and Cortisone on the severe eczemas of infancy. What a godsend!

Jack Wood received word of his selection for the oral Pediatric Boards following his departure. We cabled the information to him in Honolulu. Dr. Sutow was also selected and his request for transportation and leave is now being considered by the Army.

Lt. Renwick is presently in Korea. A letter has been sent to Col. Watt eliciting his aid.

We have just received two rather distressing communications from the Army. The first has to do with Nationals other than U.S. (See copy) The second communication pertained to ourselves. This attaches us to the United States Embassy for PX, Commissary, gasoline privileges. In short, the use of MPC's; but denies us Army billets. General Shambora has just visited us and, although sympathetic with our plight, feels that because of the nature of the Administrative Agreement the United States Armed Forces, Japan, are impotent to effect changes in this memorandum favorable to our billeting. We are awaiting the reaction of the Japanese Government to a formal note delivered to them last Monday by the United States State Department. The essence of the note was simply suggesting to the Japanese that they reply to United States Armed Forces, Japan, stating that the Japanese Government has no objection. Our problem will then be to get General Hickey to change the nature of the draft referred to above. In the event this fails we will then be forced to our last procedure, which is for the Department of Defense to dispatch a communication to G-1 here in our behalf.

This morning Bruce Breeden received a cablegram indicating his father was critically ill. He left on the noon train and will be in New York Sunday morning. This makes us very short handed, particularly with Bill Moloney new to the job, but by and large I believe the medical program will be able to carry on.

Although you may not remember the CIC area in Nagasaki, we are angling to get this piece of property on a lease from the Japanese Government. As you may recall it included several buildings: a messhall, theater, and motor pool. In the face of the local, national, and international situation, and the implications of some of our analyses, I cannot bring myself to rent the Kaikan Building for $33,000. I am hopeful that we will be able to work out some arrangement for the first floor of the Kaikan Building with the Japanese Educational Association, and put the activities of floors 2 and 3 in the CIC area, along with our bachelor personnel and perhaps one family. It will interest you to know that the Wright's home in Nagasaki is presently desired by the Governor. The rent is $300 a month, and a monthly average for electricity consumed the last six months was $200; I know that an 18½% increase in the electrical rate has just been passed by the Diet.

Thank you for the helpful correspondence on the tax situation. I am hopeful that the Academy will obtain a statement from their legal talent for our personnel.

I believe I wrote you that Dr. Shimizu is no longer the Dean at Hiroshima Medical College and that Dr. Kawaishi, the man of blood plasma substitute fame, is the present Dean. He would be the one to whom those in Washington should dispatch your journals.

You should have years added to your life simply by the thought of being tax free in 18 more months, but there is much to be said for the privilege of living in and being a citizen of the United States. The longer I stay here the more I believe that the privilege is worth the taxes we pay. We were all amused at your description of the tragedy of losing 36 pounds in order to qualify for active duty and the loss of your Commission on 28 April. The real tragedy is that it is the Army's loss.

When Lady Mountbatten visited us she repeated an amusing story which she said was not flattering to the British women, because they are all flat chested, including herself. A young British lady and her escort were dining at Claridges. During the early part of the dinner the lady turned to her escort and complained of severe heartburn. The escort, who was a medical officer, quickly appraised the situation and said, "If you'll take your teat out of the soup, you will be all right."

Warner and Becky were packed yesterday and plan to leave the 30th of May. In the meantime, Warner is dickering with the British on the chance that he may get berth spaces for himself and family on a British troop ship. Paul Carson will pack on Monday and will leave in two weeks.

I think Atala is quite a girl, starting off across the continent by herself in her Austin. She is the kind of person who would thoroughly enjoy such an experience.

Your note of 3 May arrived this morning. Transmission time is excellent. You signed it on the 6th and it arrived here the 16th.

Pat and the children are fine and join with love to you and Miss Atala.

Love,
Grant

Durham, North Carolina
October 29, 1952

Dear Polly and Jay [Arena]:

I can never repay you for the delightful party you and the Londons, Mortons, and Pachmans arranged in Chicago. It was a complete surprise. I thought I was dining with you, the Londons, Martins and Mortons, and when I found forty-eight people in the dining room I was tremendously delighted and excited. It was one of the top moments of my life.

Atala and I, not to mention Mona, Elizabeth Swett, and many others, cannot admire enough the beautifully illuminated scriptorum testimonial.

Many thanks.

Yours sincerely,
Dave

Durham, North Carolina
March 30, 1953

Dear Grant:

Many thanks for your letter of 20 March. I greatly enjoyed the editorial from Radiology. I certainly wish I knew more about statistics, but like all ignorant people, I am suspicious of things of which I have no knowledge.

Did I send you Langley Porter's comment on psychiatry, which applies equally well to me in regard to statistics? I still like every-

215

thing in per cent. If there are five cases of measles out of ten exposed, I always think of it as 50% in spite of the fact that I know that it merely accentuates my ignorance.

Atala is delighted with the glasses, and has found several species of birds which she had not known existed in this area.

As I wrote you, Banks is delighted with the microscope, although he still has several gadgets which he has not tried, such as darkfield and rotary motion.

Atala joins me in best wishes.

Yours sincerely,
Dave

Durham, North Carolina
January 29, 1955

Dear Talmage [Peele]:

I was delighted with your cartoon of our office. I didn't know that we had so much room. It is sad to think that eight of the thirty-three shown in the old 1930 photograph are now dead, nearly 25% of the original group.

With best wishes, I am

Yours sincerely,
Dave

Durham, North Carolina
May 2, 1955

Dear Bill [W. W. Francis]:

One of our pathology residents, Dick Blaisdell, when he was in charge of the laboratory of the Fourth General Hospital of Chiang's Army in Formosa, named the medical library the William Osler Medical Library.

When he returned to this country he notified the Army Post Office to send any books and pamphlets addressed to him to the William Osler Medical Library of the Fourth General Hospital, Taiwan. He has just received the following reply:

"Dear Sir:

The above mentioned mail cannot be turned over to Mr. William Osler. This person does not have APO privileges at APO 63 and is not authorized to receive mail through the APO."

With best wishes, I am

Yours sincerely,
Wilburt C. Davison

Durham, North Carolina
October 31, 1955

Dear Tarcila [Mendoza]:

Mrs. Swett, I and several of your other friends were delighted with your letter of October 23rd. We are so happy that you have returned to medicine. My wife, as you know, returned to pediatrics after twenty years during which the children were growing up.

When the war broke out, someone was badly needed to run the school clinics, so my wife was drafted for the work and enjoyed it thoroughly.

I am greatly intrigued by the "Moore examinations." I hate to show my ignorance, but I have never heard of them. I am making inquiries and if I obtain any information, I shall send it to you.

I feel as you do that examinations are a very poor way of gauging a student's ability. As you probably remember, Dr. Perlzweig used to give an occasional examination, but the rest of us, at the end of a term indicate whether we think a student, from our impressions of his or her work, should pass or fail. They are the only two grades we use. Fortunately, most of them are passes.

An occasional student who has done exceptionally good work will

217

get a "pass high" and a few of them who are not as bright as they should be will get a "pass low," but our records are mostly "straight pass."

I greatly appreciate your comments on "The Compleat Pediatrician." My daughter, Jeana, who was a little girl while you were here, was married during the War. Her husband is a physicist at the University of Michigan, so she interned and did her residency work there in Pediatrics and is now an instructor in pediatrics. She and I (mostly she) are revising "The Compleat Pediatrician," and hope to have it finished sometime in the spring. Needless to say, I shall send you a complimentary copy when it is finished.

We have just finished our twenty-fifth anniversary, and in case you have not received the Duke Alumni Register for September and a program of the reunion activities, I am sending them under separate cover.

I often look back with great pleasure on your husband's, brother's and your many kindnesses to me while I was in Manila in 1954, and hope that sometime I can return and bring my wife with me.

Should you ever be interested in pediatrics, there is an internship here for you. I am sure that you would enjoy coming back.

With best wishes to your husband, brother and you, I am

Yours sincerely,
Wilburt C. Davison

Durham, North Carolina
April 21, 1956

Dear Barbara [Howell]:

Seeing you at Captain and Mrs. Galloway's party was like a light from heaven, not only because of my temperature and illness, but it brought back so many happy memories of our youth together at Duke.

I envy you living in Cairo and I know that you are doing a splendid job. I had hoped to call on you later, but we had a full schedule.

I returned by way of London and Prestwick, and am now up to my ears in medical meetings as well as budget discussions for the coming year.

Miss Sherwood, Jerry Harris, Angus McBryde, Jay Arena, Susan Dees and your many other friends send you their best regards. They were filled with admiration for the opportunity you are having to see life abroad and to be a part of it.

With best wishes from Atala and me, I am

Yours sincerely,
Dave

Durham, North Carolina
April 1, 1959

Alumni and Alumnae:

April is my saddest month in the year, not only because it brings me another birthday and also the task of filing my income taxes, but chiefly because the Medical Center budget must be balanced. This year is particularly difficult because the Medical School (not including the Hospital) needs much more than we had last year just to maintain our present standards without raising them.

Even with the increased and very welcome contributions from the Alumni and other gifts and grants, the only way in which the budget can be balanced seems to be by raising the tuition to $1200 (for the nine months' year). Even that figure is just the average for the better medical schools, and furnishes less than one quarter of the operating costs (see the Table below).

If the tuition is raised, it will be the fifth, and I hope the last, increase. The original rate in 1930 was $450. It was raised to $600 in 1946, to $750 in 1948, to $900 in 1952, and to the present $1020 in 1957.

Best wishes,
Dave

Expenses of the Medical School (1958-59)

Salaries (Instructors, Secretaries, Technicians)	$1,171,046.00
Supplies & equipment	80,125.00
	$1,351,171.00

Revenue

Tuition	$ 324,500	(24.0%)
Alumni	32,000	(2.4%)
National Fund	36,000	(2.7%)
AMA Foundation	6,000	(0.4%)
Gifts & Grants	185,660	(13.7%)
Duke University	767,011	(56.8%)
	$1,351,171	(100%)

In addition we receive over one million dollars annually for research but not for teaching, from the National Institutes of Health, Cancer Society, Heart Association, Foundation for Infantile Paralysis, Cerebral Palsy Fund, etc.

DEAN DAVISON'S EVALUATION OF CHICAGO RESTAURANTS IN THE 1950'S (SENT TO FACULTY, HOUSE STAFF AND STUDENTS)

Chicago, Ill.

*   Barney's (steaks), 741 W. Randolph
      Beachcombers, 101 E. Walton Place
*   Berghoff (German), 17 W. Adams (closed Sun.)
(E) Bit of Sweden, 1015 N. Rush
      Boston Oyster House, 21 S. Clark St.
(E) Allgauer's Old Heidelberg, 14 W. Randolph
(E) El Bianeo (Italian), 63 & California
      Epicurean, 316 S. Wabash
(E) Erie Grill (steaks), Erie & Watts
      Esquire Pub (steaks), 43 W. Monroe
      Gene & Georgette (steaks), 500 N. Franklin
      Gibby's (steaks), 192 N. Clark
      Guey Sam (Chinese), 2205 S. Wentworth
      Gus's Steak House, 420 N. Dearborn
(E) Italian Village, 71 W. Monroe
      Jacques, 900 N. Michigan
      Feritzel (steaks), State & Lake
(E) Kungsholm (Swedish), 100 E. Ontario
      London House (steaks), 360 N. Michigan
      Morrison Hotel, 79 W. Madison
      Oyster House, Clark St.
      Papa Milanca (Italian), 951 & 1160 N. State
      Pete's Steaks, 165 N. Dearborn
      Petit Gourmet, 619 N. Michigan
(E) Ray's Steak House, 112 E. Illinois
(E) Red Star (German), 1528 N. Clark (closed Sun. lunch)
(E) Ricardo's Studio, 437 Rush (Italian)
      St. Hubert Grill, 316 S. Federal
      Sirloin Club, 4178 S. Halsted
      Stockyards Inn, 42 & S. Halsted
      Ireland (Seafood), 62 N. Clark*

(E) Henrisi, 71 W. Randolph
     Mona Lisa (Italian), 422 N. Rush
     House of Eng (Chinese), 106 E. Walton
     George's Diamond (steaks), 512 S. Wabash

* — Best; E — Excellent; G — Good; F — Fair.

Durham, North Carolina
June 23, 1959

Dear Jay:

Many thanks for sending me the June 10, 1959 number of Medical News with the interesting articles in it on tuberculosis and rooming in. I had missed it and am glad to have the material to add to the next addition of the "Compleat Pediatrician." I wish more people would read that paper because everything I have seen in it has agreed with my point of view (which does not necessarily prove that either is correct).

With best wishes, I am

Yours sincerely,
Dave

Durham, North Carolina
[No date]

Dear Jay:

Many thanks for the "piracy" on the skirt story. I stole it from someone else.

Sincerely,
Dave

Durham, North Carolina
October 30, 1959

Dear Polly and Jay:

Just a note to tell you how much Atala and I enjoyed your delightful party Thursday evening. Your manicotti is better than I have ever had at Del Pezzo's in New York, and that is the highest praise which I can give it.

I have a note in my "black book" to do something for Carrither's daughter but cannot remember the details. Please ask Jay to drop me a note about the family and daughter so that I can go to Mrs. Persons about her application.

With love and many thanks from both of us, I am

Yours sincerely,
Dave

January 20, 1960

Dr. Jay M. Arena
2032 Club Boulevard
Durham, North Carolina

Dear Jay:

Hearty congratulations on your appointment as
Co-Chairman of the Durham County 1960 White House
Conference Committee and on your appointment by the
Governor as a State Delegate to the Golden Anniversary
1960 White House Conference. All of us are proud of
the work which you have done and are doing and of the
credit and honor which you have brought to Duke.

Also, many thanks to you and Polly for bringing
back all of my baggage including the wet bathing suit.
I felt like a heel in wishing off the four pieces of
baggage on you but you certainly saved me considerable
headache in Washington as well as saving me considerable
excess baggage on the plane.

The week in Palm Beach is one of the happiest ones
I have ever had, thanks to you and Polly, Dave and Joanna,
and John and Elisa Renzulli.

With best wishes, I am

Yours sincerely,

Dave

W. C. Davison

222

Dr. John P. McGovern   May 13, 1961
3509 Montrose Blvd.
Houston, Texas

Dear Jack:

      I certainly enjoyed seeing you in Houston and
wish that we could get together more often. I was
particularly happy to have your reprints, and congratulate
you on the work which you are doing.

      Did I write to you about your article entitled
"Megalopyge Opercularis"? I meant to, because I had never
heard of the puss caterpillar which invaded Chapel Hill
and Durham last summer, and which Dr. London recognized.
However, I was very chagrined to find that I had described
the symptoms of the bites of puss caterpillars in the
paragraph on bites, section 41. I wish I could remember
everything in that book with which my friends have supplied
the information.

      I am asking Mrs. Thomas to enclose some recent
reprints of mine. I have written over two hundred articles
in the last forty-eight years (1913-1961) but only one of
them, namely "Sweating Sickness" seems to be popular. I
have had more requests for that article than any other one
which I have written.

      With best wishes, I am

          Yours sincerely,

          Dave

          W. C. Davison

PS-I enclose my check for fifty-cents.
                  WCD
WCD/mm

*Editors' Note: It was Davison's custom to give any student, intern, resident or other
colleague a dime if they found an error in his* The Compleat Pediatrician; *a check for
fifty cents followed the discovery of an omission from the book. Through the years
the editors received numerous dimes and checks. One of the latter is reproduced
here.*

Durham, North Carolina
November 7, 1960

Dear Jay:

With your clever detection of Chlordane Poisoning and Morton Bogdonoff's article on Berylliosis, both in the October Number of the *North Carolina Medical Journal*, the public will soon realize what you and I have known for a long time. Namely, that under your leadership, Duke has become the outstanding poisoning center south of New York.

With congratulations and best wishes, I am

Yours sincerely,
Dave

Durham, North Carolina
June 28, 1961

Dear Nick [William N. Nicholson]:

I enclose letters which I have received from Lou Spector, a former pediatric resident. Apparently, Jay Arena invited Edythe, Lou's wife, to sing. She has a magnificent voice and has sung in opera. However, can you and Cal answer her questions?

As far as music is concerned, I am hopelessly ignorant (as well as in many other fields), and the only music that I like is the "Volga Boat Song" (probably because I can recognize it when I hear it) and Gilbert and Sullivan songs (also because I can recognize them).

Let's not have "Dear Old Duke," "Old Nassau," or "The Star Spangled Banner" (which I also recognize).

With best wishes, I am

Yours sincerely,
Dave

Roaring Gap, North Carolina
May 6, 1963

Dear Jack [McGovern]:

Many thanks for thinking of naming your library after me. I am very flattered and accept the honor with pleasure.

I am as happy over it as Wiley Forbus was when he found that one of the doctors in Taiwan (Formosa) named his pathology laboratory the Wiley Forbus Laboratory.

I am sorry for the delay in sending you this Curriculum Vitae and the High Points of My Life.

Congratulations on your Directorship in the Allergy Society.

Please give my best regards to your charming wife whom I remember very well from my visit to your office two years ago.

Affectionately,
Dave

CURRICULUM VITAE

April 28, 1892: Born, Grand Rapids, Michigan, but left for Long Island at the age of six weeks. My father was a Methodist preacher and my mother had been a school teacher.

1898-1900: Lived near Fort Hamilton, New York, at which my father was a volunteer chaplain.

1904-1908: Jamaica High School, Long Island, New York.

1908-1909: Because of a football injury I was tutored by a Harvard man, and it was the only education I have ever had.

1909-1913: Princeton (rowing, water polo, Phi Beta Kappa).

1913-1914: Rhodes Scholar from New York at Merton College (finishing the first two years of medicine in one year, including rowing, water polo, ice hockey and track).

1914-1915: Served with the American Ambulance Hospital at Neuilly, France and later in the typhus epidemic in Serbia (Yugoslavia); returned on Sir Thomas Lipton's yacht from Salonika to Naples, then crossed Italy, Austria, Germany and Holland to England.

June 1915: B.A. degree (First in the Honour School of Physiology).

1915-1917: Senior Demy, Magdalen College, Oxford.

1915-1916: Osler's intern at the Radcliffe Infirmary, Oxford, England. Studied triple typhoid-parathyphoid vaccine with Prof. Georges Dreyer and A. Duncan Gardner. Studied solubility of anesthetics with Sir Charles Sherrington.

June 1916: B.Sc. for the triple vaccine thesis.

Oct. 1916-Apr. 6, 1917: Senior student at the Johns Hopkins (M.D., Apr. 7, 1917).

Nov. 1916-April 1917: Did research bacteriology with Atala Scudder in Stanhope Bayne-Jones' laboratory.

June 2, 1917: Married Atala Thayer Scudder.

June 1917-Mar. 1919: 1st Lieutenant and Captain in the Medical Reserve Corps in the A.E.F.

July 1917: Received the Alvarenga prize of the Philadelphia College of Physicians for the triple vaccine thesis.

1919-1927: Assistant resident, instructor, and later acting head of the Department of Pediatrics. Assistant dean and editor of the *Johns Hopkins Bulletin*, 1923-1927.

1925: Wrote Pediatric Notes.

1926: Helped S. A. Waksman write Enzymes and revised the 9th Edition of Holt and Howland's Diseases of Infancy and Childhood.

1927-1961: Dean and Professor of Pediatrics, Duke University Medical Center.

1934: and every three or four years since (for eight editions): wrote *The Compleat Pediatrician*.

1942-1945: National Research Council, Washington.

Aug.-Dec. 1945: Civilian Medical Consultant on Medical Education attached to headquarters at Frankfurt.

1948-1960: Consultant to the Oak Ridge Institute for Nuclear Studies.

Spring of 1949: Consultant on Medical Education to the Far East Command in Japan, Okinawa, Shanghai and Manila.

Spring of 1951: Consultant to the Atomic Bomb Casualty Commission at Hiroshima.

1953: Became a James B. Duke Professor.

Summer of 1954: Consultant to the National Taiwan University College of Medicine and to the Atomic Bomb Casualty Commission at Hiroshima.

1955-1963: Civilian Health and Advisory Council, Department of Defense.

1956 and 1959: Consultant to NAMRU-3 in Cairo.

1957: Attended NATO Medical Conference in Paris; Trustee of ECFMG; National Advisory Committee on Chronic Disease.

1960: President of Alpha Omega Alpha.

1960-1961: Leave of Absence.

Feb. 28, 1961: Elected a Trustee of the Duke Endowment.

Aug. 31, 1961: Retired as Dean and Professor of Pediatrics.

HIGH POINTS OF MY LIFE

Marrying Atala Scudder '17

Rhodes Scholarship '13

Osler's friendship '13-'19

Rankin's friendship '27-

Asst. Dean & Acting Ped. Hd at JH '23 & '26
Dean & Prof. Ped Duke '27-'61
James B. Duke Professorship '53-
Eight editions CP '34-'61
NRC & Lew Weed '42-'52
Stopped smoking '48
Trustee of the Duke Endowment '61

Daily Routine: At Princeton, in my day, it was a disgrace to study excessively and to be a "greasy grind." Princeton, unlike Yale, under Woodrow Wilson was the best country club in America, and studying beyond getting a "third or gentleman's group" wasn't done. However, I wanted to obtain a Phi Beta Kappa Key, and my "P," and a Rhodes Scholarship, as well as to be elected to a club, so I began to get up at five or six o'clock and work until breakfast at eight without anyone, except my roommate knowing about it. Besides I was so tired at night after rowing and swimming that I would fall asleep studying in the evening. I have continued this nefarious habit for fifty-four years, so far. Now from five to eleven, I write, dictate or read.

At eleven, when in Durham, I go to the hospital and remain until three or four in the afternoon. When at Roaring Gap or Puerto Rico, I swim at eleven.

At three or four, or earlier if I can, I take a siesta. At five or six, if the weather is clear, I walk for half-hour to an hour. At seven-thirty, I go to medical meetings, movies, or in my declining years look at television or read Westerns.

Roaring Gap, North Carolina
August 2, 1963

Dear Polly and Jay:

Knowing of your interest in large families, I thought you would be amused at the enclosed quotation from an ancient copy of the *Reader's Digest*, which I read while I was in New York.

With love from Atala and me to both of you and the children, I am

Yours affectionately,
Dave

BIG HAPPY FAMILY

Neighbors of ours recently took their eight small children to baptismal services of their newest-born, ninth child. During the proceedings the three-year old began crying and getting out of hand. Her father turned to her and quietly warned, "Suzie if you don't behave, I won't bring you next year."

Contributed by W. F. Minnick, Jr.

The mother of a large family was explaining to me why she dresses her children alike, right down to the youngest baby. "When we had just four children, I dressed them alike so we wouldn't lose any of them. Now," she added, looking around at her brood of nine, "I dress them alike so we won't pick up any that don't belong to us."

Contributed by Mrs. Leslie Williams, Jr.

[Reprinted with permission from the July '62 *Reader's Digest*]

Roaring Gap, North Carolina
July 6, 1964

Dear Sister Gilmary:

Your letter of June 23 made Atala and me very happy. We pored over the splendid photographs and could visualize you at your work.

I am glad you took the Korean boards in Pediatrics, and I know that you will receive a high mark. If I can be of any help with the joint board in obtaining approval for your intern residency program, please let me know because most of the members on the Board are friends of mine, and I know will be greatly interested in the work which you are doing.

The Accreditation Board is doing a splendid job, but the questionnaires are bothersome. Duke had two rows with the Accreditation Board, first because we had no hospital by-laws. We contended that we did not need them, and if we had them we would change them every week. Finally, I borrowed the by-laws from the Watts Hospital and had it re-typed with Duke Hospital instead of Watts Hospital, and that satisfied the Board for several years, and then they insisted that we have a set of by-laws of our own. Connie Gardner, whom you may remember, corresponded with his friends in hospitals throughout the country and finally drew up a magnificent set of by-laws, which were promptly adopted by Duke without reading, and as far as I know, no one has ever looked at them since, but they satisfied the Board.

The other quarrel we had with the Accreditation Board was that all orders must be signed by the physician, which meant a tremendous amount of work because orders are written by interns, assistant residents, residents, radiologists, bio-chemists, etc. It was like my experience in the Army when I was in charge of the Wasserman Laboratory, which handled 4,000 or more blood specimens per week. I was required to sign all of them, so I had a rubber stamp made and was promptly reprimanded by the chief surgeon, so I applied for an extra enlisted man who spent all of his time signing my name to the 4,000 reports.

From whom do you purchase BCG? I am a member of the Advisory Board of the Research Institute, and if you wish, I can ask the Director if reduced rates or an appropriation can be made.

I am taking the liberty of passing your letter and the photographs to Jay Arena, Susan Dees, and your other friends at Duke.

With best wishes in your wonderful work from Atala and me, I am

Yours sincerely,

W. C. Davison

Roaring Gap, North Carolina
August 7, 1964

Dear Jay:

Can you arrange with the Editor of InterCom or with Tal Peele to write a tribute to Mona to be published either in the InterCom or in the Duke Medical Alumni News? Many, many students would like to read a tribute to her. I enclose a copy of a poem which David Daniel wrote about Mona several years ago at the meeting of the Duke Pediatric Society in Chicago. I also sent a copy of the poem, as well as Mona Morgan's tribute to Carl Rogers at his funeral to Bill Morgan.

Atala is still on Long Island with Mrs. Paul Baum, but expects to be back in Roaring Gap around the 20th. In the meantime, Mary and Deryl Hart are seeing that I do not starve to death.

With love to Polly and you, I am

Yours affectionately,

Dave

Here's to Mona Morgan
May her tribe increase
Without her love and guidance
My med. life would have ceased,
She kept me going forward
When I would say, "O No!!"

So here's to you, Dear Mona —
A debt I truly owe.

                              David Daniel

                              Roaring Gap, North Carolina
                              September 2, 1964
Dear Jay:

When Bill Nelson's Eighth Edition of Pediatrics appeared, I wrote him a letter of congratulations and told him that Jeana and I had finished our Eighth Edition two years ago, but that you and Dave Martin were working on a Ninth Edition.

I also reminded him that when I wrote to *TIME Magazine* several years ago for permission to quote some figures on tuberculosis, I received a very formal letter giving me that permission, and then written in longhand at the bottom was a note, "Daddy says you are his worst competitor." She was working as an Assistant Editor of *TIME* at that time and is now helping Bill with the textbook on pediatrics. It also explains his handwritten note at the bottom of his form letter to those who had sent in congratulations about the new edition òf his book.

With love to Polly and you from Atala and me, I am

                              Yours affectionately,
                              Dave

                              New Orleans, Louisiana
                              March 1, 1965
Dear Dean Davison:

This past Saturday I spent a delightful evening with Jack and Kathy McGovern in their home. The Davison Library which Jack has established is truly marvelous, and we spent some exciting and interesting hours with the books and reminiscing about our experiences with you.

I was in Houston participating in the Post-Graduate Course, "Immunologic Basis and Practical Treatment of Allergic Disease," which Jack and his group organized and sponsored for the Academy of Pediatrics. The conference was well attended and a real success in every way.

I spent last year teaching at Union Theological Seminary and helping the school reorganize its program of psychiatry and religion. While there I put the finishing touches on a little book of mine and sent it to the publisher. Under separate cover I am sending you a copy which I hope you enjoy. Please pardon the somewhat grandiose title of *A Psychiatrist Looks at Religion and Health*.

The year 1953-54 which I spent with you at Duke was a most meaningful and helpful one for me. I especially remember a weekend at Roaring Gap where I found you awake and working at 6 A.M. when our usual bedtime hour had been 2 or 3 A.M. You told me all about your study and work habits, shared with me some of your philosophy of life, etc. — all of which I have treasured through the years.

Jack and I have just completed a little book in which we have reviewed the literature dealing with the emotional components in allergic illness. We have given it the preliminary title *A Review Primer of Allergy and Human Emotions*. Jack has developed at his clinic a "holistic" approach to patient care and gives his patients the best in the blending of the science and the art of medicine.

Jack and I have been hoping that you would take a quick look at our manuscript and write a brief foreword for it. Jack's secretary is re-typing it now. When she finishes it, I hope you let us send it to you in spite of your busy schedule and numerous responsibilities.

With kindest personal regards.

Sincerely,
James A. Knight, M.D.

Roaring Gap, North Carolina
April 5, 1965

Dear Jim:

I was very happy to receive your letter of March 1. It brought back many happy memories of 1953-1954 while you were at Duke.

Now that I am retired, my wife and I live at Roaring Gap in a small cottage (we sold the larger one) from March 1 to December 1, and then go to the Caribbean area for three months to avoid respiratory infections. Many, many thanks for sending me a copy of your "A Psychiatrist Looks at Religion and Health." I congratulate you on it, and I know that it will help many of us who have tried to combine a belief in religion with the facts of life.

My motto is the one which I inherited from Osler, namely, "I would rather be wrong with St. Paul than right with Aristotle."

As you may know, my father was a Methodist preacher, and most of the problems of his congregation were psychiatric. His study was a source of comfort and help to many of his church.

Needless to say, I shall be very happy to write a foreword to your and Jack's "A Review Primer of Allergy and Human Emotions."

I like Jack McGovern's term, the "science of the art of medicine." Most of the graduates of the past few years have known more science than they did art, and unfortunately have lost interest in patients as human beings, and instead have regarded them as bio-chemical complexes.

Bill Anlyan, my successor, told me of the pleasant visit he had with you at Tulane two weeks ago. Bill is doing an excellent job at Duke.

With thanks and best wishes, I am

Yours sincerely,
Dave

Roaring Gap, North Carolina
April 5, 1965

Dear Jack:

I certainly appreciated your kind letter of March 16, and there is nothing I would rather do than visit Kathy and you.

Congratulations on your smoking resolution. I found the first two years were the hardest, but not having smoked since 1946, I feel very virtuous.

My weight is increasing, and I have thought several times of starting to smoke in order to bring my weight down, but Nicholson and other friends say that if I haven't stamina enough to reduce my diet, they doubt that smoking will be of any help. At any rate, I have not seriously considered a return to smoking after these eighteen years without it.

Congratulations on your Bibliography on Sarcoidosis, and thank you for sending me the first copy. I am very proud of it, and I know that it will be of great help to everyone who works in this vague field. I am glad that you included Marty Cummings' Reference 1402, Reference 2345, and Reference 2387, in your survey of the disease. Marty always had an idea that had something to do with the distribution of pine trees. Marty was graduated from the Duke Medical School in 1944 (my son, Bill's, class), so I knew him very well. He is now Director of the National Library (the former Surgeon General's library). You probably remember him because he was in the class a year ahead of yours.

I also enjoyed Marty's foreword.

Needless to say, I am not only flattered, but very pleased, to write a brief preface or foreword to your and Jim Knight's book dealing with the "Role of Emotions in Allergic Disease." As you may remember, our daughter, Jeana, who was graduated from the Duke Medical School in 1950, had terrific dermatitis every time she had to take an examination, so I am sure that a book on the "Role of Emotions in Allergic Disease" is badly needed.

Congratulations on your postgraduate course.

I know that you will be very happy when you move into your new clinic. I am looking forward the greatest pleasure to seeing it and you and also to meeting Kathy.

I hope that Kathy and you will visit us in Roaring Gap this summer. We are very happy here.

Please give Atala's and my love to Pat and Grant Taylor, and with love from both of us to Kathy and you, I am

Affectionately,
Dave

Roaring Gap, North Carolina
September 27, 1965

Dear Jay:

Many thanks for the reprint of "The Infamous William Osler." I had never seen the article, and needless to say, I disagree with it.

However, I heard Osler say many times that he made many enemies while he was at the University of Pennsylvania because he went there as one of the professors of medicine, yet, he had never had any clinical training. All of his years in Montreal were devoted to pathology. However, I also heard him say that because so few physicians would refer patients to him he spent most of his time studying the patients in the old Blockley Hospital which had one or two wards devoted to old people, in whom he was intensely interested, in spite of his quotation from "The Fixed Period."

I persuaded Osler to talk to the American Club one night, and he referred to this "sixty years, then chloroform," with the comment that it was meant as a humorous comment, and he ended by saying that he hoped that medical students would not read any more books by Anthony Trollope. Needless to say, I obtained a copy of "The

Fixed Period" by Anthony Trollope in the near future and read it and could see how he could make humorous allusions to the book provided the individual had read the book.

Atala is resting at Greenwich with her stepmother because the trip home, due to fog, was twenty-four hours. I know that if she were here she would join me in love to Polly and you.

Yours affectionately,
Dave

St. Croix, Virgin Islands
February 6, 1966

Dear Jay:

I am rewriting an "unexpurgated" edition of the history of the Duke University Medical Center and can expand into many details which I could not do in the expurgated edition.

I should like to have a paragraph on the AOA installation at Duke in 1932 in which Dr. Root and Dr. Bierring presided. Have you a program of that event, or can you recall Dr. Root's and Dr. Bierring's full names and also the date of the installation? Dr. Bierring's first name was Walter, but I cannot remember his middle initial.

I have all of this information in my AOA file at Roaring Gap, but if you can locate it without much difficulty I should greatly appreciate it.

I enclose the last letter which I have received from Sister Gilmary together with some interesting photographs. She also enclosed a letter to Miss Duke which I have forwarded to her together with a recommendation for an appropriation.

The encephalitis epidemic must be terrible. We had a small one in Japan while I was there and also one in Taiwan. The patients look exactly like TB meningitis, and the mortality is equally high. Some of the patients remained in coma for months.

Atala and I are thoroughly enjoying our visit at St. Croix, but we shall be back in Durham on February 28. Both of us send our love to Polly and you and the children.

Yours affectionately,
Dave

Roaring Gap, North Carolina
March 7, 1966

Dear Jay:

I have always maintained that Josh Turnage and Jimmy Warren were great assets to Duke University Medical Center. I have had many letters like the last paragraph of the enclosed Xerox.

Yours affectionately,
Dave

Boston, Massachusetts
January 4, 1966

Dear Dr. Davison:

It was nice to hear from you in your letter of December 6th, and I read your reprint with a good deal of interest. I certainly agree with your description of the problem, although I am not in complete accord with you on the question of causes.

I am enclosing two things: One, my presidential address for the AAMC in which I took a stab at defining some of the causes from my point of view. The second item is a speech given by one of our people who would suggest that at least one medical school is taking active steps to deal with the problems, as you have outlined them.

I still recall our visit to you several years ago and particularly the barbecue. Hope things are going well with you.

Best wishes.

Sincerely,
George A. Wolf, Jr., M.D.
Vice President for Medical and
Dental Affairs, Tufts University

Roaring Gap, North Carolina
April 21, 1966

Dear Jay:

Atala and I were greatly distressed to learn that Polly was in the hospital, but hope very much that by this time she has made a complete recovery.

Do you know the history of the disc operation? As far as I remember the story, a neurologist at Harvard sent a patient to Sam Harvey, the surgeon at Yale, with a diagnosis of a tumor of the spine. Sam operated on the patient, and saw this thumb-like protrusion between the vertebrae and did not know what it was, so he cut it off.

He could not find a tumor. The patient made a complete uneventful recovery. That was in 1929, and, as some wag said, that operation now keeps the Mayo Clinic from being in the red. Formerly, the orthopedist did the operation, but now the neurosurgeons have taken over.

Atala and I send our love to Polly, you and the children.

Yours affectionately,

Dave

THE DUKE ENDOWMENT

1500 North Carolina National Bank Building

CHARLOTTE, NORTH CAROLINA 28202

HOSPITAL AND CHILD CARE SECTIONS
WILBURT C. DAVISON, M.D.
CONSULTANT ON MEDICAL EDUCATION

(704) 376-0291

PLEASE REPLY TO:
ROARING GAP, N. C. 28

May 11, 1967

Dr. Jay M. Arena
Duke University Medical Center
Durham, North Carolina 27706

Dear Jay:

Many thanks for your letter about the "history." I enjoyed writing it, but wish that I had not sent it to so many critics who "expurgated" the choicer items. However, I am working on an uncensored edition to be published after my death.

Many thanks for the "After Seventy-five Years Osler's Text Revised." I was pleased to see Jim Wyngaarden's comments.

While Osler was at The Johns Hopkins from 1889-1905, his salary was $5,000 per year, and his consulting practice was just sufficient to pay his expenses. He also said he never took a dollar out of Baltimore except from his book. In 1917 he turned it over to Tom McCray of Philadelphia who in turn gave it to Henry Christian who dropped the word Osler from the title.

With love to Polly and you from Atala and me, I am

Yours affectionately,

W. C. Davison

mc

Dictated 5/10/67

Montreal, Canada
May 14, 1968

Dear Dave:

Many thanks for the extract from page 451 of the diary of W. C. Davison with its reference to Dr. Saike, a student of Osler in 1882. I am interested to know that you have a diary that is so well organized that you can quote from page 451. Don't write me a special letter but, the next time you write, if you remember, tell me when you began writing it and what type of material you include in it. If you have seen my biography of Alan Gregg, you know about my discovery that he kept a secret commonplace book in which he put aphorisms of various types but nothing of the material that ordinarily goes into a diary.

For my own part, I wrote regularly to my mother, as you will remember, and continued this up to 1935 when she died. Those letters have all been put together and form a pretty good journal. After she died, I began to write very occasionally in what might be called a commonplace book. Sometimes it has turned into a diary during trips abroad; most of the time it is a place for writing out one's current thoughts. I wonder when you began your diary. I don't remember, when we were rooming together at the Hopkins, that you kept one but then I probably wouldn't have remembered anyway.

Rankin's reminiscences of Osler are straightforward and I am sure they should be included in the memorial number.

Give our love to Atala.

As ever yours,
Wilder Penfield

Evansville, Indiana
June 4, 1968

Dear Polly and Doctor Jay,

The nicest thing you could ever have done for me was sending me your Article about Dean Davison. I have thoroughly enjoyed reading it. It is beautifully written — and so true. Congratulations to you! I know I can be counted among the multitude of men who are better citizens for having known Doctor Davison so well. Truly, he is one of the finest men I have ever known.

Affectionately,
Harvey
[Harvey C. Hallum]

New York, New York
June 6, 1968

Dear Jay:

Thank you for the reprint on "Dave." What a wonderful guy! I saw him last several years ago at an Academy meeting in Chicago. He, Borden Veeder and I went over to a German restaurant for lunch. The place was crowded and we finally found places at a table occupied by a man who was contentedly eating his sauerbraten and knödel. As we sat down, Dave was in the midst of an autopsy report on an interesting case. He continued to relate how the body was opened and how the pathologist reached in and pulled out the lungs — and more gory details — totally unaware that our fellow-diner was growing paler and paler and was sweating profusely. Pretty soon, the poor fellow deserted his sauerbraten and rushed off in the direction of the men's room. Dave, totally unaware of the stranger, continued his report.

A very nice thing that Dave used to do was to send a brief note with a comment on the publication of a paper. Needless to say, it was warming to receive favorable notice from someone in Dave's eminent position.

Yours,
Harry
[Harry Bakwin, M.D.]

[TRANSCRIPTION OF MATERIAL ON BACK
OF DAVISON PORTRAIT]

Eleanor, West Virginia
June 6, 1968

Why did I sketch and frame your picture? Another "Pepys' Diary" involving us both.

I was born in Muir, Pa., Aug. 6, 1899. Finished Porter Twf. Schools in 1915, attended Keystone Normal School to 1918. The next 15 years of my life were "hectic," *remember the depression.* I was involved in losses of about $350,000. My father Thos. E. Moser always said "a good education is the most joyful treasure on earth, can't be lost or taken from you." Brother Paul graduated at Jefferson, got me interested in medicine. I returned to Lebanon Valley College got a B.S., 1935. Then I journeyed to the U. of Pitt. Med. Center to interview Dr. Meredith, Duke's representative. He had faith in me, I repaid his kindness when I interned there, 1939, by assisting a surgeon to remove his appendix.

You also had faith in me, for this and many more reasons I sketched and framed your picture. Art is a relaxation and fascination, it offered me exercise for my arm and hand, having suffered a partial hemiplegia right in February, 1964. I didn't rust out, be assured, I played out, filled out 16 and ½ lbs. of gov. blanks per mo.

1. You organized for Duke a "class A Med. School" from date of inception. 2. Wrote the "Compleat Pediatrician" a masterpiece. 3. organized first "Planned Parenthood" Clinics in N.C. 4. gathered books and sowed the seed for one of the best med. libraries. 5. As a co-worker for the sick, your colleagues, students, nurses you were kind and indefatigable. 6. As a pediatrician you cared for the child. I think to feed, clothe, shelter, protect, educate the child, teach him to sing, never cause him to weep, teach him humility, not fear and superstition, to teach him, "To plant a rose." This is the most noble work of all mankind.

When I ran across Leonardo da Vinci's Volumes I came upon a lake of knowledge, I wanted to dive in head first, but other duties calling, I could just dip in a great toe to test the water, turn about, walk sadly away into a slough of despondency, never to return to that lake again.

You have not only my love, devotion and respect, but that of all my classmates. Who holds the slightest animosity or jealousy for you is small indeed. I spent my life making *thinkers* out of believers. "Unsettle the mind, and inflame the intellect."

"Be more than you seem to be."

Dr. Lyle A. Moser
6-6-68

If you think this picture good enough, hang it in the Med. dining room, so all, by your watchful and trusting eye, will always be inspired to do *their very best*.

Durham, North Carolina
June 10, 1968

Dear Dr. Arena:

Your sending me the delightful Davison saga has touched and pleased me more than I can say. I deeply appreciate it. You write with vigor and charm. Thank you for the pleasant inscription. I wish

I had had this article before Columbia University tape-recorded my life. I longed to pay appropriate tribute to Dr. Davison but felt entirely unequal to it. Without Dr. Davison and those of you with whom he surrounded himself, there would never have been the distinguished medical school we have or indeed we might not have had one at all. Nothing Dr. Few said to Mr. Duke impressed him so much as the dearth of medical education in the South between Tulane and Johns Hopkins — a vast area. Mr. Duke told me that what *really* made him set up the funds for Duke was a question Dr. Few asked him. It was this: "Mr. Duke, don't you want to do some permanent good on the earth?"

I appoint you "chronicler of Duke." I know no one who could do the job so well.

With best wishes,

Sincerely,
Mary R. Few
[Mrs. William Preston Few]

[LETTERS PUBLISHED IN *DUKE MEDICAL CENTER ALUMNI NEWSLETTER*, JULY, 1968]

I'm sure that people more eloquent than I will pay proper homage to Dean Davison for his tolerance, teaching abilities, administrative wizardry, and for all other facets which made him a great Dean.

I remember some of the personal humane qualities. When I was a lonely medical transfer from the University of Alabama, Dr. Davison took me, as he did others, to his lovely mountain home in Roaring Gap, fed us, played golf with us, and rode us over the narrow rocky mountain roads looking for "Mountain Dew." Except for the terrible fright of the automobile to and from Roaring Gap, during which time the dean drove with his knees while he lighted his pipe, these represented memorable weekends.

J. Lamar Callaway, M.D.
Dermatology, Duke Medical Center

It was indeed a great pleasure working with Dr. Davison when he was Dean of the Medical School, but when he brought in some suitcases full of autobiography and said to me, "I want you to make me some books out of this," I looked it over and it seemed to be a very hard task for me. So I came to a conclusion that I could not do it,

240

but he said to me, "You can!" And so, he with great patience sat down and showed me just how it could be done. By carefully studying it and telling myself I can if I try, there were three books made which were much satisfaction to Dr. Davison and many others; so thanks to Dr. Davison.

Jesse W. Ferrell
(Successor to Carl Rogers)

My wife and I are very sorry not to be able to come to the Duke Dinner on Wednesday 19th, the more so as I have a special affection for San Francisco.

You may remember it was "Dave" who arranged with Francis Scott Smyth, that Desmond Pond and I should transfer to U.C. for a semester, and it was Florrie and Tom Schnoor who gave us introductions to ensure our visit being enjoyable. To all of them please convey our warmest greetings.

Desmond is now Professor of psychiatry, but although I see an increasing number of crazy people I still call myself a general physician.

Kind regards,

Yours sincerely,
George Rankins '44
London, England

There are several things about Doctor Davison that I remember so well. One is the time I was in service and went to Chicago to take my American College of Radiology Boards. I ran into "Dave" (I have never been able to call him Dave to his face) in the hotel. He asked me out to have dinner with him which we did. Then after the dinner we went to a movie. He decided that if I didn't know enough about Radiology by then, studying that night wouldn't do any good! Incidentally I passed and got my Boards so I'm sure he was right. We did see the entire movie that night, however.

Another time when his 25-year picture appeared on the Alumni Register, he was wearing the same tie. It was the Oxford blue but I didn't know it at the time. I went out and bought him another tie and I understand that many other people sent him ties too. I also remember that when I came to Duke for an interview for entrance into Medical School, the class had already started. When I talked to him at the end of seeing four other men he said to me, "If you go to

241

the football game with me this afternoon I will let you into the Medical School." Of course I went to the game! One thing about "Dave" that I always remember also are his consultations in the men's room across the hall from his office.

Jerry W. Kerner, M.D. '37

Thank you for your note of 28 June. It just missed me in Germany and had to be forwarded to me here. I have been taking some leave and visiting for the past month. Now I am just roasting and resting here in the sun.

I am enclosing a clipping that I think you will be interested in seeing. It is from our local paper in Wiesbaden. It represents my last official act over there in the theater. It also finishes a career. You gave me my first real chance in June, 1931 when you let me come in late and try for admission to Duke. I hope I have shown you that your opinion was correct. I know you did not have another Duke man that has ever reached two star rank nor one who has received the DSM. It has meant a great deal to me and I hope it means something to you that one of "your boys" has reached this status. Thank you again Dr. Dave for the many words of advice and assistance you have given to me in the past. I am very proud to have been one of "your boys."

Ray T. Jenkins, M.D. '33

Roaring Gap, North Carolina
July, 1968

Dear Jay:

Helen Thomas told me that you wanted me to write you a letter about Atala's and my activities, so here goes.

We live in a five-room cottage at Roaring Gap at an altitude of 3,000 feet from March to December. We then go to St. Croix in the Virgin Islands for three months.

Thanks to Nick Nicholson, Banks Anderson, Marty Kreshon, Cal Callaway, and others I am in good health in spite of having arthritis, glaucoma, lymphocytic leukemia, and old age.

Atala, thanks to Billy Peete who removed a thrombosed vein, is in perfect health.

I see patients on the mountain, except between the hours of one and five when I generally take a nap, though not for the whole period. I believe I am the only physician who has such a rule of having office hours for twenty hours and no patients for four hours. I

242

enclose a copy of the sign on my door which all of my friends on the mountain respect and observe.

I am still driving the Lincoln Continental which the Alumni and Trustees gave me in 1961 when I retired. It has now gone 69,000 miles and is running better every year.

Our son Bill is practicing orthopedics in Port Huron, Michigan; our daughter, Jeana, is working in the Forrest Laboratory at Berkeley; and Sandy, our younger son, is practicing forestry up and down North Carolina with headquarters in Hillsborough.

We have nine grandchildren and manage to see all of them at least once a year.

During the nine months at Roaring Gap I go to New York, Washington, Durham or Charlotte at least every two weeks so that I am traveling about as actively as I did fifty years ago.

I am going back to my 55th Princeton Reunion tomorrow and then to the A.M.A. Meeting in San Francisco and to see my daughter and her three children in Berkeley.

We are thinking of going to Portugal, Madeira, the Canary Islands, Casablanca, and Tangier in August.

W. C. Davison

P.S. We sold the cottage which you remember in Roaring Gap and bought a small five-room cottage all on one floor a mile and a half away from the other cottage. I reached 76 on April 28 and Atala did likewise on June 3. We had our 51st Wedding Anniversary on June 2.

THE DUKE ENDOWMENT
1500 NORTH CAROLINA NATIONAL BANK BUILDING
CHARLOTTE, NORTH CAROLINA 28202

HOSPITAL AND CHILD CARE SECTIONS
WILBURT C. DAVISON, M.D.
CONSULTANT ON MEDICAL EDUCATION

(704) 376-0291
PLEASE REPLY TO:
ROARING GAP, N. C. 28668

August 12, 1968

Dr. John P. McGovern
McGovern Allergy Clinic
6655 Travis Street
Houston, Texas 77025

Dear Jack:

Atala and I are delighted that Kathy and you may visit us in St. Croix. We expect to arrive in St. Croix on December 13, 1968, and leave on February 21, 1969. I think both of you would enjoy it. We shall be staying at the Club Comanche, One Strand Street, Christiansted, St. Croix, Virgin Islands 00820. I think both of you would like the Club Comanche, though it is not as fashionable as the other hotels on the island.

243

I plan to reach Durham on November 7 but can go earlier if you wish.

I know that you will enjoy your trip to Puerto Rico. We spent four winters there and liked it very much.

Although I was a Charter Member of the American Board of Pediatrics in 1932, I am not altogether sure whether the Boards have been good or bad. I certainly was glad to get off the Board after three years.

I greatly enjoyed your and Bill Bean's editorials on Osler. Osler probably would be in favor of the Boards because he was responsible for the establishment of two medical societies, namely, the American Pediatric Society and the Association of American Physicians.

I came to know Dr. Pirquet quite well in Vienna, *(in 1922 and 1925.)* He had been Professor of Pediatrics at The Hopkins from 1911 to 1912 or 1910 to 1911, and because he and his wife acquired Trichinosis from eating raw ham, as they do in Vienna, he resigned and returned to Vienna. Both he and his wife acquired the morphine habit as a result of the pain from Trichinosis, and the year after I knew them in Vienna they committed suicide by jumping out of a window. As a matter of fact, they made two attempts and the second one was successful.

Dr. John P. McGovern
Page 2
August 12, 1968

Bela Schick was Pirquet's resident in Vienna and helped him write his book. Schick came to the states about 1930 and was in charge of pediatrics at Mt. Sinai and died about six months ago. His Schick Test was not intended as a test for susceptibility to diphtheria, but at Pirquet's request Schick was trying to see how small a dose of diphtheria toxin could produce sensitivity. He later found that none of the children to whom he had given attentuated doses of diphtheria acquired diphtheria, so that a great discovery was made by accident. (See P. S.)

Atala joins me in love to Kathy and you and looking forward to seeing you in November, as well as in St. Croix, and in the spring of 1969 at Roaring Gap.

Yours affectionately,

mc

Dav

Air Mail   W. C. Davison

P.S. Schick later found that several of the patients who had red skin reactions to the diphtheria toxin later acquired diphtheria but that all of those who had negative skin tests had previously had diphtheria. Hence, he concluded that a positive test, which is now known as a Schick Test, indicated susceptibility to diphtheria and that a negative test indicated immunity - a pure case of serendipity. Now that practically all infants are immunized against diphtheria, polio, whooping cough, measles, etc., the Schick Test is used only to test the efficacy of the diphtheria immunization.

Miss Sherwood was Schick's Chief Nurse at Mt. Sinai before going to the Hopkins where I was so impressed with her that I persuaded her to come & Drs. Schick & I have been close friends since I met him in Vienna 1922 until he died about six months ago.

Dav

244

Little Switzerland, North Carolina
August 17, 1968

Dear Jay:

I have just returned from a trip abroad and find "Duke's Mixture" on my desk. Thank you for sending it to me. I know it was a labor of love for you. It warmed my heart for I loved Dr. Davison too, had observed many of the events you related and had been the recipient of his wit, his austerity, his frugality, his generosity and his informality (he detested my addressing him as Dr. Davison — but I just couldn't bring myself to call him Dave). I never felt that he had a very high regard for me, but I didn't think there was anything personal about it as I believed he had little regard for all surgeons!

You are right when you say that he has left a permanent imprint upon the Medical Center. I hope that his bitterness over his belief that the medical school was ruined by a reorientation away from an emphasis on training the generalist in medical care toward the encouragement of research oriented medical scientists since 1960 is allayed by the passage of time and the realization that the changes were not as catastrophic as he feared and actually were necessary for the continued development of a prestigious medical school.

With esteem and best wishes.

Clarence E. Gardner, M.D.

Roaring Gap, North Carolina
October 17, 1968

Dear Jack:

Many thanks for your letter of October 12. If you will send me your mother's initials I certainly shall write her a letter of warning to use a walking stick when walking on a level and to use handrails when walking up and down steps.

I shall tell her that I also have to be careful to avoid falls because a broken hip at my age of 76 would be very unpleasant.

I enjoyed your letter to your mother on the same subject, and I shall call on her when I am in Washington in April, 1969.

I appreciate your enclosing a copy of your and Coleman Harris' article on "Writing for Medical Journals" and congratulate you both. I am glad that you emphasized that the most important asset to a journal paper is brevity. I learned it the hard way from John Howland at The Hopkins. Whenever I wrote a paper he told me to cut it in half, even though I said I could not cut it in half. I would finally reduce it by 50 percent and he would tell me to cut it in half again, and as a result I am sure the article was much improved.

I am so glad that Elizabeth Sherwood sent you a copy of Bela Schick's tribute to Mildred Sherwood. I could not find my copy of it and so I asked Elizabeth to send one to you and one to me.

Atala joins me in love to Kathy and you.

Yours affectionately,
Dave

THE DUKE ENDOWMENT
1500 NORTH CAROLINA NATIONAL BANK BUILDING
CHARLOTTE, NORTH CAROLINA 28202

HOSPITAL AND CHILD CARE SECTIONS
WILBURT C. DAVISON, M.D
CONSULTANT ON MEDICAL EDUCATION

(704) 376-0291
PLEASE REPLY TO:
ROARING GAP, N. C. 28668

March 26, 1969

Dr. Jay M. Arena
Box 3024
Duke University Medical Center
Durham, North Carolina 27706

Dear Jay:

While Atala and I were in the "Food Fair" in Winston-Salem on the way to Roaring Gap last week, a courtley gentleman and his wife introduced themselves as Mr. and Mrs. Pfohl, parents of the baby whom I thought had Oppenheim's or Werdig-Hoffman disease, but whom you were sure had polio. At any rate, the infant made a complete recovery on a treatment of Amino Acids, Glycine, and gelatin. Obviously, you were right, and the parents are very happy.

This infant eventually went to Duke Woman's College, graduated, married, has several children, and lives in Georgia. Congratulations. The parents think you and Duke are wonderful.

With best wishes, I am

Yours affectionately,

Dave

W. C. Davison

mf

246

Roaring Gap, North Carolina
May 13, 1969

Dear Jay:

If it is still possible to correct the Duke Medical Alumni Directory, please insert the name of Dr. Chiung-lin Chen as Chairman of the Department of Pediatrics of National Taiwan University Hospital, Taipei, Taiwan, Republic of China.

Dr. Chen was a resident or fellow in pediatrics in the late forties or early fifties, but the 1961 Duke Alumni Directory did not list him. It listed three other Dr. Chens.

Dr. Chiung-lin Chen was very helpful to Ross Porter, Je Harned, and me while we were in Taiwan in 1954.

With best wishes, I am

Yours sincerely,
Dave

Roaring Gap, North Carolina
June 4, 1969

Dear Jay:

I told Banks Anderson about the left handed compliment I received in Chicago for "The Compleat Pediatrician" from the wife of a friend of mine. She thanked me for "The Compleat Pediatrician" because she brought up her children by it instead of by Spock's book so that her children are normal and not delinquents. I thought you might be amused by Bank's reply which I am enclosing.

With best wishes, I am

Yours sincerely,
Dave

Durham, North Carolina
May 13, 1969

Dear Dave,

Theoretically, the Compleat Pediatrician is correct in proscribing such drugs as Probanthine for Glaucoma patients. However, I have yet to see an acute Glaucoma triggered by an Anticholinergic drug. The incidence is probably about the same as Thrombophlebitis with the pill. As long as you keep your pupils small you will be safe with Probanthine.

My own paternal responsibilities will be terminated, by mutual consent, when Charles, our youngest, marries on June 6th. As I

247

recall the gas and club bills over the last few years I get some inkling of what Shakespeare must have meant when he spoke of "parting is such sweet sorrow" — maybe not too apropos since Romeo was speaking — but anyway a wrench and a little lasting ache. My three fortunately came along before the Spock era. Mildred swore by the Compleat Pediatrician. Incidentally, I shall have to check on your spelling of, as typed in your letter "Compleat Pediatrician." Wouldn't Isaac W. have dropped in an a after the p? Furthermore, Isaac himself may have been a drop out. I suspect he was, maybe didn't even know how to spell. I've forgotten how close was your association with the Compleat Angler, and being at the office cannot verify the connection, but in spite of, or perhaps because of, the remark of the lady at the ACP meeting, J. Arena should look further into the fisherman's behavior before the tenth addition. Don't construe this a defense of Dr. Spock.

As you remember, this is the season for "going away parties" at Duke. Some are apparently not associated with unrequited sorrow, on the contrary, in some quarters there is undisguised jubilation, and even in the conservative block a sly amusement over a situation in which night falls over a disenchanted campus.

Even I, no partisan, hors de combat, and essentially benign, if I could learn to knit, may find a place in the stands and enjoy seeing a few more heads roll as I count my perls. I'm afraid, however, that mass decapitation will not solve Duke's problems.

We may be out of town, at our wedding, and later at the AOS meeting at Hot Springs during your next visit to Durham, but give us a ring and let us arrange to have you and Atala for dinner if we are in town.

Our best to you both.

Sincerely yours,
Banks
[Banks Anderson, Sr., M.D.]

Roaring Gap, North Carolina
June 4, 1969

Dear Jack:

Many thanks for your letter of May 12, and many apologies for delay in answering, but as you know I have been attending meetings.

I enjoyed seeing you at Pinehurst, and I also enjoyed the trip to Durham with the splendid country ham breakfast.

I think you are right in omitting some of the material such as "papers presented." Like you, I keep a file of "talks" with the date and place so that I shall not repeat myself.

I enclose Dr. Starr's letter. I had previously written him that I own some Xerox stock which I bought by mistake for Clorox.

Many thanks for the pictures which you took. I am sending you under separate cover the additional pictures and the invitation and program for my retirement dinner which I found in my briefcase when I reached Roaring Gap.

I enclose a clipping about the Canadian stamp in honor of Osler and have asked Mrs. Hilda E. Wainwright of the Osler Library to send me two sets of the stamps and two first day covers, one of which I shall send you.

I also enclose a copy of a letter from Al Henderson, which is very sad. I had not known that he had such a serious eye condition. I certainly hope he recovers.

Roaring Gap is at its peak now, and Atala and I are looking forward to Kathy's and your visit.

The only engagements which I have are meetings in Charlotte on June 9, 10, and 23 and 24. My grandchildren are coming on June 20 and 21.

I shall be in Charlotte on July 14 and 15 and shall join you in New York for the Alumni Meeting on July 16. I shall also be in New York from July 27 to 30. As far as I know, everything is clear in August and September except for September 15 and 16, 26 and 27, and 29 and 30. However, I probably can shift most of those engagements if they interfere with your visit.

Many thanks for the rowing stamp which you sent me. I had not seen one.

Atala joins me in love to Kathy and you.

Yours affectionately,
Dave

New York, New York
May 20, 1969

Dear Dr. Davison:
Your wish is our command. Dr. McGovern shall have your

249

memoir, Xeroxed on bond. I appreciate his willingness to reimburse us, for this office gets along on mighty thin rations.

Your happy mistake in buying Xerox stock amused me. I stumbled into it myself about ten years ago, and bought my present house on the astounding results.

Cordially,
Louis M. Starr
[Oral History Research Office,
Columbia University]

Roaring Gap, North Carolina
July 16, 1969

Dear Jay:

Colonel John A. Feagin, M.D., who is the orthopedist at the United States Military Academy at West Point, was the first of the West Point and Annapolis graduates who attended Duke Medical School. John was graduated in 1961 and was my assistant at Roaring Gap during the summer of 1960.

I believe someone could write an interesting article on the careers of the West Point and Annapolis graduates who studied medicine. Practically all of them are back in the Armed Services, and like John have received senior grade rank.

Atala joins me in best wishes to Polly and you.

Yours affectionately,
Dave

THE DUKE ENDOWMENT
1500 North Carolina National Bank Building
Charlotte, North Carolina 28202

HOSPITAL AND CHILD CARE SECTIONS
WILBURT C. DAVISON, M.D.
CONSULTANT ON MEDICAL EDUCATION

(704) 376-0291
PLEASE REPLY TO
ROARING GAP, N. C. 28668

November 13, 1969

Dr. John P. McGovern
McGovern Allergy Clinic
6655 Travis Street
Houston, Texas 77025

Dear Jack:

First of all, many, many thanks to Kathy and you for our delightful Duke Medical Alumni Reunion. I enjoyed every minute of it, including my fall after receiving your splendid Medallion. Fortunately, I had my English cap in my right pocket so that I was not very badly bruised.

Second, I humbly apologize for my Sam Houston speech. I went up to receive the Medallion after your splendid talk and had the full intention to point out that receiving a Medallion at Josh Turnage's Barbecue was the height of my ambition, first because of the Medallion and second because Josh Turnage's is my favorite habitat. I noticed that several people in the audience thought that they were in for a long series of reminiscences from a garrulous old man, so I quickly swallowed my remarks and told the Sam Houston story.

I have worried about it ever since thinking that you believed I was rude. I wish I had all of the splendid qualities which you described in your excellent presentation speech, but I shall try in the future to live up to your ideals. As a matter of fact, I made the first step by apologizing to Terry Cavanagh for being rude to him five years ago when I was furious that the Medical Library did not have the list of names of the members of the Cosmos Club. I regularly sent it to the Medical Library, but apparently it was transferred to the Perkins Library for safekeeping, so I did one good deed on Saturday by apologizing to Terry for grumbling about it.

I forgot to bring "A Gift of Joy" by Helen Hayes when I went to Durham, so I am mailing it today under separate cover. Atala and I were delighted with it and envy you having such a remarkable cousin.

I found on our return to Roaring Gap the enclosed ambiguous letter from Clem Smith. I have kept a Xerox of it but shall not answer it until after I hear from you.

In the meantime I followed your advice and phoned Ashley Weech in Cincinnati who said that he would be interested in reading the editorial but could not publish it before the February number because the proofs were already in.

Dr. John P. McGovern
Page 2
November 13, 1969

Ashley is a friend of Chuck Roland's and Talbot, and I believe he will accept the "Osler and Pediatrics."

I forgot to send the enclosed photograph to Ashley Weech, but if you think it should be included, his address is Dr. A. Ashley Weech, Children's Hospital, Elland and Bethesda Avenues, Cincinnati, Ohio 45229.

On our return to Roaring Gap on Saturday, we had "tea" with a nephew of Fred Hanes and several others who were enchanted with the silver and the bronze Medallions. They all said that the Medallions were a far better gift than the Lincoln of 1961.

With love to Kathy and you from Atala and me, I am

Yours affectionately,

W. C. Davison

mf

Air Mail

Roaring Gap, North Carolina
November 14, 1969

Dear Jay:

I am like a lovesick girl writing you so many letters, but I meant to ask you for a copy of the 1968 and 1969 deaths in the class. I usually write to the widows, and I may have written to several on the list, but certainly not as many as the list you read out for 1969.

Atala joins me in love to Polly and you.

Yours affectionately,
Dave

Roaring Gap, North Carolina
March 24, 1970

Dear Sam [Samuel L. Katz]:

Many thanks for your letter of March 17. I knew that the total Pediatric Staff of 52 included several duplicates, but even 27 pediatricians is quite a contrast toMcBryde, Arena, Susan Dees, Arthur London, Jerry Harris, and me in the thirties and forties.

These figures are no criticism of you but merely an indication of the rising cost of medical education and hospitalization, as well as in the cost of living. I wish more of the Duke medical faculty would go into active practice throughout North and South Carolina where they are so greatly needed.

With best wishes, I am

Yours sincerely,
W. C. Davison

Louisville, Kentucky
April 6, 1970

Dear Doctor Davison:

I have just received the prints from the first book which I edited and am enclosing for you a copy of the foreword. I am sure you know of the high esteem that I have had for you as a teacher, educator, friend and counselor.

My curriculum vitae has not kept up with your expectations for me; however, the twig is proceeding in the way it was bent. Last fall I took on the added responsibility as chairman of the Department of Pediatrics and now have begun the big swim in the ocean of medical education.

Faye and I have very warm memories of our days at Duke and

especially of the personal contact with you. I would honor and treasure very much a portrait of you to be placed in my office along side a picture of the Duke University Medical School, for all of my students, house officers and friends to see. I am very proud of the education you helped me to receive and am most grateful for all of the kind references and recommendations you have made for me.

With warm personal regards,

Very sincerely yours,
Billy F. Andrews, M.D.

Roaring Gap, North Carolina
May 6, 1970

Dear Kathy and Jack:

I had meant to send my ardent letter of thanks to you both as soon as I returned to Durham, but I had to go to a meeting in Greenville, South Carolina, on Monday and Tuesday, and a meeting in New York on Thursday, Friday, and Saturday. Today is Sunday and the first opportunity I have had to use my newly repaired Dictaphone.

You will never know how much Atala and I appreciate the most pleasant week we have ever had. Seeing all my old friends, as well as you both, brought back many happy memories.

My only regret was the miserable paper which I gave, but I have now revised it three or four times since I returned, and I shall send you a Xerox of it to get your comments on it before the paper is published.

We bought our Checker Cabs yesterday. Atala's is light blue, and mine is green, and I have given the 1961 Lincoln Continental which the Alumni Association, students, and Trustees gave me in 1961 to the Duke Medical Alumni Association; I hope that it will give as good service to them as it has given me over the past ten years.

Atala and I are going to Roaring Gap tomorrow morning, she in her ten-year-old Peugeot and I in the new Checker. She does not feel confident about power transmission, power steering, etc., so she will practice with my green Checker on the side roads of Roaring Gap, and Sandy will bring up her blue Checker when she becomes more acquainted with my Checker.

I am trying to persuade her to give her Peugeot to the Duke Medical Library to run errands and deliver books, but she is not convinced that she will ever master the Checker Cab, and besides she is devoted to the small car.

With love from both of us to both of you and thanking you again for making our visit to Texas such a happy one, I am

Affectionately,
Dave

P.S. If you have one or two extra copies of the Osler number of JAMA, I would appreciate it if you would send them to me as I have only one copy. Also, if you have an extra one, please send it to Mrs. William P. Few, the widow of Dr. William Preston Few who was President while you were at Duke. She is greatly interested in all of the activities of the Duke Medical Graduates.

W. C. D.

Roaring Gap, North Carolina
May 12, 1970

Dear Jay:

I have just received cards announcing their going into the practice of medicine from William R. Harris, J. Thomas Foster, W. Hampton Lefler, Leroy Allen, William Lester Adcock, Jr. and Carroll L. Mann III.

Are any of them Duke medical graduates, as I should like to write "best wishes" to them?

Affectionately,
Dave

Roaring Gap, North Carolina
June 29, 1970

Dear Polly and Jay:

Many thanks for sending me a card from Berghoff's. You made me very envious.

In the course of a conversation with Jim Davis about a prospective surgeon for Sparta, he told me how much pleasure he had when you and Jay introduced him to Berghoff's. Did you try the new Berghoff's at 123 North Wabash Avenue? I sat next to a man in the old Berghoff's one day, and he told me that he liked both of the places equally well.

With love from Atala and me, I am

Yours affectionately,
Dave

Dear Jack:

My humble apologies for the delay in answering your interesting letter of September 8, but Dr. Rankin died that day, and after attending his funeral I have not felt like writing letters. The enclosed note from Bert Persons and my answer express my feeling of loss.

Can you send me a list of those who are contributing to "Humanism in Medicine" together with the titles of the articles so that I can start work on the Foreword? I am glad that Emile and Wilder are sending you reprints for the Holman and Penfield section of the library. I have just started reading Wilder Penfield's latest book entitled "Second Thoughts." Terry Cavanagh loaned me a copy; it was published in 1970. Wilder's previous book was entitled "The Second Career" published in 1963.

Congratulations on Thomas C. Gibson's review of "William Osler: The Continuing Education."

I appreciate your sending me a copy of it.

Needless to say, I was delighted that you have been appointed by Mr. Nixon as a member of the Board of Regents of the National Library of Medicine. Not only is it a very distinguished Board, but it is actually getting things accomplished through the Public Health Service which those of us who were on the previous Board could not get done through the Army. I hated to vote to turn the Surgeon General's Library over to the Public Health Service, but as a famous bank robber stated when he was asked why he robbed banks "You go where the money is."

I appreciate your mention of Russell Blattner. He certainly has a good memory because he and I have not seen each other for the last fifteen years.

I appreciate a copy of the list of Charter Members of the Osler Society and also the stationery which Al Henderson designed which now includes the Honorary Members.

I am glad that you are joining the American College of Physicians because the State and National meetings of the College are very interesting. I have written a letter of endorsement for you for the American College of Physicians. I think you will enjoy membership in it.

Congratulations on being appointed to the 1970 White House

Conference [for Children and Youth] for the Allergy Foundation of America.

Jay Arena, Sam Agnello, and two TV technicians spent a morning here two weeks ago, but as I was cautioned not to say anything disagreeable I think the film probably is very dull. At any rate, Arena said he liked it, but I haven't seen it.

I also am returning to you the booklet of the American College of Physicians.

Atala joins me in love to Kathy and you.

Yours affectionately,
Dave

Asheville, North Carolina
October 2, 1970

Dear Dean Davison:

I want to thank you very much for your sincere interest on my behalf in moving from the academic world in Durham to the private practice of Thoracic and Cardiovascular Surgery here in Asheville, North Carolina. Your notes to Doctors Craig, Raper, Gilbert, Burns and to Ralph Jennings have in each case been followed through by a personal contact on the part of all concerned. I have been very graciously and warmly received in the community which I attribute to a great extent to your kind words to each of these people. My partner, Dr. Charles Keller, by winning a great deal of esteem for himself and practicing a high caliber of surgery has paved the way considerably for my coming to town.

There are many challenging opportunities here, as well as an on-going strong program which makes the practice of medicine quite a lot of fun. The major difference thus far that I have seen between Asheville as a regional hospital center and Durham is that we seem to be able to get things accomplished more reasonably and quickly because of the smaller size of this particular place. Needless to say, I have always been a great proponent of Western North Carolina and living up in the hills and now that I am here I know that I have been right all along. The surrounding countryside is beautiful and thus far we have had an occasional opportunity to enjoy it. I know that Elon has always envied you the Roaring Gap home and has repeatedly stated that he would love to live in the hills of Carolina. He was up a week or so ago and greatly enjoyed his visit as we enjoyed having him.

Please let us know if you expect to be in this neck of the woods as we would all love to host you in some way. I look forward to seeing you on my return to Durham, or perhaps we might drop by and say hello if we drive up to Galax to see Bill Waddell. Again, many thanks for your interest and support. My best wishes for your continued good health.

Sincerely,
F. Maxton Mauney (Mac)

Roaring Gap, North Carolina
October 7, 1970

Dear Jay:

Many thanks for your letter of September 30, and I wish that I could attend all of the festivities of the 40th anniversary celebration on November 19-21. However, unless my checkup at the hospital next week improves my knees, I will be unable to attend, except possibly the dinner on Friday, November 20, at 6:30 p.m. and the barbecue on Saturday, November 21, at 11:00 a.m.

I have heard that Jimmie Warren sold Turnage's Barbecue to Blue Light. Is it as good as usual?

I certainly am sorry that you will not be present during the celebration.

Atala joins me in love to Polly and you.

Dave

[No Date]

From Dr. W. C. Davison to Dr. Arena:

Knowing of your interest in poetry and in THE BIBLE, I thought that you would be amused at the enclosed writings of The Reverend John Cotton who was the Vicar in the village in which the Sixty-fifth General Hospital, the Duke unit, was stationed during the war.

Atala and I visited the village in August on our return from Copenhagen. The hospital, which I had not seen since 1945, was unchanged and John Cotton and his wife were as delightful as ever.

Seeing that I was driving a rented English Ford, he presented me with his version of the Twenty-Fourth Psalm and then because I refused a drink during the visit that morning, he gave me the enclosed poem on the dangers of temperance.

257

Twenty-Fourth Psalm

The Ford is my car I shall not want another,
It maketh me to lie down in wet places;
It soileth my clothes
It leadeth me into paths of ridicule for its namesake
It landeth me in deep waters
It prepareth a breakdown for me in the presence of mine enemies
Yea, tho I run down the valleys, I am towed up the hills
I feel much evil whilst it is with me
Its rods and its engines miscomfort me
It anointeth my face with oil; its tank runneth over
Surely to goodness, the damn thing won't follow me
all the days of my life or I shall dwell in the
habitation of the insane forever.

The cow and the horse live thirty years
and nothing know of wine or beers;
The goat and sheep at twenty die
without the aid of rum and rye;
The sow drinks water by the ton
and at eighteen is nearly done;
The cat in milk and water soaks
and then in ten short years it croaks;
The dog at fifteen cashes in
still ignorant of scotch and gin;
The honest bone dry thrifty hen
lays eggs for years then dies at ten;
All animals are strictly dry
They sinless live and swiftly die
But sinful ginful beersoaked men
Survive for three score years and ten
And some of us the mighty few
Stay pickled till we're ninety-two.

Roaring Gap, North Carolina
November 13, 1970

Dear Grant:
  Many thanks for your letters of November 4 and 9 enclosing Dr.

258

Hinohara's letter and the delightful article about Pat Sullivan. Please contratulate both of them.

Would there be any chance of getting Dr. Hinohara's book on Osler for the University of Texas Library or Jack McGovern's Library, or the one at Duke or the National Library of Medicine?

In spite of the talent of Duke Hospital, no one has discovered why my knees get tired so quickly after walking 50 yards or standing a few minutes. I then start stumbling and fall about once a week which so far has not been dangerous but very painful.

Atala joins me in love to Pat and you.

Yours affectionately,
Dave

Roaring Gap, North Carolina
December 1, 1970

Dear Moffitt [Howell]:

I have just heard from Jack McGovern about your coronary and hope that you are taking care of yourself. I often heard Osler say that the key to a long life was to have a coronary and then treat wisely as you have done.

I also was unable to attend the Silver Anniversary Reunion, but my knees wear out after I have walked twenty-five yards or have stood for fifteen minutes or more. I never realized that arthritis could be so crippling.

With best wishes, I am

Yours sincerely,
W. C. Davison

Lakeland, Florida
December 11, 1970

Dear Dean Davison:

Of all the letters that I have received during my convalescence during my recent disability, which from the present time I feel no ill effects whatsoever, I do not know of any of those that I have appreciated and have felt more sincerely than the one of yours recently.

It was very difficult of me to not attend our Silver Anniversary back at Duke, particularly with the hopes that you might be attending a portion of it, and I think that it is fantastic that you are able to keep track of your "wandering herd" as well as you do. It is difficult to realize that I received my M.D. degree under your excellent auspices back in 1945.

I just wanted to let you know how very much I sincerely appreciated your remembrance, and kind words, to me, and I also sincerely trust that your physician will be able to alleviate your arthritic condition and make you as active as you ever were and as you would wish to be now, I am sure.

With best personal regards and sincere appreciation, I am

Sincerely yours,
Moffitt Howell

Houston, Texas
February 1, 1971

Dear Davy:

I was recently reading about a computer developed by Dr. N. A. Nash, of London, England, that can answer 700 million questions, and costs $10.00. It can be carried in a medical bag. Dr. Nash calls his device a Logoscope "a marshaling yard for trains of thought." It is really a slide rule. I could not help but think as I read the description of Dr. Nash's Logoscope of the format of the *Compleat Pediatrician*, and how advanced you were in presenting the material it contained. Without doubt you were the first programmer in the clinical sciences. Unfortunately, those who objected to the format had little foresight as to what has now become an accepted way of presenting information. I am enclosing a copy of an announcement on the Logoscope.

Do hope your leg has improved and that you are enjoying your vacation. I understand that Durham is now in the grips of a severe winter storm. Each joins with love to you and Atala.

Sincerely,
Grant

Roaring Gap, North Carolina
April 2, 1971

Dear Grant:

Many, many thanks for your letter of March 5 and for the reprint of Dr. Shigeaki Hinohara's report of the hijacking and of his affection for Osler. Atala and I have read it word for word and shall file it with the Osler articles.

260

Atala gave me a first edition of Aequanimitas many years ago, and I have tried to follow Sir William's advice.

I certainly should need that advice on a hijacking experience such as that of Dr. Hinohara.

Hijacking in this country is getting entirely too frequent, particularly for those of us like Atala and me who go to the Virgin Islands. Several planes flying out of Atlanta and Miami have been hijacked, held for a few hours, and then allowed to go on their way. David Smith was hijacked last month out of a plane leaving Atlanta for Durham. He said they had to stay in Havana for two hours, and all they could buy there were souvenirs.

I hope that you will send a copy of OSLER'S PEREGRINATIONS IN ASIA to David Smith. I believe it would cheer him up. Fortunately, Susan was not with him.

The reason for my delay in answering your letter of March 5 is that I have just recently been loaned a Dictaphone to replace the one which I took to St. Croix and which for some reason has refused to function. There was no use in my answering letters in longhand because no one can read my writing, so I filed all my correspondence in three groups: "immediate," "before April 15," and "after April 15." Needless to say, your letter of March 5 is in the "immediate" file.

I am sure that I have not answered a previous letter from you, and I shall hunt through the files for it.

Atala joins me in love to Pat and you.

Yours affectionately,
Dave

Roaring Gap, North Carolina
April 23, 1971

Dear Fetter [Bernard F. Fetter]:

I was delighted to read that you had received the Golden Apple Award of 1970 as well as election to AOA. Hearty congratulations and best wishes.

Yours sincerely,
W. C. Davison

Durham, North Carolina
May 3, 1971

Dear Dave,

Thank you for your letter of the 23rd. I don't see how you have time to read all the material which might come across your desk. Since you gave me an appointment, I am glad you noticed this news item. As I told somebody not too long ago, there is not much to teaching. All you need is an enthusiastic group of students. Such a group will make anyone look good. I appreciate your letter very much.

Sincerely,
Fetter

Roaring Gap, North Carolina
May 18, 1971

Dear Bill [Andrews] :

I am just catching up with the correspondence which accumulated while I was in St. Croix and found that I had not answered your kind letter of December 7.

Atala and I greatly enjoyed your visit with us in Charlotte even though the dining room of the White House Inn was closed.

In addition to my arthritis, leukemia, and glaucoma, I have had several severe falls which have handicapped my walking. However, I never liked to walk any way, so I enjoy being chauffeured around by Atala and riding in a wheelchair at the airports.

As a matter of fact, physical exercises have improved my lameness, and I am sure that by summer I shall be much more limber.

Atala joins me in best wishes to your wife and you.

Yours affectionately,
Dave

Roaring Gap, North Carolina
May 18, 1971

Dear Pam [Leight]:

Many thanks for sending me copies of the correspondence with Mrs. Noss. I am glad that "The Compleat Pediatrician" was useful to her in Africa.

One of the speakers at the dinner given me in October, 1961, was a Polish woman doctor representing the League of Nations. She said that someone sent her during the war some underclothes and a copy

of "The Compleat Pediatrician." Both of them, she said, were useful.

With best wishes, I am

Yours sincerely,
Dave

Roaring Gap, North Carolina
November 2, 1971

Dear Polly and Jay;

Many, many thanks for your kind message from the Chicago
meeting. I certainly wish I could have been there and seen so many
of my old friends. Some of them I have not seen since they went out
to practice in different parts of the United States, but I remember
and love all of them.

With love to both of you from Atala and me, I am

Yours affectionately,
Dave

Roaring Gap, North Carolina
November 24, 1971

Dear Jack:

I certainly enjoyed our telephone conversation this morning and
enclose a photograph of Sir William in which I had assumed he was
holding a cigarette. Looking at it more closely, I believe that he was
photographed in front of some flowering vine and that the supposed
cigarette in his left hand may have been a flower in the background.
At any rate, I don't know the history of it. The picture was given to
me by one of my best friends, Joe Moore.

Joe's mother ran a restaurant in Roaring Gap, but the authorities
refused a beer license because Joe was under sixteen years of age.
He settled the controversy by joining the Marines and was
wounded, and I had a battle with the Veterans Administration to get
a pension for him. The pension board said he was not entitled to a
pension because he joined the Marines at the age of fourteen and
stated that he was sixteen years of age. At any rate, he got a small
pension and also a hearing aid because some bazooka had gone off
near his head while he was working with the Army in Korea as a
medic.

After some persuasion, Joe returned to grammar school (he had
only gone through three grades), then high school, and then the

University of North Carolina, supporting himself by being a registered embalmer. He wanted to go to medical school, and I did everything I could to persuade my colleagues that he was the type physician which we ought to produce, but Joe gave up his ambition, got married, and then ran the syphilis control program in Fayetteville, North Carolina, adjacent to Fort Bragg. That explains his reference to lues control on the back of the picture.

I think I gave Joe this picture, but I had always thought that Osler was leaning on an automobile. Instead of that, it is a steel armchair. If you copy it, please send me back the original because of Joe Moore's note on the back.

With love to Kathy and you from Atala and me, I am

Yours affectionately,
Dave

Durham, North Carolina
March 31, 1972

Dear Jay (if that's the kind of bird you are):

I'm surprised at Davison maligning me. In fact, I didn't know he was until I read all the tripe he sent me. You tell him those are the worst puns I ever heard. I wouldn't even punish a dog with that stuff. In fact, I love my dogs. If they knew how well bred they were, they wouldn't go in the field with me. But, tell him I appreciate him thinking of me in any terms. I love the kind of dirt his mind is made out of; it's rich for any soil. Tell him, for God's sake that in spite of everything, I still love him. Give him my love, will you.

Sincerely yours,
Raney S.
[W. Raney Stanford, M.D.]

Roaring Gap, North Carolina
April 18, 1972

Dear Jack:

Many thanks for your letter of April 8 which traveled to St. Croix and then to Roaring Gap.

Atala and I left St. Croix on April 3, spent a week in Charlotte seeing friends, and then came to Roaring Gap on April 8. We have had two clear days since that time — the others have all had smog or were cloudy with occasional rain. However, it is very comfortable at Roaring Gap in spite of the gray sky.

I had no thought of polio until Bob Graves found that my right calf was four centimeters less than my left calf in circumference. Since that time, the difference has increased. I had previously assumed that I probably had polio during the 1900 epidemic in New York because so many thousands of other children did. However, I worked in the polio hospital of the New York Board of Health in 1916 where we always had at least 3,000 polio cases, so I assumed I must be immune. I had no recollection of the 1900 epidemic but assumed that it was in that epidemic when I acquired polio after Bob Graves spotted the difference in my two calves.

In spite of that, I was fairly active in athletics — football, rowing, ice hockey, shot-putting, hammer throwing, water polo, and one or two other activities at Princeton and at Oxford. I was always second-rate but at times would pick up a stray medal.

Atala and I would be delighted to have Kathy and you arrive here on June 2. I have already made reservations at the High Meadows for your room. I am sure that the sun will shine when you arrive.

I certainly appreciate getting the extra copies of the transcript of your, Wilder's, Emile's, and my interviews in Galveston. I have had several complimentary letters from doctors, students, etc. throughout the country who have seen the article in The Roche Image for February.

Our 57th wedding anniversary will be on June 2, and Atala and I are looking forward to Kathy's and your visit at that time. Atala's birthday is June 3, but her mother felt that it was bad luck to get married on one's birthday, so the wedding was held on June 2. Naturally, I made no objections to the earlier date, especially when I knew that I was going overseas within a few days. I was commissioned on April 17, 1917, before I was graduated from The Hopkins. General Gorgas personally gave me my commission on the strength of Dr. Welch's statement that I was graduated even though the regular graduation date was June 15.

With love to you both from Atala and me, I am

Yours affectionately,
Dave

P.S. I certainly am sorry that I shall not be able to attend the meetings of the American Association for the History of Medicine and of the Osler Society in Montreal in May.

W. C. D.

Dear Dr. Arena:

I was very much shocked with the news that Dean Davison has passed on June 26. About two months before his death I still got a letter from him dated on April 24. The letter reminded me of his persistent kindest regards to us and his gracious character of humanity. The letter was so warm and vivid that I could not imagine he would die so soon.

I was so stupid that I heard the news of his death only when I saw the "Festschrift in Honor of Wilburt Cornell Davison" of the September issue of *American Journal of Diseases of Children* which reached my hand yesterday. Although it passed already more than four months since he died the news was new to me and I was shocked very much.

The relation of Dean Davison to me started in 1950 when I studied at the department of pediatrics of Duke Hospital. At that time my image of Dean Davison was a teacher. His dynamic (on time and tireless) and comprehensive teaching at the teaching round was very impressive. My second impression was that he was a teacher of humanity. Although I was his student, at that time he used to take me with his car to the party of Bar-B-Q and once to a seminar three hundred miles far away from Durham.

Our relationship was enhanced since Dean Davison came over to Taipei and spent four months to help us to develop the new curriculum of the clinical departments of our medical college. His office was at my next door. During his stay in Taipei he not only helped us to develop a new curriculum but also gave lots of advice to our department of pediatrics and gave a special lecture on "Advances in Pediatrics" at our meeting of Pediatric Association.

We gave him dinner parties several times and excursion with our staff of pediatrics to the vicinity of Taipei. Personally I invited him to my house for the dinner and went to a picnic to Yangminshan with him. It was that time that I learned he liked swimming. We swam in the pool. I was impressed that he swam very well with such a bulky body.

Our friendship continued after Dean Davison left Taipei. I sent Christmas card every year and some letters. He also never missed to respond to me.

When I wrote him telling that I was going to England to make further study he sent many letters of recommendation to the pediatricians in England. (I did not request!) I appreciated his kindness very much.

Once I wrote to him about our findings of favism in Taiwan and the results of G-6-P-D study in these cases he responded quickly and enclosed a dime in his letter saying that it was his rule to give a dime to a person who suggested him to revise his book of "Compleat Pediatrician." He would put G-6-P-D deficiency in the part on favism or acute hemolytic anemia.

I was disappointed that I could not meet him when I visited Duke Hospital again in 1967 but I learned that he was still well and active. After I came home I received a letter from him apologizing his being out of Durham.

I am very sorry that I have lost a great teacher and a good friend. His portrait and his book "Compleat Pediatrician" which he gave me with his signature will always remind me of his greatness and kindness.

With cordial regards.

Yours sincerely,
Chiung-Lin Chen, M.D.

In Memoriam

WILBURT CORNELL DAVISON, M.D.

1892–1972

Memorial Addresses

Delivered at Duke Chapel

November 17, 1972

 Mary D. B. T. Semans
Trustee of Duke University and
The Duke Endowment

IN SPEAKING ABOUT Doctor Davison on behalf of the Boards of Trustees of Duke University and the Duke Endowment, I find it impossible not to speak also for myself.

On January 19, 1927, President Few of Duke University appeared in Doctor Week's office at the Johns Hopkins Hospital, sent for Doctor Wilburt Cornell Davison and greeted him with the words, "I have come for you." This was a lustrous moment in the history of American medicine. It was the beginning of the Duke University Medical School and the life-long dedication of its pioneer dean to this institution and the total University. It was the forging of the links between them—and the laying down of a total campus concept of cooperation and close association.

"Make your own policies and when you get in trouble, let me know and I shall help you," Doctor Few had said. Doctor Davison years later made the statement, "Doctor Few always helped me." It can be documented that during these consultations Vice President Flowers, who later succeeded Doctor Few, was always called in. This continuity and confidence contributed a vitality to the whole Medical School-University relationship.

From the bare earth Doctor Davison guided the construction of this institution, bought books, created the library and built a faculty. He brought with him a vigorous optimism and a fierce determination that this school, rising from the ground, would be the best in this country in our lifetime. We are thankful for his faith. From the first day he had the courage to act on his convictions. Both his fixing of the goal on excellence and his confidence that it could be achieved derived from his deep belief in the teachings of his mentor, Sir William Osler.

To the question in many minds at the time about where the hospital patients would come from, Doctor Davison said, "I had great faith in Osler's statement that in spite of the belief of many people, a huge metropolis was not essential to a medical school." The results of this confidence were reflected in the Dean's writings twenty years later. "Duke Hospital has been accepted as a source of academic and scientific personnel with people from all over the world coming to Duke's door."

It is the philosophic sweep of thought behind an institution which is the key to its development. Here too, Osler's tenets held for Doctor Davison. "Look heavenward," he said, "if you wish, but never to the horizon—that way danger lies . . . the frauds, the quackeries . . . which have deceived each generation—all beckon from the horizon, and lure men not content to look for the truth and happiness that tumble out at their feet." "Shut close, then, the great fore and aft bulkheads, and prepare to cultivate the habit of a life of Day-Tight Compartments."

In addition to his sense of immediacy, Doctor Davison gambled on young talent as Osler had done. He brought in a core team of young Hopkins men who had been trained in a climate of highest quality of scientific learning, bedside teaching and hospital techniques and he reached out for other youthful candidates of the highest national promise. He established Duke Medical School chairmanships as continuing positions of greatness. Together these chairmen and the Dean shaped policy in an atmosphere of excitement and highest expectation. In his words, "The faculty and staff have tried to keep in a state of more or less continuing dissatisfaction with themselves and their *status quo*. So long as they desire to have more than they have and do more than they are doing, there is hope for continued progress in the School and Hospital."

The Duke Medical School possessed a sort of joyous determination to provide medical leadership, a willingness to experiment with curriculum, an insistence on teachers' engaging in original and productive investigations and, above all, the requirement for meticulous and compassionate medical care for all segments of the population. The success was, as Doctor Weed expressed it, "the research spirit of the originating faculty . . . sailing out with Doctor Davison on an unknown sea of educational procedure."

We are grateful for Doctor Davison's lifelong dedication to the aspirations of Duke's founder. He had an unusual attitude of reverence for Mr. Duke's primary philanthropic objective; namely, to improve the quality of medical care in the Carolinas. In helping to promote the ideals of the Duke Endowment he secured the cooperation of Duke University, joining in a mission to upgrade the standards of North Carolina's medical practice by reviewing the quality of professional care, helping to staff new hospitals, adding to their resources and assisting them in gaining accreditation. These objectives spurred him on to a second career after retirement from the Medical School and, working for the Duke Endowment, he dedicated the rest of his life to finding solutions to the problems of medical care in North Carolina.

Dave's open door policy, the promises he kept, his hearty but dignified informality, his ebullience, his belief in students and his gallantry toward them, his unswerving loyalty and limitless capacity for capturing friendships and maintaining them endeared him to the whole Medical School family.

A few weeks ago, I met a physician from Florida who had been a Duke house officer in the early years. We spoke of Dave. "It will never be the same again," he said. I knew he was right, but there was something beyond that which we needed to say.

When Dave started this Medical School, he "built-in" its future. His hearty camaraderie, crackling humor and overflowing enthusiasm may be with us as but permanent imprints on our memories; but his visions, demands and accomplishments day-by-day were so significant that the Duke Medical School's greatness can be permanently sustained.

This school did not have to wait for traditions to evolve slowly through generations. They sprang up around Dave during his lifetime. He understood the history of his profession. He knew medicine as an art. Just as the gold doors of the Cathedral in Florence are Ghiberti's— the Duke Medical School is Doctor Davison's masterpiece.

Thanks be to God for sending him here.

II   William G. Anlyan
Vice President for Health Affairs

"DISSATISFACTION IS OUR goal." Those were the headlines quoting Doctor Davison in the newspaper in the early 1950's. "Dissatisfaction is our goal"—a startling and almost shocking headline attributed to one of the world's leading figures in the health field. However, as one read the rest of Dave's statement, the profoundness of his message became apparent. "Dissatisfaction with the world as it is" had been one of the prime motivating forces throughout his career.

As one examines Dave's professional lifetime, it is obvious that he was at the cutting edge of change in health care and health education, at times highly unorthodox for his day, defying the artificial rigidities of tradition yet preserving the excellence of proven quality. Let us remember some of his accomplishments and objectives that placed him at the *avant garde*.

Despite the highly structured curriculum of the Johns Hopkins School of Medicine, he managed to tailor a highly individualized and flexible course of medical studies for himself between Hopkins and Oxford University where he was tutored by Sir William Osler. His personal experience with flexibility was highly influential in his subsequent stewardship at Duke.

His studies at Oxford were followed by voluntary service to his country and to the Allies during World War I. Weaving in and out of enemy territory and relaying important information to the Allies, he would have made the CIA of today envious. The respect he earned from the Armed Forces led to his becoming a consultant to our Army thereafter and especially during World War II when he commuted regularly to Washington.

He founded our Medical School and Medical Center with a young, untried faculty and flexible educational policies. To this day, the leadership of the Medical School has persisted with young faculty in key positions and perhaps the most flexible curriculum in the nation.

He foresaw the need for some form of health insurance and, along with George Watts, Sr., founded the Blue Cross Hospital Insurance Program in our state over considerable opposition from organized medicine of that day.

Forced by the austerity of the depression, he and Deryl Hart, M.D., conceived the "geographic fulltime system" for the attraction and development of the clinical faculty. The PCD system, as it is now known, was heresy in the academic medical circles of the United States at a time when all schools were trying to mimic the fulltime Johns Hopkins model. Today, many of the nation's leading academic medical centers are trying to institute a variant of the Duke system.

His concern for the unmet health care needs in rural areas led to the tutorials with selected practitioners in this region. Subsequently, as a Trustee of the Duke Endowment, he helped provide the funds for summer scholarships for students to work in selected communities. The Duke Endowment summer program covers all students at the four academic medical centers in North and South Carolina and has reached across the Atlantic Ocean to develop relationships with counterpart groups in Great Britain. The Student AMA of today has enlarged such a program on a national basis.

On the national scene, one of Dave's prime accomplishments was in his capacity as Chairman of the Armed Forces Medical Library. He was a key figure in converting it to the National Library of Medicine, which is now headed by one of his former students, Martin Cummings, M.D. In the Davisonian tradition, the National Library serves the entire world in its health information needs.

The *world* was Dave's perimeter of professional activity though his base of operations and his love were Duke and North Carolina. He was an avid internationalist known throughout the globe—from Formosa to Egypt to Northern Europe. He made good use of the airplane in the pioneering days of air travel. It was not unusual to receive a postcard from Dave in the morning mail with the postmark in Bangkok and then find him, the same day, presiding at the lunch table in the Duke Hospital dining room. The familiar greeting he uttered on such occasions to his faculty colleagues was typical of his one-upmanship— "Welcome back," he would say, placing the faculty member on the defensive.

As a result of his world travels, many physicians from other countries reciprocated by visiting Dave and Duke. The only catastrophe that I can recall was when a delegation of Pakistani Moslem physicians arrived; as was customary, they were taken to Josh Turnage's for dinner. The incompatibility of the *specialte de la maison Turnage* and the Moslem religion soon became apparent but the ingenuity and adaptability of Dave and Josh Turnage met the challenge and the hens that roamed Turnage's back yard were sacrificed for the occasion.

Though Dave is no longer with us physically, he has left his indelible imprint and style: youthful faculty leadership; flexibility; informality; involvement in innovation and change at the international, national, regional, and local levels; devotion to Duke University; and above all

275

the desire to meet the needs of our people with love and compassion. In the Davisonian tradition, we too are constantly dissatisfied and we seek to fulfill the ideals prescribed by Dave.

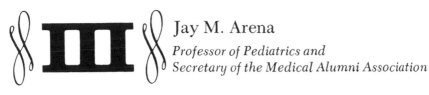

Jay M. Arena

Professor of Pediatrics and
Secretary of the Medical Alumni Association

As one of Duke's first medical graduates, present alumni secretary-treasurer, and long-time member of the pediatric faculty, I speak from a forty-two-year, happy and rewarding association with Doctor Davison in all of these areas. Our relationship was such that it is most difficult for me today on such an occasion as this to express in cold words what lies in the heart. Perhaps two brief anecdotes will best illustrate how we all felt about this unique, unpretentious and lovable man—the Dean—who was totally and unequivocally dedicated to Duke.

In the forty-two years that I had the pleasure and privilege of knowing Doctor Davison as a student, as a house officer, as a member of his staff and faculty, and as a warm and thoughtful friend, never once did I hear him say "I did this" or "I did that"—it was always, "Duke did this" or "Duke did that." The first anecdote I would like to recall concerned a senior student who had the misfortune of being caught with a case of whiskey in his room. The president of the University wanted him dismissed immediately and he called Doctor Davison to this effect. Doctor Davison's reply was "Absolutely not." No way would he dismiss a fourth year student, for not only was this student an exceptionally talented individual but Duke had four years invested in his education. "Anyhow," Doctor Davison said, "where else could you safely hide a case of whiskey but in your room?" That student is here today, sitting somewhere in your midst, and I assure you he has had a most distinguished medical career.

The second anecdote I'd like to recall was in the fall of the year 1955—Friday, October 14, to be precise—when a private plane from the Ross Laboratories of Columbus, Ohio, dropped down from a rain-laden sky to pick up a group (Doctor Davison and some members of his pediatric staff) to attend the Duke-Ohio State football game the following day. Incidentally, Duke won 20-14 in spite of being overwhelming underdogs and in spite of Ohio State's All Americans Cassidy and Parker. The flight to Columbus was a rough and stormy trip and, believe it or not, the topic of death was being bantered about. Doctor Davison suddenly turned to me and said, "Arena, you don't need to fear death; you and the Pope are such good friends. Surely you'll go straight to heaven. As for me," he said, "if there is such a place, I will never make it." There flashed through my mind at this time a passage from the Bible (Matthew 25:24–40) which I recounted—a slightly altered version to be sure—perhaps my own version. The version goes like this and I think you are all familiar with it: "Then the King will say to those on his right hand, 'Come, you whom my Father has blessed, take for your heritage the kingdom prepared for you since the foundation of the world. For I was hungry and you gave me food; I was thirsty and you gave me drink; I was a stranger and you made me welcome; naked and you clothed me, sick and you visited me, in prison and you came to see me. Then the virtuous will say to him in reply, 'Lord, when did we see you hungry and feed you; or thirsty and give you drink? When did we see you a stranger and make you welcome; naked and clothe you; sick or in prison and go and visit you?' And the King will answer, 'I tell you solemnly, insofar as you did this to one of the least of these brothers of mine, you did it to me.' You have done all of these things many, many times, Doctor Davison," I said, "and your chances of getting to heaven are better than mine." I knew he was pleased with this passage and with my reply, for he said after a long pause, in an uncharacteristically subdued voice for him, "Maybe I'll make it after all." Those of us who have known "The Dean" all these years—his former students, house officers, colleagues, and warm devoted friends—know that *Dave has made it.*

IV John P. McGovern
The Davison Club

M<small>RS.</small> D<small>AVISON,</small> <small>DISTINGUISHED</small> faculty, fellow alumni and honored guests —if ever there was a labor of love, this is one: helping to pay tribute to our beloved Dean Davison. Love, because that was the emotion he stirred in all of us who knew him. But labor, too, in the sense that it is a well nigh impossible task to distill this man's greatness into a few brief words.

I am representing The Davison Club today, the group of former students, colleagues, friends and patients who seek to honor the Dean through support of the Duke Medical Center. Enthusiastic as I am about the club, I must speak today not only as one of its charter members, but also as a close friend and former student of the Dean and one who cherishes some unforgettable memories.

In its ongoing support activities, The Davison Club serves as a living memorial to a great man. But, in a larger sense, all of us who knew him are testimonials to his memory, for the Dean left his mark upon us all. No one who knew him could be unaffected by the experience. We all came away somehow different, perhaps a little bit better, certainly changed by our encounter with him.

It has been documented that he was a man who made things happen, who boldly innovated in all directions while keeping a steady hand on the helm of the medical school he was building. He pioneered in unpopular areas, such as hospital insurance. He took the best ideas in medical education as practiced here and abroad and blended them with his own ideas into a new and stimulating curriculum and medical way of life. He was not afraid to buck a trend; while he insisted upon excellence in the specialties, he also encouraged students to become well-rounded family physicians. Of Dean Davison it might be said, as Shaw wrote, "Some men see things as they are and ask why? I dream dreams that never were and ask why not?" (George Bernard Shaw, *Back to Methusaleh*).

But it was not only what the Dean did that endures, it was how he did it. One doubts if a group such as The Davison Club would have come into existence simply to honor a great teacher, physician and administrator. He was all three, but much more: he was the most human of human beings I have ever known. And it was the humanity of the

279

man that struck an answering spark in those around him, inspiring students and colleagues to band together in such a club to emulate his example and honor his name.

I called the Dean "the most human of human beings I've ever known." This was his own description of Sir William Osler, under whom he worked as a Rhodes Scholar at Oxford and who was *his* own lifelong hero and inspiration. Like Osler, Dean Davison was a true "man for all seasons." He was physician, researcher, scholar and humanist, a lover of his fellow human beings. This was the rare quality in the Dean that men saw and responded to—that much misunderstood and often confused commodity called love. The Dean honestly loved people—without guile, without affectation and without caring at all whether the recipient was great or lowly. He showered the same warmth and affection on everybody who came within his orbit, be he an orderly or a high official. And when you saw him, it was as though the sun had come out.

Bursting with energy, rumpled, impatient with trivia, sparing with words and dry of wit—that was the Dean, with tongue firmly planted in cheek where his own achievements were concerned.

No wonder his students and colleagues and patients loved him. People gravitated to the Dean as metal filings to a magnet. Somehow, mysteriously (because he was an exceedingly busy man), he always had time for them. He knew each student by name and kept track of them after they left Duke, following their careers with genuine interest and concern. I said "mysteriously," but to the Dean there was nothing mysterious about it. He was the *compleat* humanist-physician, and he once put it very simply: "Humanism is liking people." He said that, by the way, during a 1970 symposium sponsored by The University of Texas System to explore the place humanism has in today's medicine. As Osler's youngest living American student (then seventy-seven), he was an honored speaker at that symposium, which focused on Osler's life and its contemporary relevance.

It is fitting that one of the Dean's last professional appearances was concerned with such a subject, for he was the prototype of the humanistic physician. It was the patient that engaged Dean Davison's attention, not just the symptom. It was the person who counted with the Dean, and the rest could go hang. He believed in you, and somehow what you were capable of doing enlarged and grew, and you found yourself achieving more than you had thought possible—because of this man's faith and love.

And so we pay tribute to our lifelong hero, benefactor and friend whose life so enriched our own that I can truly say about the Dean what Hamlet said about his father: "He was a man, take him for all in all. I shall not look upon his like again." (William Shakespeare, *Hamlet, Prince of Denmark*, Act I, Scene 2.)

Prayer of Thanksgiving

JAMES T. CLELAND

Dean of Chapel and
First Honorary Alumnus of the Medical School

Almighty God,

God of our fathers, and their fathers, and our God;
Gladly have we called to mind, in Thy presence, the man whom we
delight to remember at this service in his honor.

✿ ✿ ✿ ✿ ✿ ✿

For the home into which he was born, against whose tenets he somewhat
rebelled, yet remaining true to them—after his fashion;
We give Thee thanks and praise.

✿ ✿ ✿ ✿ ✿ ✿

For the amazing academic career of this brilliant iconoclast,
Who was totally human, remarkable in judgment, without affectation;
We give Thee thanks and praise.

✿ ✿ ✿ ✿ ✿ ✿

For his love of medicine: preclinical, clinical, postclinical,
organizational,
Where his benevolent despotism moulded a great School, and trans-
formed the P.D.C. heresy into orthodoxy;
We give Thee thanks and praise.

For the home which he made for himself, with the gracious lady, who is
    Atala;
For the house by the side of the road, where folk were welcome;
For his inexplicable love of Turnage's;
 For the informality which never forgot courtesy;
For his enthusiasm for enthusiastic people, of all kinds and colors and
    conditions;
We give Thee thanks and praise.

✿ ✿ ✿ ✿ ✿ ✿

For this stalwart, flexible individualist, with a knack for cooperation,
Who met the needs of sick people, with the love which is compassion;
We give Thee thanks and praise.

✿ ✿ ✿ ✿ ✿ ✿

We are glad that, according to the teaching of Thy Son, our Lord, such
    a man automatically inherits the Kingdom:
For he fed the hungry, gave drink to the thirsty, welcomed the stranger,
    visited the sick.

✿ ✿ ✿ ✿ ✿ ✿

So he has heard Thy "Well done, good and faithful servant."
We leave him in Thy care.
Amen.

THIS IS THE HOUSE THAT DAVE BUILT

FIFTY YEARS AGO a young unorthodox medical educator opened the doors of a brand new academic medical center located in a small semi-rural community. It was at the height of the Great Depression. Despite the unsettled times and setting, his brilliance, lack of orthodoxy, informality and powers of persuasion attracted a young and vigorous team of faculty leaders. Even the first students were selected in competition with the leading established medical schools.

Together, they built a "launching pad" — a medical school, a teaching hospital, a school of nursing, a program in hospital administration and selected allied health programs. Through Dave's leadership and the collective ingenuity of the faculty, the Private Diagnostic Clinics were established as one of the key mechanisms for self sustinence and institutional growth. During Dave's "reign" as Dean, the Medical Center grew as meager resources could be lumped together — a new department, a key new appointment, a new wing. The institution was spartan and austere but established its reputation for excellence in whatever was undertaken. The informality and lack of communication barriers became the imprint of the modus vivandi.

In 1960, when Dave retired, the launching pad was complete. From the side-lines and his vantage point as a Trustee of the Duke Endowment, he continued to support the next generation.

Today, we enjoy sharing the highest orbit of excellence with other institutions. Our challenge for the next half-century is to sustain and maintain that reputation. As one reflects on the first 50-year history, one can truly say . . . "this is the house that Dave built."

William G. Anlyan, M.D.

INDEX

to Columbia University medical school,
26; aims in attending, 23, 227; in
athletics, 24–26; daily routine, 227; at
Democratic Convention of 1912, 28;
entrance examinations, 20, 22; financial
assistance for, 22; first experiences with
surgery, 26–27; graduation, 28; political
activities, 28–29; Rhodes Scholarship
awarded to, 23, 27–28; at tenth reunion,
93
in retirement, 176–84; Checker Cab for,
253; as Duke Endowment trustee, 177,
180, 275; farewell dinner for, 178, 180;
goals for retirement, 177–78; Lincoln
Continental given to, 178, 180, *181*, 183,
193, 243, 253; medical school building
named for, 180, 183; in Oxford robes,
1968, *188*; Puerto Rican winter
vacations of, 176, 227; a reflective pause
during retirement, *186*; at Symposium
on the Commonwealth of Children,
178, *179*, 180, 183–84
tributes to, 189–205
works of: communicable diseases paper of
1941, 151; *Enzymes*, 97, 99; *Pediatric
Notes*, 97, 138. *See also Compleat
Pediatrician, The*
in World War I, 74–86; at American
Ambulance Service Hospital, 46–48; at
Army Laboratory No. 1, 73, 76, 77, 78–
80, 82–85; at Army Medical School, 73;
at Base Hospital 33 in Portsmouth,
England, 85–86, 87; becomes medical
officer in U.S. Army, 59; as chief surgeon
on the *Erin*, 52–53; dog Chienne,
84–85, 124; in France with American
Expeditionary Force, 72, 74; in Germany
during the war, 53–54; hunting in
France, 83; loses his first patient, 47–48;
with patients at French hospital, *81*;
promotion to captain, 83; reports on
Italian news for *Daily Mail*, 52–53, 54;
returns to U.S., 86, 87; riding a

motorcycle, 84; with Serb surgical team,
48–50; in uniform, *75*; visit to Joinville
estate, 84; voyage to France, 74; while at
Oxford, 46–56

during World War II, 149–59; Cuba and
Yucatan holiday in January 1942, 149;
in Germany after the war, 156, 157, 158;
jobs done by, 151; living conditions in
Washington, 153–54; railroad travel,
151, 153; at tank laboratory, 151, *152*;
teaching tropical medicine, 155; wants
to get into Medical Corps, 149; in
Washington after the war, 159

Davison, William L. (father): as
administrator of his father's estate, 23;
boredom in retirement, 177; churches in
Michigan, 5; at Fleet Street Church, 23;
going to fires, 9; at Grace Church in Bay
Ridge, 6; independence of, 5; letters of
recommendation for WCD's Rhodes
Scholarship, 28; photograph of, *13*; as
Princeton graduate, 5, 22; ptomaine attack
of, 19; as smoker, 17–18; at Williams
Avenue Church, 12

Davison Club, 279–80
Davison Medallion, 194–95, 251
Davison Scholarship, 180, 183
Day, W. A., 117
Dean, H. R., 140
Deaver, John B., 27
Dees, Susan C., 153, 218, 229, 252
Dieuaide, Francis R., 91
De Nyse, Adrian (Uncle Ad), 7
Department of Defense Civilian Health and
Medical Advisory Committee, 173, 175
Derby, Richard, 46
Desjardins, Arthur U., 47
Dewey, (Admiral) George, 7
Diarrheas, infant, 88, 174
Diphtheria, 9, 59, 80
Disc operation, 235–36
Diseases of Infancy and Childhood
(Howland), 97–98, 136